# POWER MACHINE TOOLS

## A₁
### First Industrial Revolution

**SCREW-CUTTING LATHE—1800**
*Maudslay          London, England*

First master lead-screw was made. Then duplicate screws [coul]d be machine-made. Next, by [u]se of change gears, duplicate [screw]s of varied pitch could be [made] from a given lead screw.

*Rotating workpiece, lateral cutter movement*

**The DRILL PRESS—1840**
*Nasmyth          Manchester, England*

[Fi]rst drill with automatic power [feed.] This feature made metal-drill-[ing p]ractical by controlling the rate [and] direction of cutting action.

*Rotating tool penetrates in direction of axis*

**The BORING MILL—1775**
*Wilkinson          Bersham, England*

[B]oring mill made Watt's steam [engin]e a success by machining [the] cylinder holes true through-[out th]eir entire length.

***[Thu]s the Power Age was born***

*Tool moves along axis of bore — enlarges and trues bore.*

**The PLANER—1817**
*[Roberts] Manchester, England*

[The fl]at bed and ways of this [planer] were made with a chisel [edge], by hand. It was the first. [So tha]t other flat surfaces could [be ma]chined with accuracy.

*Reciprocating tool cuts on forward stroke*

**MILLING MACHINE—1818**
*[Whi]tney          New Haven, Connecticut*

[This m]iller performed the first truly [accur]ate duplicate-part produc-[tion b]y mechanically controlling [the co]urse and cutting motion of [a rota]ting, multiple-cutting-edged [cutter.]

*Rotating multi-edge cutter, reciprocating workpiece.*

**THE BAND SAW — 1933**
*Wilkie          Minnesota*

[B]and saw did not become a [metal]working machine tool until [1933 a]lthough it had been used [in wo]odworking from an early [date. T]his last of the basic machine [tools r]esulted from the develop-[ment o]f a rigid, precision machine [and al]loy band saw blades specif-[ically] designed for metal cutting [by] means of butt welding the [blade.]

*Milli-toothed, ribbon-like vertical cutter*

*ANY DIRECTION*

*ANY ANGLE*

**The GRINDER—1880**
*Typical Tool Grinder*

[Gui]de plate placed over the [grindin]g wheel began the transfer [and] control in surface grinding [to mec]hanical control. This evolved [into] completely automatic ultra-[precisi]on contour and flat grinding [machin]es.

  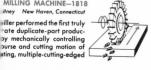

*Rotating abrasive cutter, reciprocating workpiece.*

# SEMI-AUTOMATIC MACHINE TOOLS

## A₂
### Mass Production

**LATHE**

**RADIAL DRILL**

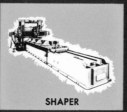
**BORING MILL**

**SHAPER**

**MILLING MACHINE**

**BAND SAW**

**SURFACE GRINDER**

# FULLY AUTOMATIC MACHINE TOOLS
### Industrial Revolution

**REPEAT CYCLE MACHINES**

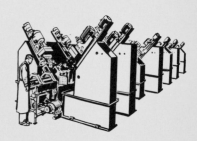

**TRANSFER MACHINE**

## A₄   SELF-CORRECTING MACHINES

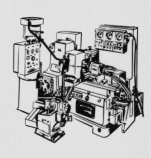

**FEEDBACK CONTROL GRINDER**

## A₅   EQUATION SOLVING MACHINES

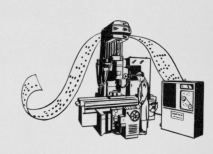

**NUMERICAL COMPUTER CONTROLLED MACHINE**

# FROM HAND TOOLS TO AUTOMATIC PRODUCTION

WILKIE BROTHERS FOUNDATION
DES PLAINES, ILLINOIS
AMBER & AMBER DETROIT
© 1962

# Anatomy of Automation

GEORGE H. AMBER, P. E.
PAUL S. AMBER, P. E.

*Amber and Amber*
*Consulting Engineers*

**PRENTICE-HALL, Inc.,** Englewood Cliffs, N.J.

# DEDICATIONS

*To inventor, scientist, and philosopher H. Stafford Hatfield, who, back in the 1920's, foresaw and detailed today's automation.*

*To mathematician Norbert Wiener, whose cybernetic interpretations of the roles of men and machines stimulated the authors' work in automation.*

Second printing .... January, 1964

Library of Congress Catalog Card No. 62-12103

Printed in the United States of America

03530—C

# Preface

This book is intended for use by pre-engineering, business administration, and management students in a course on production and automation fundamentals; also, by men already in industry and management. Principles and methods are stressed rather than equipment design details.

Alert educators are aware that the engineers and executives of tomorrow have commonly been taught how to develop yesterday's machines.

Education must be redirected to basic principles if engineering and management students will be able to meet the problems of the future.

*Anatomy of Automation* is not intended to be a "popular" book, nor is it only for engineering specialists. It is meant to give a basic foundation in the principles and philosophy of automation without neglecting conventional nonautomatic methods. Of particular value to the man now engaged in industry are the how-to-do-it aspects of introducing automation to the fabricating industries, and the discussions of the most important pre-automation activities.

We favor the use of many examples to help the reader understand the subject. To avoid disrupting the main discussion, examples and notes are largely in panel chart form, where the information is organized and compared.

Some of the information upon which we build our structure of automation is from our personal experiences and observations. Most of our basic information is from recent technical magazines, engineering journals, conferences, interviews, plant visits, and textbooks.

We appreciate the contributions to automation and automatic practices made by our fellow workers in the field who have published their experiences and developments. We particularly value the help received from Charles F. Hautau of Oxford, Ohio (formerly Detroit, Michigan), an independent consultant, who pioneered the design of radically new automation machinery. We are also indebted to our clients who permitted us to use material originally developed for them pertaining to automation feasibility studies, automatic measurements, automatic dull tool detection, automatic quality control, and mentor control systems.

The assistance of the General Electric Company in sponsoring our studies on automatic measurements for automation is particularly acknowledged. Thanks is also due to *Production Magazine* for making it possible for George Amber to research automation developments while engaged as their engineering and automation editor; also to the Ford Motor Company who made it possible for Paul Amber to participate in their Automation Group projects on the development of engine plant automatic manufacturing systems.

Some of the material used herein was presented in lectures before classes of Industrial Automation at the Applied Management and Technology Center of Wayne State University, Detroit. The aid of the students and the faculty is appreciated.

*Anatomy of Automation* developed from a series of articles bearing the same title, written for *Electrical Manufacturing* magazine (now named *Electro-Technology*). We are indebted to them for permitting us to use material in which they have copyright interest. Thanks is also due to the Wilkie Brothers Foundation and to editors, publishers, and manufacturers for permissions listed in the Credits and Acknowledgements.

Comments from readers are welcomed; they are, in fact, most necessary.

*George H. Amber*
*Paul S. Amber*

*Detroit*

# Credits and Acknowledgements

Front and back endpapers, Wilkie Brothers Foundation, Des Plaines, Illinois (hereafter abbreviated "WBF"). Front endpaper, $A_4$ machine, Heald Machine Co., Worchester 6, Mass.

Chapter 1. Drawings, pages 4, 5, 6, 7, WBF. Cartoon, page 6, *Automation Progress*, London. Cartoon, page 8, *USSR* Magazine. Chart, page 12, sources cited.

Chapter 2. Drawing, page 16, Federal Reserve Bank, San Francisco. Drawing, pages 21, 22, F. Jos.

Lamb Co., Detroit 34. Drawing and captions, page 26, General Electric Co. Drawing, Page 28, Charles Hautau, P.E., Oxford, Ohio. Essay, page 30, *Encyclopedia Americana*.

Chapter 3. Drawings, pages 36, 37, 41, 42, WBF. Chart, page 49, *Mass and Flow Production*, Frank G. Woollard, Illiffe Books, Ltd., London.

Chapter 4. Drawings, page 60, *Product Engineering*. Drawings, pages 63, 68, 71, WBF. Drawing, page 65, Cincinnati Milling Machine Co.

Chapter 5. Drawing, page 77, Westinghouse Electric Corp. and *Product Engineering*. Drawing, page 84, *Electro-Technology*. Chart, pages 86, 87, *American Machinist*. Drawings, page 89, W. H. Folger and *Tool and Manufacturing Engineer*.

Chapter 6. Chart, page 109, *Production Magazine*.

Chapter 8. Drawing, pages 116, 118, Richard C. Shafer and *Western Electric Engineer*. Drawing, page 134, *Production Magazine*.

Chapter 9. Pages 152, 153, Automobile Electric Association, Detroit.

Chapter 10. Drawing, page 161, Turchan Follower Co., Detroit. Drawing, page 162, EMI Electronics Ltd., England. Drawing, page 163, Friden Corp. Drawing, pages 164, 165, Bendix Corp. Drawing, page 166, Kearney & Trecker Corp. Glossary pages 167, 168, Sluis and Wharen, *Metalworking*.

Chapter 11. Drawing, page 180, Elliot Ltd., England. Drawing, page 181, Autonetics Division, North American Aviation Corp. Drawing, page 182, RCA.

Chapter 13. Cartoon, page 190, *Automation Progress*, London.

Chapter 13. Music, page 198, from *Illiac Suite for String Quartet*, Hiller and Isaacson, Theodore Presser Co. Cartoon, page 202, WBF.

Chapter 14. Drawing, page 221, Driam Corp., Manitowac, Wisc. Drawing, page 222, Litwin Engineering Co., Wichita, Kansas.

Appendix. Chart, page 224, *Instruments and Control Systems*.

Typing and secretarial services: Verona Shoch, Lausanne, Switzerland; Grace Walton, Miami, Florida; Evalyn Wheaton, Dearborn, Michigan.

Authors' illustrator: Bernice Forrest, Oak Park, Michigan.

# Contents

CHAPTER THREE

# PRODUCTION FUNDAMENTALS                    31

CHAPTER FOUR

# METHODS, TOOLING, AND OPERATIONS          51

CHAPTER FIVE

# PRE-AUTOMATION ACTIVITIES                  75

CHAPTER SIX

# HOW-TO-DO-IT                               91

CONTENTS

# Automation Yardstick

1

The word *automation* was first used early in the 1950's to mean automatic materials handling, particularly equipment used to load and unload stamping presses, but it soon bore many additional meanings. For example, the act of making things automatic came to be called automation mainly because automatization was a tongue twister. Nonenergy tasks, those involving infor-

mation, were referred to as automation by both the public and engineers, for the term made its appearance just in time to describe all systems that can to some extent replace men.

Consequently, automation has become a general term. It now refers both to services performed and to products produced automatically; and it refers to information-handling tasks as well

Chart 1-1. Yardstick for Automation

| ORDER OF AUTOMATICITY | HUMAN ATTRIBUTE MECHANIZED | DISCUSSION | EXAMPLES |
|---|---|---|---|
| $A_0$ HAND TOOLS AND MANUAL MACHINES | NONE—Without self-action properties. Does not replace human energy or basic control but may include built-in guides and measurements. Includes all hand tools. They increase workers efficiency but do not replace human function. | Includes all muscle energized machines. They give mechanical advantages but do not replace man's energy or control. Simple machines are: lever, inclined plane, wheel and axle, screw, pulley, and wedge. | Shovel, knife, pliers, axe, crowbar, hammer, scissors, wrench, file, handsaw, bellows, paintbrush, trowel. Block and tackle, pencil sharpener, bow and arrow, bicycle, typewriter, churn, wheelbarrow, tirepump, desk stapler, jack, hand lawnmower, handloom. |
| $A_1$ POWERED MACHINES AND TOOLS | ENERGY—Muscles are replaced for the basic machine function. Machine action and control completely dependent upon operator. | Uses mechanical power (windmill, waterwheel, steam engine, electric motor) but man positions work and machine for desired action. | Snag grinder, cement troweling machine, portable floor polisher, electric hand drill, drillpress, air hammer, power lawnmower, spray gun, belt sander, electric (or spring wound) shaver. |
| $A_2$ SINGLE-CYCLE AUTOMATICS AND SELF-FEEDING MACHINES | DEXTERITY—Completes an action when initiated by an operator. Feeds tool to the work by power. | Includes all single cycle automatic machines. Operator must set up, load, initiate actions, adjust, and unload. However $A_3$, $A_4$, or $A_5$ control systems may be superimposed on basically $A_2$ machines to reduce the dependence on operator skills. | Pipe threading machine, radial drill, electro-erosion machine, precision boring machine (without accessory automatic control system), machine tools, such as grinder, planer, mill, shaper, lathe. |
| $A_3$ AUTOMATIC; REPEATS CYCLE | DILIGENCE—Carries out routine instructions without aid by man. Starts cycles and repeats actions automatically. | Includes all automatic machines. Loads, goes through a sequence of operations, unloads to next station or machine. Open loop (not self-correcting) performance. Obeys internal (fixed) or external (variable) program, such as cams, tapes, or cards. Includes transfer machines and "Detroit" automation. | Engine production lines; self-feed press lines; automatic copying lathe; automatic gear hobbers; automatic assembly of switches, TV's, relays, locks, valves; machines for making springs, bottles, hinges, chain, cartons, doughnuts; automatic packaging. Also record-playback and numerical programmed machines which are not self-correcting. |
| $A_4$ SELF MEASURING AND ADJUSTING; FEEDBACK | JUDGEMENT—Measures and compares result to the desired size or position and adjusts to minimize any error. | Although feedback control of the actual surface of the workpiece is preferable, positional control of the machine table or tool is of great value too. A process may use more than one $A_4$ subsystem operating independently. | Feedback from product: automatic sizing grinders; size-controlled honing machines, dynamic balancing; color matching or blending; level control; weight control; chemical milling; process controllers. Positional feedback: pattern tracing flame cutter; servo-assisted follower control; feedback control of machine tool table, saddle, and spindle; tape controlled machines (only if self-correcting). |
| $A_5$ COMPUTER CONTROL; AUTOMATIC COGNITION | EVALUATION—Is cognizant of multiple factors on which machine or process performance is predicated, evaluates and reconciles them by means of computer operations to determine proper control action. | Any process or problem which can be expressed as an equation can be computer controlled. This includes automatic cognition, the awareness of variations in materials, in process conditions, and in the work. Mentors are simple limited purpose computers used to accomplish $A_5$ computer control. | Rate-of-feed cutting; machinability control; maintaining pH; error compensation; turbine fuel control; dynamic positioning; selective assembly; self-optimizing (maxima-minima); Auto-QC calculations; interpolation between data points. |

Chart 1-1. Yardstick for Automation (Continued)

| ORDER OF AUTOMATICITY | HUMAN ATTRIBUTE MECHANIZED | DISCUSSION | EXAMPLES |
|---|---|---|---|
| $A_6$ LIMITED SELF-PROGRAMMING | LEARNING—Machine sets up and tries subroutines, based on the general program. By remembering which actions were most effective in obtaining the desired results, the machine "learns by experience." | The subroutines are a form of limited self-programming. This may be preferable to providing the necessary memory storage and recall apparatus for complete programming in a complex computer. | Utilization of intercity telephone circuits, sophisticated elevator dispatching; "mock tortoise"; mechanical "maze running rat," neurological models, "telelogical" machine. |
| $A_7$ RELATES CAUSE FROM EFFECTS | REASONING—Ability to forecast trends, patterns and relationships, from incomplete facts. Exhibits "intuition" by going beyond available data. | Theory of Games, Monte Carlo method, and other strategies may be the basis of operation. Inductive reasoning $A_7$ is not the same as deductive reasoning $A_5$; analysis requires deduction. Synthesis requires induction. | Sales prediction, weather forecasting, "champion" chessplayer, automatic OR, population patterns, lamp failure anticipation, actuarial analysis. |
| $A_8$ ORIGINALITY | CREATIVENESS—The ability to originate works to suit human tastes and preferences. Not copying, imitating, or following plans and instructions. | The program only designates the general form of the desired action and eliminates clashes, discords, and disharmonies. The actual result is original. | Write music; design fabric patterns; formulate new drugs and chemicals; write poetry? design products? create paintings? create original automatic machines? |
| $A_9$ COMMANDS OTHERS | DOMINANCE—Governs actions of men, machines, and other systems. Acts as a "commanding general" or as a "dictator" to achieve results. Machine is no longer servant but master. | An $A_9$ supermachine capable of superior energy ($A_1$), dexterity ($A_2$), diligence ($A_3$), judgement ($A_4$), evaluation ($A_5$), learning ($A_6$), reasoning ($A_7$), and creativeness ($A_8$), would be able to dominate man. | The authors decline to cite examples of $A_9$ automation. Science-fiction writers are talented in conjecturing such machines, so examples of higher orders of automaticity are best left to their imaginations. |

as to energy-converting tasks. Automation covers all instances where intensive use is made of automatic methods.

As the many ways in which automation is used have caused confusion, a number of attempts have been made to define the term by words. Verbal *definitions*, as in Chart 1-2, are valuable. But also needed is a logical *classification*, as in Chart 1-1, to relate automation's various forms.

Following is a classification of automation devised by the authors. It is a refinement of the original method first disclosed in January 1955 in an Amber and Amber paper. The classification is constructed on the premise that all work requires both energy and information, and that these must be provided by man or by a substitute for man, a machine. Man has certain faculties for accomplishing energy or information tasks, many of

which can be done by machines. Whenever a machine assumes a human attribute, it is considered to have taken on an "order" of automaticity.

The more human attributes performed by a machine, the higher is its "order" of automaticity. Automaticity is here considered to be the self-acting capability of a device.

It was found that ten classifications of automaticity are adequate for discriminating all present and future self-acting devices. The first half of the automaticity scale contains the machines and devices known to exist today. Its second half projects into levels of self-action exhibited by machines which are largely conjectural.

The character *A* is taken to represent the automaticity scale, just as F has long been used to represent the Fahrenheit scale. The "vertical" level of automaticity (its range) is shown as a subscript, denoting the *order* of automaticity. The "horizontal" intensity of automaticity (relative amount of automatic operation), is shown as a superscript, denoting the *degree* of automaticity. This is consistent with algebraic usage which uses an exponential superscript to indicate the degree of a term.

All machines and devices that are not self-powered are considered to have the *zero* order of automaticity. Powered devices and machines comprise the first two orders of automaticity. Machines that are entirely self-acting and can work by themselves form the third order of automaticity. At this level, all the *energy* required is completely mechanized. Higher orders of automaticity indicate further automatization of *information* functions.

In its most general sense, the term *automation* embraces all applications of devices and techniques that involve any degree of self-action. As applied to manufacturing operations, it will be shown that automation refers to the third and higher orders of automaticity, which are capable of self-action without human intervention, either repeatedly or for an extended cycle.

Used as an adjective, *automation* is functionally synonymous to *automatic*. Used as a noun, it represents the state of performing work automatically and can be considered to be a shortened form of *automatization*.

*Mechanization* refers to the first and second orders of automaticity, which include semi-automatic machinery. *Mechanization* is also used to indicate the assignment of an operation to a machine, even if it is not mechanical. For example, using a machine (computer) to do arithmetic may be referred to as the *mechanization* of the arithmetic operation, even though the computer works on electronic rather than mechanical principles.

## ORDER OF AUTOMATICITY

### HAND TOOLS AND MANUAL MACHINES, $A_0$

Hand tools, including what we term "manual machines," constitute an important class of machines. Our civilization began with the introduction of hand tools, and we will always depend on such muscle and hand-powered devices for some of our work.

There are many types of hand tools, and even wider variety of machines which depend on muscular energy. However, they replace none of man's faculties, for such devices provide neither the energy nor information needed to do a job. All hand tools continually require man's muscle

Band cutting, $A_1$

(energy) and brain (control). Therefore, hand tools and manual machines comprise the class of devices having the *zero* order of automaticity. This is designated symbolically as $A_0$.

Muscle-powered machines do not include stored energy devices, such as music boxes or clockwork that function for an extended period without man's attention or efforts. Even though the original source was man, the wound spring or raised weights become the effective energy source, and the mechanism is no longer a non-powered device. Therefore, clock type mechanisms are not classified $A_0$. However, a muscle-powered machine, such as a water pump, bow and arrow, or screw jack is $A_0$.

### POWERED MACHINES AND TOOLS, $A_1$

*Power Tools* are the simplest substitutes for man's efforts. They provide most of the energy required to do a job. Thus, they greatly reduce the need for man's muscular energy. Man's efforts when using a power tool consist mainly of starting and stopping the power tool and positioning it or positioning the material being worked on.

Guiding and positioning a machine often demands appreciable muscular effort. However, the necessity for man to provide the basic energy necessary to do a job has been eliminated by the use of a power tool. This self-action constitutes a quality of automaticity.

Self-powered machines and tools exhibit the *first* order of automaticity, represented symbolically by $A_1$. Such $A_1$ machines require continuous guidance by an operator.

## SEMI-AUTOMATIC DEVICES, $A_2$

Single cycle (semi-automatic) devices are fully powered. They have the ability to perform a complete cycle of operation without human intervention once they have been set up to do a specific job. Such machines provide the energy to do the basic job as well as the auxiliary actions, such as feeding a workpiece to the machine.

The most familiar examples of semi-automatics are the self-feed power tools. They represent a significant step forward on the automaticity scale, for the feed function requires appreciable energy from an operator. When the feed function is also provided by a machine, it possesses the second order of automaticity, $A_2$.

The discussion that follows uses manufacturing operations as examples. However, $A_2$ covers all single cycle *automatics* (which are really semi-automatic) such as the coin-operated washing machine.

$A_2$ machines provide all of the necessary energy except for the very small amount needed for control. With $A_2$ devices, control of the machine is still entirely the duty of the operator. He must set whatever controls are not predetermined by the design of the machine, properly position or insert the workpiece and start the operation. Then he can stand by until the operation is completed. Commonly, a machine automatically stops operating when the job is finished.

An example is the power hacksaw which stops after the cut-off operation is completed.

The $A_2$ machine is considered semi-automatic because once the work is in position and the job started, the remainder of the work cycle is self-acting.

The complete cycle may even involve more than one operation. For example, a pipe-cutting machine may withdraw the cutter and then ream out the burr. However, semi-automatic machines require an operator for loading, unloading, and for initiating operations.

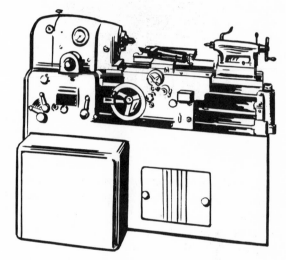

Tool room lathe, $A_2$

Most machine tools (grinder, planer, mill, shaper, lathe) are semi-automatics. They require a skilled machinist to operate them but relieve him of all energy requirements. The machines can finish a cut with automatic power feed once the operator initiates action.

Higher order control systems can be superimposed on basically $A_2$ machines to reduce the demands on operator skills and dexterity. One example is automatic coordinate setting, whereby a standard $A_2$ boring machine is converted to incorporate automatic positioning of table and cutting tools. This may be in response to manually set dials or to a taped program (numerical control). Spindle speeds and feeds, as well as locations on the workpiece, can also be preprogrammed.

Removing critical adjustments from operator

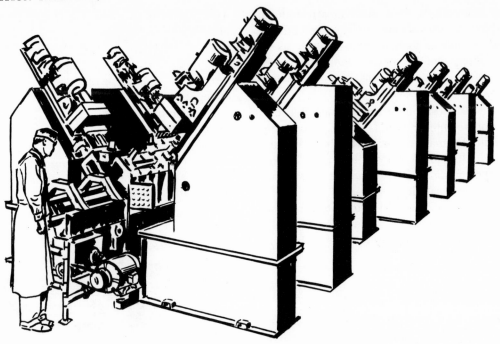

Transfer machine, $A_3$

control improves machine performance, for human error and the time required for manual resetting are greatly reduced. Semi-automatic machines adopting automatic features are particularly valuable for short runs and one-of-a-kind production where fully automatic manufacture is not justified.

It should be noted that even though the auxiliary control apparatus may include higher order features, such as feedback (self-correcting) control and computer control, the machine still requires an operator and is classified $A_2$. Semi-automatic machines with higher order auxiliaries are sometimes referred to as *semi-automation*.

## AUTOMATIC MACHINES, $A_3$

Fully automatic machines exhibit the third order of automaticity. They can be entirely self-acting for an extended period of time as they reload and recycle automatically.

The popular interpretation of *automation* is the use of $A_3$ industrial machines, in conjunction with some machines having higher levels of automaticity.

The power drive and power feed machines previously discussed supply all of the energy necessary to accomplish their purpose. However, they demand that an operator continually supply

Detroit automation—British viewpoint

information by his controlling actions. If the *orders* to the machine can be given in advance and if the machine can *obey* them, the operator may be dispensed with.

6

The instructions to a machine (what to do and how to do it) are called the *program*. Simple versions of programming consist of cams, stops, slides, and the physical configuration of the machine. More complex versions may use coded tapes. An example of a programmed machine is the old-time player piano, with removable rolls. Industrial forms of external program may require subsidiary apparatus of a higher order of automation.

Automatic cycle machines, transfer machines, and specific product machines are ordinarily all of the third order of automaticity.

## SELF-MEASURING AND ADJUSTING, $A_4$

Machines or processes which can monitor their own performance and self-correct themselves as their output varies can be said to have some judgment. That is, they can make simple decisions. Such self-correction is commonly known as *feedback* control or *closed loop* control because information of machine performance, which is continually measured, is fed back (or *looped* back) into the process. The term *automatic reset* is also used to denote self-correction.

Self-correcting systems, either a machine or an entire process, constitute the fourth order of automaticity, $A_4$.

Feed back control is based on measuring the workpiece or the output of the process, comparing the measurements to a standard value, detecting the magnitude and sense (direction) of any error, then adjusting the process or machine to reduce that error. The standards to which feed back measurements are compared may be in the form of master gauges, dial settings, templates, patterns, models, master parts, or coded information on cards or tapes.

A simple $A_4$ automatic system is one which (a) obeys a simple command; (b) senses a single condition; and (c) varies a single factor. An example is the common household thermostat controlling a furnace, where (a) the command (thermostat setting) is "maintain 71°F"; (b) the condition sensed is the room temperature, 69°F; and (c) the factor varied is the fuel to the furnace, which is increased to reduce the differential

between the 71° temperature setting and the 69° temperature reading.

An industrial example of $A_4$ is the automatic grinder which checks the size of the part produced and automatically compensates for wear of the grinding wheel.

## COMPUTER CONTROL, $A_5$

The simplest self-correcting machine senses and corrects one varying condition. Some control systems must compensate for more than one variable factor. Whenever a process requires the

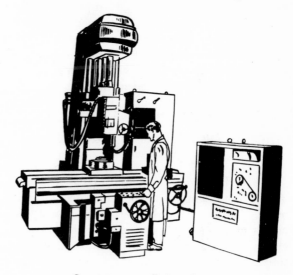

Computer controlled machine, $A_5$

awareness (sensing) of multiple conditions affecting its product, it has the property of *automatic cognition*. When it is necessary to sense more than one condition, or to vary more than one factor, computer control is required to relate the dependent and independent factors properly.

Machines, devices, and processes that make use of mathematical equation-solving operations as part of their control system display the fifth order of automaticity. Almost any process action can be described by mathematical equations. A process can therefore be regulated by equation-solving control devices which manipulate signals that represent each of the pertinent factors affecting the action being controlled.

An example of this is a power plant. The command may be "maintain maximum boiler efficiency." The conditions sensed are steam demand, flue gas temperature, and $CO_2$ in flue gas. The factors varied are fuel input and combustion air.

This is a self-optimizing control system, quite typical of $A_5$ computer control. The computing device automatically solves equations which relate the effect of these five principal factors on the operation of the power plant and automatically achieves maximum efficiency.

The computer used for the control system may be a large, general purpose computer. More likely, it is a fairly simple, limited-purpose computer specially designed for the specific control problem. Such limited-purpose computing devices used for control and for instrumentation are termed *mentors* to distinguish them from the general purpose types used mainly for performing large scale calculations and data processing.

## HIGHER ORDERS OF AUTOMATICITY—
### $A_6$ TO $A_9$

The higher orders of automaticity, of which only a few examples can be cited, do not exist on the factory floor. However, by classifying orders of automaticity beyond present-day machines, we are better able to understand the similarities between automatic control and human action.

### LIMITED SELF-PROGRAMMING, $A_6$

A machine or process that can *learn by experience* illustrates the sixth order of automaticity. Such a machine or process attempts to attain its goal by several different methods. If one approach does not prove to be satisfactory, another is tried.

The trial-and-error sequencing of self-learning machines is not fully programmed. Although some possible alternate actions are *built-in*, the proper choice depends on the circumstances encountered.

The $A_6$ self-learning machine should be able to remember its best solution or approach to a problem so that it can avoid unsuccessful at-

A fabricated doodle

8

tempts when a similar problem is faced in the future.

Such a development would be desirable in a computer, for example, for it would reduce the drudgery and detail necessary to plan all of the steps a computer must take. It may be simpler and less costly to create a computer able to program itself than to provide the necessary memory storage and access apparatus. In other words, in a very complex computer it may be more efficient to program basic routines from which the computer can devise (learn) its own subroutines, than to program the subroutines in detail. Some work along these lines has already been done by computer experts.

A possible application for $A_6$ self-learning automation is for the control of elevators in a skyscraper. The controls (using a computer) would build up a history of the passenger load and direction (up or down) at various hours. The elevators would then be dispatched to carry the passengers most quickly. Use would be made of express runs, fast returns, number of passengers, and so on.

The key to such $A_6$ operation is that a control computer would *try* different modes of operation and *remember* the results of those attempted. Thus, the best program of automatic elevator dispatching could be re-used when the same passenger load conditions are re-encountered.

Other areas for possible $A_6$ control are self-selection of intercity telephone circuits, distribution of mail-order catalogs for maximum sales, and a chemical plant which experiments with the system parameters, seeking best results, although lacking an absolute program.

The key to the $A_6$ machine is its ability to remember the outcome of a series of actions, as a guide for future work.

$A_6$ self-learning machines are mainly curiosities at present. Some have been built by physiologists and neurologists to simulate brain action and to demonstrate conditioned reflex, learning, avoidance of obstacles, and free will. One type, a *mock tortoise*, will even return home for *rest and recuperation* when near exhaustion. Learning by experience is not the same as learning by memorization. *How* men or animals learn is a controversial topic. Just what constitutes *learning by machine* is still open to argument.

## RELATES CAUSE FROM EFFECT, $A_7$

Reasoning is the ability to determine logical relationships, such as attributing causes to observed effects. A system or machine capable of reasoning would exhibit the seventh order of automaticity. An $A_7$ system is able to synthesize a plan or mode of action from known responses. The $A_7$ system would go beyond the basic instructions to program itself in response to past occurrences and operating variables. Such behavior may be based on statistical and probability criteria. However, automaticity of the seventh order may never go beyond talking stages.

$A_7$ machines need not confine their activities to a strict program or to trial-and-error experiences. Instead of learning in a conventional manner, $A_7$ relies on *intuition* and attempts some modes of operation directly, bypassing others.

A possible example would be an automatic chess player which does more than just act on preprogrammed criteria of *good* and *bad* moves. This champion chess-playing machine would consider its opponent's previous plays, and by inductive reasoning, decide on the most favorable move. Thus, it could profit by past mistakes and would exhibit considerable *freedom of action*.

Research hints that simple $A_6$ machines-that-learn are theoretically possible. The likelihood of the $A_7$ intuitive machine is less probable.

## ORIGINALITY, $A_8$

Creativity is a high-level, human attribute. Creativity ranges from originating a new cookie recipe to writing a movie scenario; from developing a new refining process to formulating a general law of physics.

A machine that exhibits creativity is considered to have the *eighth* order of automaticity. Such a machine or process would be able to produce an original product or result. The $A_8$

machine is not instructed as to exactly what form its output is to have. Rather, the programming consists of the general (not specific) characteristics required from the output of the process.

In all of the classes of automaticity below $A_8$, the process actions and methods were either fixed ($A_5$ and lower) or flexible ($A_6$ and $A_7$). However, the desired end result has always been specified. This is not so with an $A_8$ machine, where the exact form of the final result is not known until it is produced.

Routine designs, whereby the product has already been defined by equations and the machine merely runs through a series of calculations using the parameters and specifications provided, is not creativity. The difference between routine design and creative design is analogous to the difference between a skilled draftsman and an imaginative architect.

A creative machine would start with *ideas*. These could be random impulses, or memory signals, combined by permutations and combinations to fit a pattern of human tastes and preferences. Some obvious disharmonies, clashes, and discords could be omitted by programming.

Consider the problem of designing a machine to write music, which has already been accomplished (see Figure 14-1). Can we program the general rules for simple bugle calls, marches, popular tunes, or symphonies?

It would be less difficult to design machines to play music from written notes (which is a program) than to design machines to write a truly original composition. Unless the *composition* follows a predetermined formula, however complex, which renders it no longer a creation in the strict sense.

The music-creating machine probably reveals the large routine content in most music more than it proves a machine can be truly creative.

The basic precept of mechanization is *routine means machine*. Mechanizing creativity therefore infers routinizing creativity. This amounts to a paradox. Therefore, the concept of a creative machine seems to be self-contradictory. How can we routinize creativity which, by definition, cannot be routine?

## COMMANDS, $A_9$

Extending to the ninth order of automaticity, the highest level of the Amber and Amber classification reaches the human faculty of "dominance." Such a machine is superhuman. Just as man outclasses animals in intellectual ability, the $A_9$ machine outclasses man in the scope of the superhuman faculties that it possesses. That is, an $A_9$ machine is to man as man is to a dog.

This means much more than merely exceeding the *intensity* of human faculties. We all know that machines can work faster and more consistently than can man, for this is largely the justification for using machines.

The application of his faculties allows man to dominate all the world, organic or mineral. With the advent of $A_9$ machines, man's accomplishments will be surpassed by machines. Thus, man's position as top figure on earth drops to second place. The era of dominance of man by machine would exist.

The higher orders of automaticity are best suited for description in science fiction stories, so no more will be discussed here.

### SUMMARY: ORDERS OF AUTOMATICITY

Ten orders of automaticity have been established, starting with the nonself-acting $A_0$ through the mechanization of energy $A_1$ and $A_2$, mechanization of information $A_3$, $A_4$, $A_5$, mechanization of higher intelligence $A_6$, $A_7$, $A_8$; finally reaching superhuman level capabilities, $A_9$.

Machines classified according to the highest order of automaticity by which they accomplish their basic purpose, generally exhibit the characteristics of the lower orders as well.

The orders of automaticity through $A_5$ are in common use. Computer control, $A_5$, is the highest practical level. Higher orders, $A_6$, $A_7$, $A_8$, and $A_9$ may be considered as hypothetical advances stemming from $A_5$. These conjectural levels of automaticity will not be discussed further. However, this text is not confined to systems fully proven in practice. What appears ripe for increased automation is considered worthy of attention, too.

Chart 1-2. Dictionary Definitions of Automation *

| DICTIONARY & COPYRIGHT | DEFINITION | PUBLISHER |
|---|---|---|
| From The New Century Dictionary of the English Language, copyright 1959. | au·to·ma·tion (â-tō-mā′shon), n. [From autom-(atiz)ation.] A method or process of directing mechanical processes by machines rather than by men; automatic operation. | Appleton-Century-Croft, Inc. |
| From Thorndike-Barnhart Comprehensive Desk Dictionary, copyright 1958. | au·to·ma·tion (ô′tə·mā′shən), n. method or technique of making a manufacturing process, a production line, etc., operate more automatically by the use of built-in or supplementary controls in a machine or number of machines. [<autom(atic) + (oper)ation] | Doubleday & Co. |
| From The Standard Dictionary of the English Language, International Edition, copyright 1960. | au·to·ma·tion (ô′tə·mā′shən) n. Technol. 1 The automatic transfer of one unit of a complex industrial assembly to a succession of self-acting machines each of which completes a specified stage in the total manufacturing process from crude material to finished product. 2 The application of fully automatic procedures in the efficient performance and control of operations involving a sequence of complex, standardized, or repetitive processes on a large scale. 3 The theory, art, and technique of converting a mechanical process to maximum automatic operation, especially by the use of electronic control mechanisms and electronic computers for the rapid organizing and processing of data in a wide range of technical, industrial, and business information. [<AUTOM(ATIC) + (OPER)ATION] | Funk & Wagnalls Company |
| From Webster's New Collegiate Dictionary, copyright 1959 | au′to·ma′tion (ô′to·mā′shŭn), n. [automatic + -ion.] 1. The technique of making a process or system automatic. 2. Automatically controlled operation of an apparatus, process, or system, esp. by electronic devices. | G. & C. Merriam Co., Publishers of the Merriam-Webster Dictionaries. |
| From the Concise Oxford Dictionary, fourth edition, 1958. | automa′tion, n. Automatic control of the manufacture of a product through successive stages, (loosely) use of machinery to save manual labour. [irreg. formed from AUTOMATIC] | The Clarendon Press, Oxford. |
| From The American College Dictionary, copyright 1960. | au·to·ma·tion (ô′tə′mā′shən), n. the science of operating or controlling a mechanical process by highly automatic means, such as electronic devices [b. AUTOM(ATIC) and (OPER)-ATION] | Random House, Inc. |
| From Webster's New World Dictionary of the American Language, College Edition, copyright 1960. | au·to·ma·tion (ô′tə·mā′shən), n. [arbitrary coinage c. 1949], in manufacturing, a system or method in which many or all of the processes of production, movement, and inspection of parts and materials are automatically performed or controlled by self-operating machinery, electronic devices, etc. | The World Publishing Company |

* Definitions reproduced by permission of the publishers listed.

## DEGREES OF AUTOMATICITY

The orders of automaticity previously discussed are based on the extent to which man's attributes, both muscular and intellectual, are replaced by mechanical actions. This is a *vertical* classification of the *range* of automaticity accomplished. It is qualitative in nature. The orders are complemented by the *degrees* of automaticity, a horizontal classification of the relative intensity of automatic operations in a process.

The degrees of automaticity are quantitative in nature. The intensity of self-action of a manufacturing process is revealed by its degree notation. It is the ratio of automatic operations to total operations, in a machine or process.

Readers entirely unfamiliar with industrial processes (discussed in Chapter 3) may elect to bypass the remainder of this chapter.

The concept *degree of automaticity* is of particular interest and value to production engineers and planners. The degree is determined from manufacturing operation sheets, which detail every operation on a part including nonautomatic and manual operations.

The degree (intensity) of automaticity is designated by a superscript after the automaticity symbol $A$, that is, $A^{3/6}$. The example $A^{3/6}$ represents a machine which has six operations, three of which are automatic. Likewise, $A^{7/21}$ indicates the 7/21 *degree* of automaticity, or seven self-acting operations out of twenty-one total operations.

Typical industrial operations are: transport and load, position, drill, bore, ream, bend, tap, grind, invert and advance to next station, dip, dry, paint, assemble, and inspect. Such operations may be by man or by machine and apply only to work or handling directed right to the workpiece. Auxiliary actions, such as a chip removal, lubrication, coolant, cutter replacement, or indexing a machine turret are not considered to be direct working operations.

Use of the combined notations for *degrees* and *orders* of automaticity is illustrated in the following example:

An automatic screw machine is set up to make oil-line fittings from hexagonal brass bar stock. This machine recycles automatically ($A_3$) and

has but one manual operation, loading. The other eight operations (chuck, turn, drill, ream, chamfer, pipe thread, machine thread, cut-off) are self-acting. Therefore, the notation for the machine's productivity is $A_3{}^{8/9}$; $A^{8/9}$ because eight of nine operations are automatic, and $A_3$ because it is an automatic cycle machine.

A basic idea, which first made automation an everyday word, was the addition of electrically controlled conveyors which removed work from one automatic cycle machine and loaded the part into the next unit, at the same time re-initiating an automatic machine cycle. Long lines of linked automatic machines have been formed and operate effectively in many high production industries. The automatic conveyors may be long or short and of varied types, such as shuttle or transfer machines, chain conveyors, gravity chutes, and vibratory feeders.

### PROCESS FUNCTION

The *function* of any process is the sum of the individual operations of each machine or station making up the process. The *automation* of any process line is expressed by the sum of the individual automation symbols.

A transfer machine (a single multistation machine with built-in parts transfer mechanisms) is treated as a line of separate automatic machines. Thus, a typical automation line or transfer machine could be represented by:

$$aA_1{}^{1/1} + bA_1{}^{1/2} \text{*} + cA_2{}^{2/2} + dA_3{}^{4/4} + eA_4{}^{2/2} + fA_3{}^{3/4}$$

The lower-case letters represent the function code. The symbol * designates automatic conveyors and shuttles. These are commonly $A_3{}^{1/1}$ but would be $A_3{}^{2/2}$ or $A_3{}^{3/3}$ if the workpiece is inverted or reversed by the shuttle device.

The example cited is typical of Detroit automation. Note that the production line is basically self-acting but may start off with a *manual* loading operation. Very often the last operation, inspection, is also manual.

The notation of the orders and degrees of automaticity, supplemented by a function code as discussed above, helps planners, engineers, and production executives in comparing two or more proposed manufacturing systems.

12

# The Areas of Automation

**2**

## AUTOMATION AREAS

Major automation activity is confined to four areas: office, military, domestic, and industrial. These divisions tend to overlap as interarea exchange of techniques and proven components is increasing.

The office automation area covers mainly the use of automatic machines of the digital computer type to accomplish routine operations of paper work necessary for business and commerce.

Though other automation areas embrace several automatic activities, office automation depends solely on data processing. Yet, because office automation is so important and widespread, it constitutes an automation area.

Whereas industrial automation results in a *product*, office automation provides a *service*.

Office automation is important because such a large portion of all office white-collar work can be done automatically, faster and at far less cost than by traditional manual methods.

Examples of office automation are: data processing, information handling, data reduction, computation, and segregation, accounting, record keeping, distribution, billing, inventory, subscription lists, and numerical control of industrial machines. These are accomplished mainly by digital methods, discussed in later chapters.

### Military Automation Activities

The use of automatic methods to accomplish control functions necessary for military operations, constitutes *military automation*. Civil aviation and merchant marine are included as part of the military automation area because they are so similar to the air and naval services.

Military operations require intensive automation of both energy and information. This involves highly automatic machines and high performance control systems. Like office automation, military automation has no *product*. The main objective of military automation is to deliver an offensive object (some sort of projectile) to the enemy or to detect and intercept an offensive object from the enemy. The military area of automation considers performance rather than cost or savings.

It is the most advanced area of automation technically and has made available to the other automation areas a huge technology. This is due to the large amount of effort and expense devoted to perfecting military equipment which utilizes automatic guidance and other sophisticated forms of control.

Military automation includes ranging, fire control, instrumentation, training, systems engineering, operations research, and human engineering.

### Domestic Automation Activities

The *domestic automation* area concerns the use of automatic methods for the comfort and convenience of people in their everyday domestic environment. It is of particular interest because domestic automation affects us directly and personally.

Whereas most industrial, office, and military automation consists of machines, processes, and systems, most domestic automation consists of the products of automatic manufacture, namely, home appliances and automobiles. These end products of automatic manufacture are *machines* or *systems* for providing special services to the owner. Domestic automation continues to increase sharply. The domestic area of automation is especially critical to us because a power failure here may be a catastrophe.

### Industrial Automation Activities

The industrial area automation activities concern the automatic manufacture of goods, producing a product. This means intensive mechanization in the use of energy by means of machines and processes, and to a lesser extent, mechanization of information, the control necessary to accomplish the desired work. This area includes manufacture by both continuous processing and by piece part fabrication.

The industrial area of automation is important because of the continuous demand for more goods at lower cost. Many technical and economic problems hinder the development of automatic fabrication. Manufacture by processing is much more amenable to automatic methods, thus it is more highly automatized than is manufacture by fabrication.

## OFFICE AUTOMATION

*Office Automation* is automatic data processing primarily for routine paper work, such as record-keeping. This contrasts with *control*, which is automatic data processing (acting on information) to direct a machine or process. The point is that *office automation, computation* and *control* are all data processing activities and are therefore functionally similar.

Office automation has become a general term referring to all mechanized assists to business procedures not in direct control of industrial machines.

The objective of industrial automation is the production of *goods*. The objective of office auto-

Chart 2-1.  Data Processing Activities

| TERM | EXPLANATION | EXAMPLES |
|---|---|---|
| **DATA PROCESSING** | The activity of submitting data ("bits" of information) to specific operations to make the information more usable for the intended purpose. Synonymous to information handling. Includes office automation and computation. | Data processing for office automation: use of punched cards, tapes, digital computers, automatic typewriters, sorting machines; to perform arithmetic operations, comparison, sorting, distribution, and data reduction. Data processing for computation: using digital computers, analog computers, equation solvers, differential analyzers, integrators, to provide "answers" to problems. Data processing for automatic control: operating on control information by means of analog-mathematical (proportional) controls; or by means of digital-logical (sequential) controls, or by mentors (limited purpose control computers). |
| **OFFICE AUTOMATION** | Data processing primarily to do routine "paperwork." | Controlling letters, billing, and mailings of magazine subscriptions; disbursement and recordkeeping of nation-wide ticket sales for ship, train, or plane; insurance records and billing; inventory control of department store; cost analysis from time and price records; payroll; averaging and statistical evaluations; census data compilation machine, translation of languages; determining machine scheduling for large job-shop production. |
| **COMPUTATION** | Processing data primarily to obtain an "answer"; the solution of algebraic, trigonometric, or differential equations, or of arithmetic problems. | Analog computation or control is "mathematical" for it solves a real algebraic equation, by a concurrent set of operations. Best suited for solving equations and for engineering design calculations, such as of transformers or of transmission lines. Digital computation or control is "logical" for it follows a set of operating rules in a series of sequential and consecutive operations. Digital computers act by repeated summation. Used to compute ballistics tables, rocket orbits, statistical analysis, bank statements, and investment yields. |
| **CONTROL** | Data processing primarily to accomplish direct control of a machine or process. | Analog (proportional) control: speed control, servomechanism linear positioning, torque control, record-playback machine control. Digital (numerical) control: on-off, sequencing, numerical control of machine table positions, "logic control." Mentor (limited purpose computers) control: averaging, machinability, dull tool detection, automatic quality control. |

mation is the production of *services* involving the processing of information.

Chart 2-1, Data Processing Activities, describes the uses of data processing for office automation, computation, and control. In the case of automatic control, information is processed by means of controllers and mentors for the control of a machine. In the case of office automation, a large mass of information is refined and organized, usually for routine recordkeeping or to guide executive decisions.

An example of office automation is shown in Fig. 2-2.

A basic point to keep in mind is that any information that can be handled in a routine way can be handled by an automatic data-processing system; however, the work must first be reorganized to facilitate automatic data processing. Mere assignment of man tasks to machines does not succeed. It is necessary to program the work, that is, to break the task down into small elements that can be performed in sequence. Before this can be done, the work must be carefully studied and all redundant operations culled out. Then the machine can really show a great improvement over manual methods of computation and recordkeeping.

As an example, let us consider the use of data processing for mortgage loan-payment collections. In the traditional manner, the clerical staff is required to send out monthly notices, reminder notices, keep reserve accounts for taxes and in-

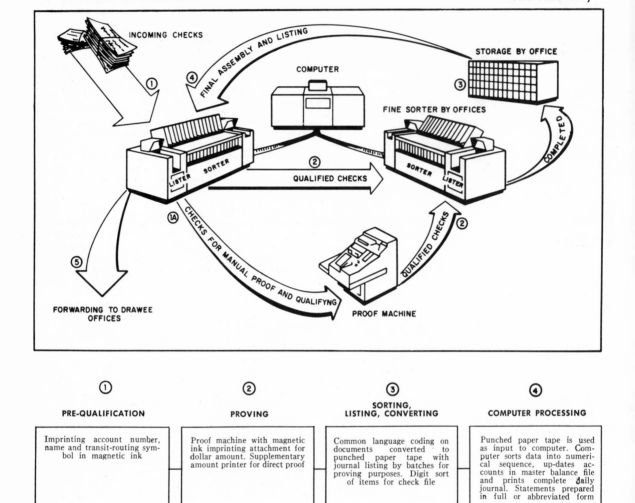

| ① PRE-QUALIFICATION | ② PROVING | ③ SORTING, LISTING, CONVERTING | ④ COMPUTER PROCESSING |
|---|---|---|---|
| Imprinting account number, name and transit-routing symbol in magnetic ink | Proof machine with magnetic ink imprinting attachment for dollar amount. Supplementary amount printer for direct proof | Common language coding on documents converted to punched paper tape with journal listing by batches for proving purposes. Digit sort of items for check file | Punched paper tape is used as input to computer. Computer sorts data into numerical sequence, up-dates accounts in master balance file and prints complete daily journal. Statements prepared in full or abbreviated form |

Figure 2-2.  Office automation for bank check processing.

surance, and credit payments against interest and principal. Before automatic data-processing can be used, the entire office procedure must first be simplified then adapted to machine methods.

The improvements in office procedures which are forced by the advent of automatic processing contribute much of the positive results obtainable by the use of automatic information-handling systems. In other words, if the procedures of the office are studied and reprogrammed for most efficient action and then automation is *not* used, a great deal of benefits will still result. One

of the contributions of office automation to business is that it compels the adaption of more efficient procedures that have nothing directly to do with electronic machines. One cannot help inferring that many of the advantages of office automation can be obtained without actually making use of electronic equipment.

The alert business manager does not immediately rush out and buy big scale office automation equipment. With a look to the future, he may call in a management consultant to help him *rethink* his operations, especially to cull out every

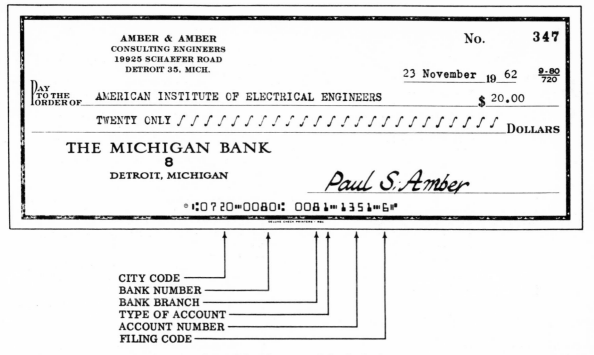

Figure 2-3. Magnetic ink bank check.

bit of superfluous paper work. After this, he can introduce automatic business machines where most needed.

Although suitably programmed digital computers are the *heart* of office automation, certain office machines are used in conjunction with the data processing action. Addressing machines, billing machines, automatic printing machines, sorters, punchers, tabulators, checkwriters and signers, money counters, automatic microfilming machines, automatic typewriters, pneumatic tube conveyors, wired TV, counters, and registers are examples. These, too, are a part of office automation.

## MILITARY AUTOMATION

The earliest engineers were military engineers. The missile control engineer of today is also a military engineer, though he would be amazed to hear it. Just as the civil engineer developed from the early military engineer, the industrial control engineer is developing from the military control engineer.

Military has led the way and continues to lead the way in engineering. No one else has had such fabulous success or such costly failures. Military developments made commercial television and nuclear power possible. Industrial users of automatic control can learn much from the military control, both successes and failures.

Chart 2-4, Military Automation Activities, shows the contribution of military developments to automatic control for commercial use, further amplified below.

### CONTROL

Control engineering is most advanced in the military area. Military control developments which contain techniques applicable to industrial automation are exhibited by military ranging, homing, and simulating equipment. The same electric and electronic techniques which are suitable for guiding the delivery of projectiles to an enemy and to guide ships and planes, are also suitable for the control of industrial machines and processes.

Military machines are just special purpose de-

Chart 2-4.  Military Automation Activities

| TERM | EXPLANATION | MILITARY EXAMPLES AND THEIR INDUSTRIAL COUNTERPARTS |
|---|---|---|
| CONTROL | The means, method and act of having a "device" (man, machine, process or system) perform as desired; usually to accomplish a specific objective. | Automatic navigation: guidance of missiles, aircraft, ships, tanks.<br>Fire control: guidance of projectiles and torpedoes, and prediction of their target location.<br>Equipment control: radar antennas, sonar heads, gun elevations and traversing.<br>Computer control: ballistic computation, simulators, navigation, range finding.<br><br>Servomechanisms, remote control, remote positioning, instrumentation and measurements, and computer control. |
| INSTRUMENTATION | The means used to display information about varying conditions, usually by indicating the numerical value of a measurement. Instrumentation includes sensor (transducer), data processing equipment (such as amplifier), and indicator (such as lamp) or instrument (such as a meter). | Direction and distance: range finders, radar, sonar, fathometer, depth gage; optical sights, infrared sights, gyro-compasses.<br>Conditions: temperature, pressure, CO alarm, fuel level, bathythermograph sea temperature indicator, miscellaneous aircraft and marine pilotage instruments and warning devices.<br><br>Automatic measurements and surveillance are the industrial versions of military instrumentation. |
| RANGING | Determining distance, altitude, depth, aspect, and velocity of a remote object. | Optical range finders, Radar, Optar, Sonar, Loran, Shoran, Decca, Omnirange.<br><br>Optical inspection instruments, "radar" heating, supersonic thickness measurement, induction thickness and hardness measurements; electronic testing; inspecting foods (eggs, fruit) by "Q" loss profile; determining size and weight of a piece part by its RF energy absorption, and by electro-mechanical resonance. |
| HOMING | Determining direction and angular velocity of a target from a remote position.<br>Seeks target by self-correction. | Direction finding, acoustical control of torpedoes, infrared tracking of bombs, proximity fuse (sensing) of shells.<br><br>Precision positioning by scanning reflection of pulsed light source; detection of dull drill by squeak; quality inspection by "ringing" piece parts; measuring temperature and position of hot objects by IR sensing; proximity switches; optical measurement of inaccessible objects such as steel billets. |
| SIMULATION | Creating "synthetic situations" for training purposes. Artificially creating a number of effects so that collectively they give the appearance of a realistic situation. | Radar and sonar simulators, gunnery trainers; link trainer, submarine trainer, anti-submarine warfare trainer, bombing trainer, operational flight trainer, tank combat trainer.<br><br>Chemical process trainer, nuclear pile simulator trainer, learning stimulators (sic), design by analog substitution, mentor control of machines and processes. |
| OPERATIONS RESEARCH | Application of the scientific method to the analysis of an involved relationship of actions and effects. The method of forming a "model" (commonly mathematical) that applies to the conditions under study to aid in decision making. | Specifying best procedure and tactics for bombing, mine sweeping, anti-submarine warfare; mathematical analysis of group operations; evaluating comparative military equipment; specifying functional characteristics for radar, gunnery, communications, sonar, and fire control equipment.<br><br>Generalized formula of coil taping operation; optimum design; queueing theory; evaluation of manufacturing systems. Writing equations upon which to base $A_s$ mentor control. |

Chart 2-4. Military Automation Activities (Continued)

| TERM | EXPLANATION | MILITARY EXAMPLES AND THEIR INDUSTRIAL COUNTERPARTS |
|---|---|---|
| HUMAN ENGINEERING | The practice of measuring man's range of capabilities and limitations and designing the machine or process to accommodate man rather than vice-versa. The policy of making optimum use of men, as part of an overall system. Termed ergonomics in Great Britain. | Study of human abilities and limitations; specifying pilot's seating, control arrangement, indicators, procedures; simplifying radar display and use for quicker comprehension. Coordinated arrangement of levers, pedals (with power boosters), and alarm indicators for an excavating machine; automatic display of vital data on the graphic panel of a refinery; centralized readout (visual display) of output count and quality and of tool condition, for all machines in plant. |
| SYSTEMS ENGINEERING | Design of a complex system by coordinating all elements that make up the system, taking into account their interactions as well as their individual characteristics. Malfunctions must be considered as well as normal operation. | Airborne fire control system coordinating manual, optical, electronic, and navigation data; missile guidance system coordinating ground radar signals, computers, inertial navigation, and target sensing; design of lighter-than-air airship trainer (simulator) coordinating simulation of radar, aerodynamic properties, armaments, engines, power, sound, and all flight instruments. Automatic manufacture of quartz radio crystals; automatic statistical quality control and selective assembly of piece parts; numerical control of groups of machines; any automation machine or process; freight-car train make-up. |

vices that make use of control techniques applicable to any system, including industrial machines. Cannons and mortars can be likened to $A_1$ industrial power tools. Self-loading guns can be likened to self-feeding, semi-automatic $A_2$ machine tools such as the power hack saw. Machine guns are comparable to automatic cycle $A_3$ machines, such as automatic riveting machines.

Self-homing projectiles and proximity fuses have a resemblance to $A_4$ feedback machines, such as size-controlled grinders, for they adjust themselves to achieve their objective. The computer-controlled bombsight and fire control director are the military version of $A_5$ computer-controlled industrial machines.

### INSTRUMENTATION

Instrumentation provides the information upon which control action is based whether for military or for industrial purposes. Manual control is greatly *aided* by automatic instrumentation; automatic control *demands* automatic instrumentation.

Military instrumentation evolved from instruments which aided the operator, such as the

World War II bombsight. This led to the full automation of key operations, such as an integrated computer-controlled, fire control system. Industry, too, first adopts automatic instrumentation, then fully automatic systems. Many of the sensors used for industrial sensing and measurement were first developed to instrument military systems. Examples are precision synchros, supersonic pickups, and infrared cells.

### RANGING

Military ranging techniques point out methods for sensing and measuring objects in the process of manufacture without direct contact. They also provide a well-developed technology of microsecond timing, use of precision indicators, use of mentors (elementary control computers), and optical methods. Military ranging, such as radar and sonar, exhibits electronics at a high stage of development.

### HOMING

Military homing techniques illustrate methods for detecting locations on objects from which measurements can be made without contact. This is important because direct contact with work pieces undergoing manufacture is not always possible with a measuring transducer.

### SIMULATION

To simulate a real life situation (for training or study), the pertinent conditions that make up the situation must be determined. For simulating flights by instruments, each function (direction, altitude, wind, load, and so on) must be described as an alegbraic equation. This results in families of related equations. The instruments in a trainer are caused to respond to the solutions of the equations by limited-purpose analog computers. Models and motion picture projections are then automatically manipulated to simulate reality.

Simulation points the way to $A_5$ mentor control of industrial machines. The pertinent factors must be determined. Then control of the machine based on the automatic reconciliation (solution) of the equations is possible. Military simulators display the technique of control by computation and have made the necessary components available.

### HUMAN ENGINEERING

Human engineering developed because military machines (such as aircraft) made excessive demands on the operator, resulting in poor overall performance and failures. The ultimate result of human engineering is automation, when man is no longer asked to perform routine duties or to serve a machine.

Human engineering obviously applies to machinists as well as to jet pilots.

An early human engineering step, to help the operator work better, was to give him better controls; that is, power boosters, improved knobs and levers, and logical arrangements. The next step was to help him know what the machine was doing through automatic measurements, improved indicators, and direct reading instruments.

Once these aids exist, the stage is set to have a control system replace the operator, by arranging that certain readings bring about specific control actions, thus relieving the operator of all direct control responsibilities.

### SYSTEMS ENGINEERING

Military systems developers have learned at great cost that a *system* is much more than a mere collection of components. No matter how well described and specified, the operation of a component or unit along with other parts in a system cannot always be predicted. Hence, the *system* must consider the complex of all parts working together, not merely the summation of individual units. In addition, every factor that affects the performance of the system (including the effect of failures), is a part of the system and must be considered. Automation systems also involve the coordination of men, machines, components, materials, and operations. Successful industrial automation demands the *systems* approach.

In summary, the control engineer who is making use of complex systems for automation will take with him both the positive and negative lessons from military automation. Feedback control and computer control can serve his industrial applications well. The systems approach, rather than piecemeal design, is necessary to coordinate the interactions of the many stages and units within a system.

## INDUSTRIAL AUTOMATION

The industrial area of automation contains several groups of activities, as shown in Chart 2-5. These are the activities that directly pertain to the manufacture of products, both products of the continuous processing industries and products of the piece-part fabricating industries, which are stressed in this discussion.

### PRODUCTION ACTIVITIES

The broad designation *industrial engineering* includes tool engineers, manufacturing engineers, production planners, methods engineers, and master mechanics. Also embraced by industrial engineering is machine design, materials handling, and all quality control activities.

The *quality* activities include measuring, inspection and testing, and statistical quality control. The *materials handling* activities include both plant-to-plant transportation and interma-

Chart 2-5. Industrial Automation Activities

| | TERM | EXPLANATION | EXAMPLES |
|---|---|---|---|
| PRODUCTION ACTIVITIES | PRODUCTION ENGINEERING (Industrial Engineering) | Concerns itself with manufacturing, the production of goods. | Plant layout, arranging an automatic warehouse; designing an automatic machine or process; selecting machine and processes for a tractor plant; studies of costs, efficiencies and materials; value analysis of production methods; also specialties as methods engineering, plant engineering and manufacturing engineering. |
| | PRODUCTION PLANNING AND CONTROL | Concerns itself with the most effective methods and arrangement for the production of goods; mainly the organization and planning of the manufacturing process. | Measuring effectiveness of manufacturing process; scheduling machining operations, determining optimum machine loading. Improving efficiency and productivity of existing and contemplated production systems. |
| | TOOL ENGINEERING | Concerns itself mainly with the tools, dies, jigs, and fixtures; for cutting and forming the workpiece, guiding the tool, and for holding the workpiece. | Developing jigs and fixtures for holding and positioning workpieces undergoing the manufacturing process. Machinability evaluations; determinations of rates and feeds for optimum removal of metal; choice of metal cutting tools; determining when to replace tools; deciding best method for removing metal. |
| MATERIALS HANDLING ACTIVITIES | | Concerns itself with the task of moving materials at the proper time, place, and position. | Use of pipe lines and chutes; use of conveyors, elevators, transfer machines; automatic stock room; assembly of mixed products on one line; precision orientation, positioning and manipulation, of the workpiece; lift trucks; scrap removal. |
| QUALITY ACTIVITIES | | MEASUREMENTS: the activity of determining the numerical value of a "dimension." Usually the physical size of the workpiece, but the "dimension" being measured may be any process or product variable. | Measuring diameters of work produced by lathes or centerless grinders; measuring thickness of work pieces being milled or surface ground; measuring process variables, such as temperatures, pressures, flow rates. |
| | | INSPECTION: the activity of comparing measurements or other attributes of quality to a standard to determine acceptance or rejection. | Use of micrometers or comparators; automatic measurements using transducers, color matching, magnetic flow detectors. |
| | | QUALITY CONTROL: the activity of evaluating measurements and inspection information by statistical methods. | Averaging, determining variability, determining machine or process capability; determining malfunction and "out of control"; evaluating by sampling. |
| DESIGN | | The activity of designating by drawings and specifications, the details of a proposed product, process, system, or plan of action with due consideration to the pertinent factors. | Product redesign for automation: gas valve; television; foam rubber seats; extruded window frames; plastic buckets, dishes trays, and covers; typewriter sub assembly; Automation process design: gas valve manufacture and assembly; printed electronic circuit process; foam rubber plant; automatic extrusion process, polyethylene plastic process; automatic assembly of typewriter keys and type bars to varied keyboards. |

chine movement of parts. *Design* activities pertain to the product as well as to the process, for they must be considered together.

These industrial engineering specialties overlap. Production men, whatever their title, participate in all to some extent.

INDUSTRIAL ENGINEERING PRACTICE

Typical responsibilities of industrial engineering are: plant layout, selection of machines and processes, scheduling of work to machines, selection of tooling, coordinating production opera-

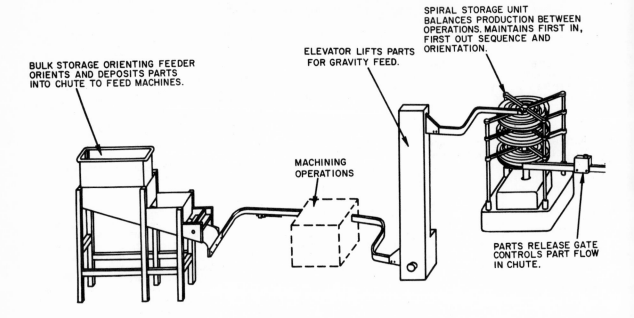

BULK STORAGE ORIENTING FEEDER ORIENTS AND DEPOSITS PARTS INTO CHUTE TO FEED MACHINES.

ELEVATOR LIFTS PARTS FOR GRAVITY FEED.

SPIRAL STORAGE UNIT BALANCES PRODUCTION BETWEEN OPERATIONS. MAINTAINS FIRST IN, FIRST OUT SEQUENCE AND ORIENTATION.

MACHINING OPERATIONS

PARTS RELEASE GATE CONTROLS PART FLOW IN CHUTE.

Figure 2-6. Automatic parts handling.

tions, cost analysis, flow study, time study, and the placement and assignment of labor. The three basic kinds of fabrication; the tool-room, the job-shop, and mass-production, require different manufacturing techniques.

### TOOL-ROOM WORK

The tool room usually makes few-of-a-kind, such as models, experimental work, tools, dies, and fixtures, and parts of special machines. Precision and adaptability are the problems here. The industrial engineer strives to get machines of greatest adaptability and precision. A typical example is the precision jig-boring machine, which can be used to jig-bore, drill, and mill, to a high order of accuracy.

For tool-room work, the set-up time of the work is often much longer than is the actual metal cutting time. Automation helps here, not by doing the job without human aid, but by means of built-in precision table and tool setting and measuring instrumentation, to ease setting up the machine and its tooling.

If several pieces must be made, means for automatically programming the machine bed and

tool positions are well worthwhile. However, absolute automation is not needed in the tool room.

### JOB-SHOP WORK

The job shop is similar to the tool room in that short runs are made, but the precision required is seldom as great, and many hundreds of parts may be produced not just a few. General purpose machines are used here because special dies and fixtures are too costly for small lot production. As a job shop makes all kinds of parts, the machines are arranged by the type of operation rather than for the *flow* of the workpieces. The production problem here is mainly quick set-up time, materials handling between dispersed machines, and production planning to keep the machines loaded, and to minimize nonproductive time.

The short runs and frequent machine resettings typical of job-shop operations may justify numerically controlled or record-playback automatic machine control. Even if the operator is still needed for loading and general surveillance, the work is thus speeded up and the chance of human error reduced.

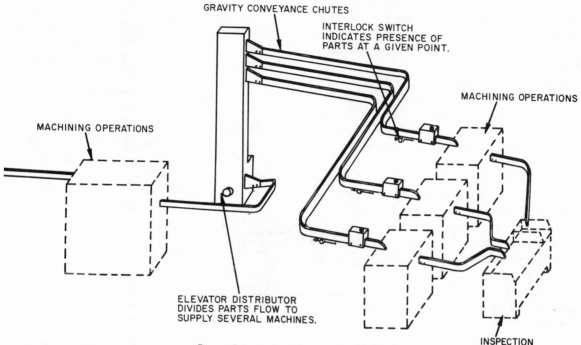

GRAVITY CONVEYANCE CHUTES

INTERLOCK SWITCH
INDICATES PRESENCE OF
PARTS AT A GIVEN POINT.

MACHINING OPERATIONS

MACHINING OPERATIONS

ELEVATOR DISTRIBUTOR
DIVIDES PARTS FLOW TO
SUPPLY SEVERAL MACHINES.

INSPECTION

Figure 2-6. Automatic parts handling.

### Mass-Production Practice

Whereas tool-room work is few-of-a-kind, and job-shop production consists of short runs, mass production concerns the manufacturing of identical goods in large quantities. This is the most familiar mode of manufacturing and is the outstanding characteristic of United States production practice.

Mass production became possible once the use of interchangeable parts was generally accepted. Prior to setting up for mass production, each part is analyzed into separate production operations. The methods by which these operations will best be accomplished are then determined. These operations are programmed in a fixed sequence and arranged physically to accomplish a smooth *flow* of the work from one operation to the succeeding operation.

Mass production can be done manually and was so done at one time. The actual operations are usually accomplished by chip-making machine tools. In the typical nonautomated factory, these are $A_1$ powered tools and $A_2$ semi-automatic self-feeding tools, fortified by some $A_3$

automatic cycle machines. Assembly is usually $A_0$, by hand.

Mass production, using powered machines, succeeded to the point where further improvements in machining operations resulted in negligible time savings because the tasks of moving and positioning the workpiece between operational stations consumed most of the time. This led to concentrated efforts to reduce the interoperation time and fostered the development of specialized intermachine materials handling devices. When the machines accomplishing mass production operations were interconnected by suitable materials handling devices so that no human effort was required, the result was termed *automation*.

This was how automation developed from the intermachine materials handling approach. The other major approach to the automation was from automatic control. Interoperation time was only partly caused by the delay in moving materials. Much of the total production time was spent in deciding what to do next. Most of the actions and decisions were of a routine nature, but they were paced by the operator's reactions and inattention. This led to the use of elaborate predecisions of what to do and how to do it. That is, machine programs for automatic control were used, which called out the decisions as necessary.

The industrial automation we have today is largely based on station-to-station materials handling. Predetermined programs govern the necessary control actions (mainly of operation sequence and part position) necessary to do the work.

Machines for the three basic forms of production can benefit from automation. However, the automatic features must offer different specific advantages for each form of production. The tool-room machines must stress quick and accurate positioning of the workpiece. The job-shop machines must stress ease of changeover and versatility. Mass-production machines must stress mechanized materials handling and automatic decisions.

### PRODUCTION PLANNING AND CONTROL

The objective of production planning is to organize machine utilization and the supply and movement of materials, and to bring about the desired number and quality of manufactured items at the right time and place. This involves planning and control of routing, scheduling, and dispatching in addition to the coordination and control of materials, methods, machines and operating times, and inspection. Data processing computers and information centers are a modern aid to production planners.

### TOOL ENGINEERING

The objective of any manufacturing process is to bring about a certain configuration to the workpiece, to *shape* it, commonly by *machining*, which indicates that a cutting action occurs. Attainment of the desired shaping of the workpiece requires use of a *tool*, the object which directly and physically forms the workpiece to the desired configuration.

Tool engineering concerns the devices that actually come in contact with the workpiece. This may be by holding it, as by a holding fixture, or by changing its form or shape, as by a drill. The purpose of machining is to manipulate the tool against the workpiece. The tool is the most vulnerable part of the entire process, being subject to wear and breakage. Tooling is therefore a sensitive spot of industrial automation.

One of the responsibilities of tool engineers is to specify when a tool should be replaced. This is not as easy as might appear, as unnecessary replacement wastes tool life and production time during changeover. Allowing tools to become dull may damage the workpiece. As a multi-operation transfer machine may have hundreds of tools, replacement is an important responsibility. This is discussed further in the topic *Dull Tool Detection*, Chapter 14.

Tools, tooling, and some aspects of production planning, machines, and processes, are further discussed in Chapter 4, Methods, Tooling and Operations, with accompanying charts.

### QUALITY ACTIVITIES

Objects possess certain characteristics which make them suitable for their intended purposes. Workpieces may have the characteristics of size, form, hardness, polish, straightness, strength, or color. Their level, by measurement, is what determines their suitability for the intended purpose. The actual measurement of such characteristics is needed by industry.

The objective of the manufacturing process is to impart the desired characteristics to the parts and to the assembled product. Therefore, manufacturing is the prime quality activity, for most specific characteristics (size, shape) are brought about by active manufacturing operations. It is evident that the *general* quality of the finished product, in the first sense, depends on each piece part attaining the proper measurable values of specific characteristics. This assumes that the product design is suitable, for the best manufacturing cannot overcome shortcomings in the design of the product.

For manufacturing purposes, the general sense of quality is not suitable. What is needed, is a specific measure by which quality can be evaluated.

The manufacturing process depends on three

secondary quality activities to evaluate the acceptability of the workpiece and to correct it for deficiencies. The secondary quality activities, a discussion of which follows, are *measurements, inspection and testing,* and *statistical quality control.* An all-embracing concept, *total quality control* (which includes both primary and secondary quality activities), will also be discussed.

### INDUSTRIAL MEASUREMENTS

Measurements serve three main purposes in the fabrication industries. These are:

1. Machine Control—as a basis for adjusting the machine.
2. Inspection—to determine the acceptability of the workpiece.
3. Quality Control—to determine trends and shifts in machine or process performance.

Whereas the objectives of these three purposes are somewhat separate, all depend on measurements of the workpieces. Automatic methods make it possible to combine all measurements operations, whatever their purpose. Instrumenting a machine for automatic measurements, provides information for machine control, for inspection, and for evaluating the performance of the machine.

### MACHINE CONTROL MEASUREMENTS

The output of every industrial machine must be measured when the machine is first set into service to do a particular job and periodically thereafter. Most production jobs have moderate or low precision requirements. The machinery can perform the work without excessive rejects after being properly adjusted. At the beginning of a production run (such as turning small electric motor shafts), the machine operator sets the tool the best he can, runs a few parts for trial, then measures them.

It is characteristic of all machines that they do not produce *exactly* the same results on each part but work within a range. The narrower the *spread* of the output, the better is the *capability* of the machine. The operator recognizes this by taking into account the range of measurements of output of the machine he is controlling. He

considers the center of the range as the centerline of the machine's performance. He measures machine output periodically to detect if the centerline of the machine performance has drifted or shows an excessively wide range (dispersion).

The operator of a machine is its control system. He is the agency providing feedback, for he determines the output of the machine, compares it to a standard, then adjusts the machine to minimize the error between the machine output and the standard, which is the dimension he desires. This is exactly what any feedback system does, whether it is a human operator or automatic control system.

This manual method of measurements and control is good enough when a man can stand by the machine and continually check on its operation. Otherwise, a large number of defective pieces will be produced if machine *drift* or *spread* is not soon detected.

Except for coarse work, if the operator merely measures a part and then adjusts the machine on the basis of this single measurement, he may actually be maladjusting the machine so that an excessive number of the subsequent batch of parts would measure outside of the tolerance range.

To set the machine properly, the operator must take into account both the range of performance of the machine and the average or centerline of performance. The range (the difference between the high and low measurements) tells him the machine's variation. If the range is tolerable, he considers the center of the range to be the centerline of machine performance. He may then align the centerline of machine performance to the design center of the part being produced. This is the normal procedure for controlling and adjusting a machine on the basis of manual measurements.

Automatic measurements can be a definite aid in cases where an operator cannot cope with a machine's speed of operation, or where one man is to care for a number of automatic machines. It is far easier for him to adjust the machine's settings in accordance with dial readings of automatically made measurements than to make

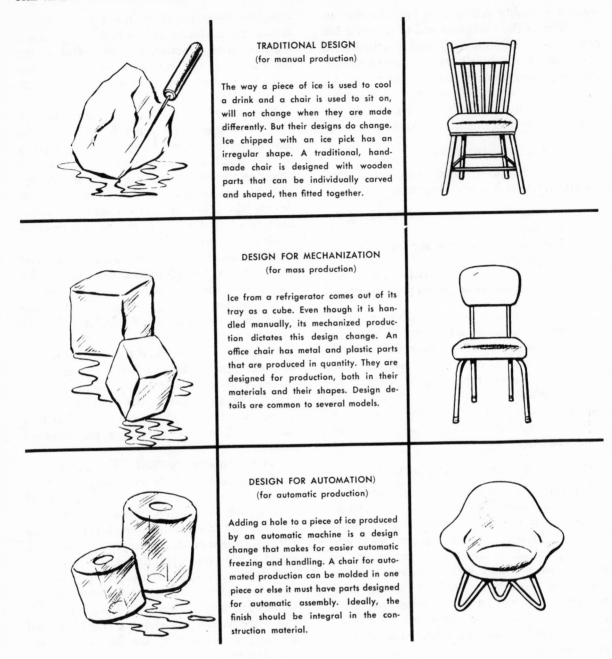

### TRADITIONAL DESIGN
#### (for manual production)

The way a piece of ice is used to cool a drink and a chair is used to sit on, will not change when they are made differently. But their designs do change. Ice chipped with an ice pick has an irregular shape. A traditional, hand-made chair is designed with wooden parts that can be individually carved and shaped, then fitted together.

### DESIGN FOR MECHANIZATION
#### (for mass production)

Ice from a refrigerator comes out of its tray as a cube. Even though it is handled manually, its mechanized production dictates this design change. An office chair has metal and plastic parts that are produced in quantity. They are designed for production, both in their materials and their shapes. Design details are common to several models.

### DESIGN FOR AUTOMATION)
#### (for automatic production)

Adding a hole to a piece of ice produced by an automatic machine is a design change that makes for easier automatic freezing and handling. A chair for auto-mated production can be molded in one piece or else it must have parts designed for automatic assembly. Ideally, the finish should be integral in the construction material.

Figure 2-7. Designing for automatic production.

the measurements himself. However, even though the measurements of the parts produced are readily displayed, the operator must still determine the range and the centerline of the machines' performance. Dials and indicators dis-playing measurements would be helpful to an operator. However, the average and the variation of the measurements, automatically calculated and displayed, would be of even greater benefit. Such a device fits in the $A_5$ order of automation.

## MATERIALS HANDLING

The movement and positioning of materials *within* a plant factory is termed *materials handling*. *Between* plants and factories, it is called *transportation*. There is no basic difference between them.

Materials handling at first was from machine to machine. Then loading and unloading of machines was included. Now machines integrate materials handling functions along with their metal forming functions.

Every improvement in materials handling directly improves automation. This is because the actual machining of a manufacturing process is usually only a small part of the production time. The major amount of time is devoted to handling materials rather than working on them. Few improvements can be expected that will appreciably shorten machining time, but there is often much room for improvement in materials handling.

Materials handling includes the simple task of moving objects from one point to another. However, in addition to bringing items to their proper location, the workpieces must be delivered at precisely the right time and be suitably orientated.

The materials to be moved may be bulk, such as plastics pellets to a molding machine. They may be highly finished instrument gears, which are easily damaged by rough handling. Large, heavy objects such as crated refrigerators must be handled quite differently from electric switches. Materials handling conveyors can be below the floor or overhead. They may make use of rollers, belts, slats, monorails, elevators, or even pipelines. Storage, industrial vehicles, shipping containers, and scrap removal are a part of materials handling, too.

For many years, industry has used machines to perform its fabrication operations. These were simply $A_1$ power tools to begin with, then power tools with power feed, the $A_2$ machines. Before long, fully automatic machines were in existence, namely, the $A_3$ machine. They were automatic but required that a man load them and that the material they machined be taken from them.

In some cases, loading $A_3$ machines was simplified, for they could receive their materials from an overhead gravity hopper and could discharge their work into another hopper. Arranging several such machines in a series constituted a simple form of automation.

Most fabricated parts had to be inserted into the machine by hand and then removed. Some automatic loading and unloading devices have been in existence for many years, but their use was not stressed mainly because the great potentialities of automatic loading and unloading were not recognized.

The role of the typical factory worker consisted of the manual loading and unloading of industrial machines. This was especially difficult and dangerous in the loading and unloading of stamping presses. Attempts to improve such operations led to the development of fully automatic materials inserting and removing devices to work with the stamping presses. Such efforts proved very successful and stimulated interest in further development of automatic equipment to handle materials in and out of machines.

### AUTOMATIC MATERIALS HANDLING

The use of automatic materials handling equipment between standard automatic industrial machines was the first widespread form of modern industrial automation.

Present-day $A_3$ industrial machines are designed to facilitate the use of standardized materials handling devices between machines. These are, in effect, $A_3$ automatic materials handling and transportation machines, the controls of which are interconnected with the $A_3$ fabricating machines.

### DEVELOPMENT OF TRANSFER MACHINES

It became apparent to some machinery designers that materials handling should be designed with the machine, not improvised later. The outcome of this line of reasoning was the transfer machine, a composite of a number of standardized machine unit stations in a row or about a common center. Each machine station performs a set of operations on the piece part. At the conclusion of a work cycle, the part is transferred to the following station in the ma-

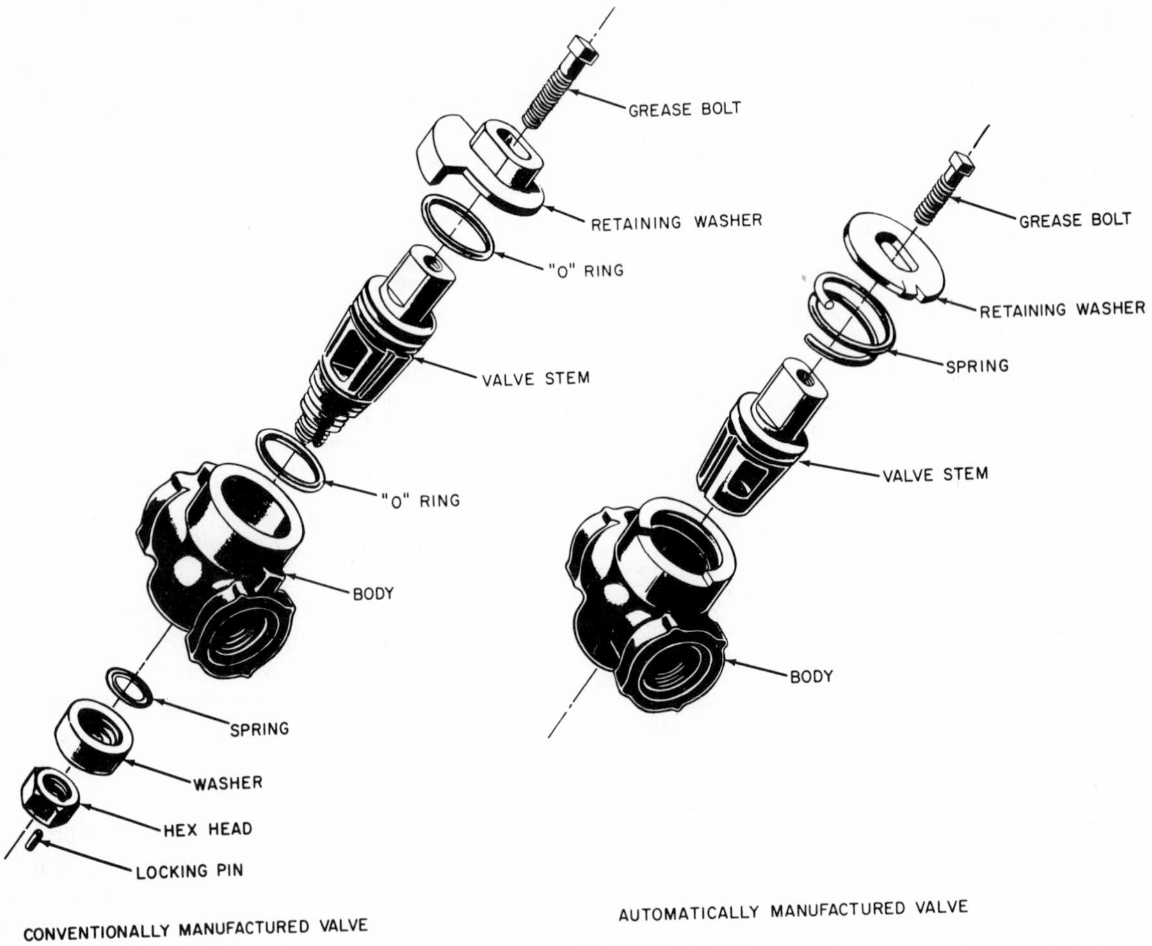

Figure 2-8. Valve re-design for automation.

chine. In this way, the part being machined proceeds from station to station, and there is no need for separate materials handling equipment. Combining the materials handling function with the metal working function of the machine has considerably simplified and speeded up the production process.

The transfer machine is not the only method that combines materials handling and machining by incorporating materials handling into the machine. Another approach is to bring the parts working machines to the materials handling system. This is done mainly by the electronics industry and electrical parts manufacturers. Their practice is to use a chain conveyor, which carries the piece part under production through the factory. Separate machine unit stations are placed at various points of the materials handling conveyor. Each station performs its specific operations, such as inserting parts, riveting, or dip soldering.

The main advantage here is flexibility of arrangement, for a variety of standard production machine stations can be positioned in any arrangement or order about the conveyor. The transfer machine, in contrast, is much less adaptable. Heavy machinery conversions may be necessary to rearrange transfer machines to accommodate product changes.

Both have their place. The heavy transfer machine saves space and results in greater precision, but the lighter conveyor-oriented automation machinery is more amenable to changes and is excellent for light assembly work.

### FLEXIBLE MATERIALS HANDLING

An example of flexible materials handling by automatic dispatching is the assembly of somewhat different engines on one assembly line. Both passenger car and truck engines are made up by using different components with the same major engine parts. The truck engine uses different carburetor, manifold, valve lifters, camshaft, and generator than the automobile does. This requires delivery of these different parts to the assembly line exactly as needed by synchronized automatic materials handling. After the engines are assembled, switches are set on the engine carriers, automatically selecting the route to the proper engine test stand and then to the loading dock. This requires flexibility of the materials handling control, as the destination and the origin of the materials are not fixed.

Automatized materials handling in the post office is a sign of what can ultimately be applied to industry. The mails transport material from a great number of points to a great number of points. This is an extreme case compared to any possible industrial application, but some transfer of method is possible.

Materials handling is a highly developed field of specialization which can only be touched briefly here. Numerous technical articles and books have shown the progress made, from simple roller conveyors to complete automatic foundries. What were once difficult materials handling problems requiring special machines can now be accomplished easily by standardized parts loaders, feeders, positioners, conveyors, and packaging machines. Although plant-wide mechanical handling systems must be designed to suit the job, most of the components, controls, and methods have already been perfected.

Figure 2-6, Automatic Parts Handling, shows that standard units can be used to make up the intermachine materials handling equipment for many automation lines. They are especially suitable for converting existing machines into an automatic continuous manufacturing system.

## DESIGN FOR AUTOMATION

It is mandatory for automation that the design of the product and its manufacturing process be coordinated. If the machine designer and the product designer work closely together, the product will be amenable to automatic manufacturing and will also incorporate advantages of being produced automatically. The goal of product-process coordination is to get the best product from the simplest machinery.

The design or redesign of the product for automation is often even more important than the automation machines themselves.

Figure 2-7, Designing for Automatic Production, illustrates the principle that a product must be designed for the process by which it is to be created. The item to be produced by mechanization is different from that made by manual methods. Likewise, if the item is to be produced automatically, the design intended for ordinary mechanized manufacture will not do.

As an example, Figure 2-8, Valve Redesign for Automation, shows how a conventional gas valve contained ten parts when it was manufactured by ordinary mass production techniques and assembled by hand. A machine could have been designed to produce each of the ten parts and to assemble them, but this would have been needlessly complex and expensive. Redesign of the valve to five parts permitted simplification of the machinery to the point where automatic fabrication of the pieces and their assembly was feasible and profitable.

## AUTOMATION, ô'to-mā-shŭn

A formal definition of the term automation will not suffice for an understanding of its implications because there is no unanimity of agreement among even the specialists as to what constitutes a complete and accurate definition. A better understanding of automation can be obtained by tracing its evolution from the earliest machines which mechanized simple manual processes.

The earliest machines invented by man made possible the manufacture of products which ordinarily required a manual skill or physical effort beyond the capacity of the operator. Usually the machine had the ability to manufacture products of uniform quality at a speed exceeding that of manual production. The most significant feature of these machines was that the sequence of operations was directly guided by the operator so that the machine and man became one. Furthermore, man supplied the prime energy required for the operation of the machine.

With the invention of the steam engine and, later, the harnessing of electrical energy man began to divorce himself from the machine for he was no longer needed as the prime source of energy. As a result, the operator and the machine became separated and as the machine took over more of the "thinking" the operator began to take on less of the character of a machine.

Modern technological developments particularly in the areas of electronics, thermodynamics, mechanics and engineering materials have made automatic or semiautomatic machines a reality. These machines perform certain functions in the overall manufacturing process of a particular product. A complex product, such as an automobile, requires a large variety of operations and a particular machine may perform one or more of these operations. The integration of the functions of these machines in the whole production process led to the concept of mass production. In mass production the actions of man and machines are integrated in a total organized effort known as the production line. Men must load, unload, and operate the machines, and control the sequence of operations of the integrated complex of machinery.

The difference between automation and mass production lies in the complete integration of fully automatic machines without the need for man as an intermediary. The machines are self-loading and self-unloading with conveyors guiding the goods in various stages of production from machine to machine. Electronic controls and actuators coordinate the functions of the various machines even to the point of correcting for errors and evaluating the quality of the finished products. Hence, from new material to finished product the entire manufacturing process is automatic without the intervention of man. The automatic controls are capable of making swift decisions when confronted with a predetermined set of variables in a variety of possible patterns.

The fully automatic factory has not yet been achieved at the production level. However, there are semiautomatic factories in existence as well as a large variety of fully automatic machines which consummate a particular group of manufacturing operations. The fully automatic office is more likely to be achieved first. The so-called electronic brains, such as digital and analog computers, are already an important factor in making decisions at the managerial and scientific level. For example, it is entirely possible to design a fully automatic office for a large industrial activity ranging from decision-making to billing the customers.

Computers can only carry through a formalized process of analysis or computation originally conceived by man. Hence, they are no more of a threat to man's intellect than the slide rule or the conventional adding machine. JOHN F. LEE, *Professor of Mechanical Engineering, North Carolina State College.*

by permission, from *The Encyclopedia Americana,* 1962 Edition.

# Production Fundamentals

# 3

Production is the economic term for making goods and services available to satisfy human wants. Production implies the creation of value by the application of useful mental or physical labor, as shown in Figure 3-1, Production: Manufacturing-Services.

*Goods* are material things such as carpets, cement, or candy. *Services* satisfy nonmaterial wants such as medicine, education, and enter-

tainment. They are the result of useful labor which does *not* directly produce a tangible commodity. Data processing, computation, teaching, planning, and design are services. Many services can be handled in the form of automatic processes by use of computers, simulators, recorders, and so on. Navigation, inspection, billing, and chemical analysis, are examples of services that can be accomplished automatically.

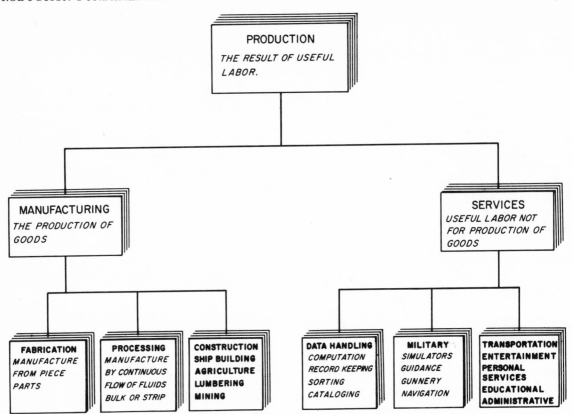

Figure 3-1. Production: manufacturing-services.

The production of services that do not pertain to industry, such as vending, transportation, and communications, makes much use of automation. The nonindustrial aspects of automation are important and interesting but beyond the scope of this book. The production of goods, *manufacturing*, commands our main attention here.

## MANUFACTURING

Manufacturing consists of making or perfecting material things (goods) for human wants. The results of manufacture are termed *products*. Manufacture also includes such processes as refining, smelting, canning, and mining.

Manufacture can be accomplished by fabrication or by processing. *Fabrication* is the making of a product from pieces such as parts, components, or assemblies. It also includes the making of the individual products or parts. Items of a

separable discrete nature, such as tires, nails, spoons, screws, refrigerators, or hinges, are fabricated.

*Processing* consists of manufacture by continuous means, or by a continuous series of operations, for a specific purpose. Items of a continuous nature, such as steel strip, beverages, breakfast foods, tubing, chemicals, and petroleum, are processed. Many products, manufactured by processing, are marketed as discrete items, such as bottles of beer, bolts of cloth, spools of wire, and sacks of flour.

Products of a separable discrete nature, both piece parts and assemblies, are made by fabrication, in a *factory*. Products which *flow* (liquids, gases, powders, strips, webs) are made by processing in a *plant, refinery* or *mill*.

We commonly hear of the *process industries*, meaning the industries such as petroleum and chemical that rely heavily on *continuous* processing. The process industries are sometimes referred to as the *flow* industries.

To a lesser extent, we hear of the *fabricating industries,* and the *manufacturing industries.* These terms refer in both cases to fabricators, such as manufacturers of clocks or tractors.

Strictly speaking, and this is the usage encouraged herein, *manufacturing* includes both fabricating and processing. The process industries are those that treat a more or less continuous product, not made up from individual parts, though various ingredients may be used. The continuous process may involve separate *treatments* to the product.

Manufacturing accomplished by fabrication from pieces rather than by continuous processing is stressed herein. In most cases, automation of fabrication manufacturing operations is more of a problem than is automation of continuous process manufacturing operations. This is because continuous process manufacturing makes use of continuous dimensions, whereas manufacturing of discrete piece parts (and assembly from discrete piece parts) makes use of discontinuous dimensions. It is easier to control continuous dimensions than it is to control discrete dimensions.

Prior to the development of modern automatic control systems, manufacturing by processing (continuous products) was considerably different from manufacturing by fabrication (discontinuous parts). These two modes of manufacture are now converging to achieve the advantages of flow production. The current trend is to eliminate production by batches in favor of an uninterrupted series of operations whenever justified by mass production requirements. This makes fabrication resemble processing more and more.

Fabrication often includes continuous process treatments such as electroplating, heat treat, demagnetizing, and extrusion forming. Thus, it is common practice to also call the continuous automatic production of piece parts a process.

Construction and agriculture are means of producing goods other than by fabrication or processing in factories. Construction is a form of production of useful goods but is not thought of as manufacturing by the public, for the work is

not done in a repetitive manner nor is it done in a plant or factory. Shipbuilding resembles both fabricating and construction.

Agriculture and commercial fishing produce real goods as the result of useful labor. Lumbering is similar to both agriculture and mining in some respects, and mining is best considered to be a form of processing. Processes which perfect or improve the raw materials from agriculture, fishing, lumbering, and mining, are, however, forms of manufacturing.

## RANK OF PRODUCTION TERMS

Production terms have a definite rank of importance somewhat like grades in the Army. Confusing *system* with *section* is akin to mistaking a colonel for a corporal. In either case, knowledge of rank is necessary, Chart 3-2. Their rank is not absolute but relative. The terms tend to overlap because of the inconsistencies of popular usage.

### SYSTEM

The highest ranking term in the production hierarchy is *system.* A system includes the apparatus, interrelations, and influencing factors (considered collectively) necessary to accomplish an end result. In its broadest sense, a production system includes men, money, machines, markets, and management. In fact, all aspects of commerce (manufacturing, sales, advertising, profit, and distribution) are involved.

Systems Engineering is a specialty which stemmed from military control systems. The armed forces engineers learned, after spending vast sums of money, that a complex system will not work successfully when made up of independently designed components however carefully the individual units are built. A radar-controlled bombsight for example, includes a target tracking subsystem, a fire-control computer, aircraft position sensors (altitude, direction, drift), and the bombsight proper. It would appear that properly · interconnecting these would result in an automatic system superior to

Chart 3-2. Rank of Production Terms

| TERM | EXAMPLES |
|---|---|
| SYSTEM | an automatic refinery; an atomic power reactor similator; missile guidance system; air line ticket reservation system; automatically assembling radios; plywood manufacture; lamp making-testing-packaging. |
| PROCESS | rolling steel, drawing wire, bottling milk, brick making, roadbuilding, distilling, also automatic manufacturing. |
| MACHINE OR SECTION | Grinding, bending, sewing, rolling, machines; bottle washing, injection molding, carton forming machines; stamping, forging presses; cigarette, knitting machines. Also machine tools, specific product machines, office machines. |
| JOB OR STATION | Typical jobs: drill, tap, countersink, blowout; fill, weigh, seal, label; insert, crimp, solder; attach carburetor, connect gas line, connect vacuum line; convey, invert, transport. Typical stations: drilling, inspection, loading, assembling, balancing, blowout, welding, sealing. |
| OPERATION OR TREATMENT | Typical operations: convey, load; shot-peen, weld; measure, sort; assemble, fit; test, tryout; fill, wrap. Typical treatments: plating, welding, annealing, blowout, dipping, etching, enameling, baking. |
| TOOL | Drills, broaches, reamers, milling cutters, grinding wheels, honing stones, dies, taps, saws. Also includes dies and fixtures. |

human control. However, experience has proved that unanticipated interactions degraded the expected effectiveness. By establishing systems engineering with systems responsibility, it was possible to properly integrate the performance of all units in a system, resulting in superior performance.

Whether or not called systems engineering, consideration of the over-all influencing factors is necessary. An industrial example is the development of a radically new process for manufacturing plate glass by floating molten glass over molten metal. Technical perfection of the basic operation was not enough. Commercial feasibility required the system-wide integration with glass industry practices and economics.

## PROCESS

A series of operations directed to a desired result is termed a *process*. This is a general term which refers to the treatment and alteration to which unfinished products are subjected. For example, injection molding, die casting, progressive stamping, spinning, dipping, assembling, testing, pasteurizing, homogenizing, cementing, and annealing are commonly called *processes*

from the functional point of view. Whereas processing implies continuous products or actions, integrated operations for continuous automatic production, such as shell mold casting, are considered to be a process, too.

Comparing *system* with *process*, the system can be considered to include the nonphysical considerations as well as the actual equipment which comprises the production process. From the control engineers' special point of view, *system* applies to control and the term *process* to the equipment being controlled. For example, the process might be a machine tool or chemical plant, in which case the control system consists of the circuitry and devices that govern the machine tool or chemical plant process.

This dual sense of the term *system* is the result of the joining of control engineering with production engineering. The correct sense is usually suggested by context.

## MACHINE OR SECTION

A machine is an assembly of related mechanisms on a frame acting together to produce a desired result. Generally, the motors, tools, controls, and auxiliary devices are included. Ma-

34

chines, such as a screw jack or can opener, need not be self-powered.

Machines may do a single operation (cut-off saw) or multiple operations (packaging) or practically an entire manufacturing process (automatic screw machine). Machines vary in size from a pencil sharpener to an elephantine forging press.

Long multi-operation transfer machines are, in actuality, semi-independent machine sections joined together to act on the workpiece in progression. Therefore, in the case of *transfer machines,* the rank of *machine* is taken by a machine *section*. A machine section generally includes those operations which affect the workpiece at the same *station*.

With flow materials, the work-in-process undergoes successive and continuous treatments, either by machines or in ovens, vats, or conditioners. Here, too, the rank of machine is taken by a section of the process—such as catalytic section, blending section, or concentrating section.

Just as *process* implies manufacture by processing, *machine* implies manufacture by fabrication, but the uses are far from pure. The ranks of *process* and of *machine* or *section* overlap. Throughout this book, any discussion pertaining to machines generally applies to processes as well.

## JOB OR STATION

Originally, a job is the work performed by a man, and station is the working place of a man on a production line.

A job is a group of related operations generally performed at one station. For example, the job at a final assembly station may consist of four operations:

1. attach carburetor
2. connect gas line
3. connect vacuum line
4. connect accelerator rod

The job of a turret lathe (a semi-automatic machine) operator may include the following op-

erations at his station: load, start, drill, index and ream, index and thread, index and chamfer, index and knurl, stop, unload, inspect.

The terms *job* and *station* have been carried over to machines without men. A job, as before, is a group of related operations generally performed at one station, and a station is a position or location in a machine (or process) where specific operations are performed. A simple machine (bench drill) has but a single station. Complex machines can be made up from standardized unit stations. The job at a station often includes many simultaneous operations, as "drill all face holes," by multiple spindle drills.

## OPERATION OR TREATMENT

An *operation* is a distinct action performed in producing a desired result or effect. Typical operations are: load, grind, or gage. Operations can be further divided into time study elements for work measurement purposes. For example, loading is made up of: picking up part; placing part in jig; closing jig. However, it is not necessary to discuss suboperational elements here.

Operations can be categorized functionally as:

1. materials handling
2. working
3. inspecting
4. assembling
5. testing
6. packaging

These basic operations may occur more than once in some processes, or they may sometimes be omitted. These six basic operations will be discussed shortly from the functional, operational, and physical points of view.

*Treatment* is a form of operation which implies that a continuous action is applied to the workpiece. It also suggests the alteration or modification of the product-in-process without the active contact of tools. Thus, we may speak of heat-treat, degreasing, or galvanizing treatments.

As usage is not precise, we must accept the fact that the terms treatment, operation, job, or station are sometimes interchanged.

THE SEVEN BASIC
MACHINE TOOLS

LATHE
turning-threading

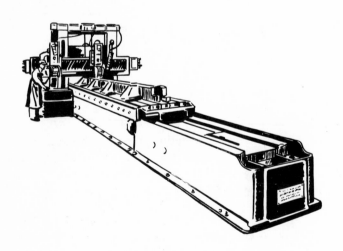

SHAPER-PLANER
straight line surfacing

MILLING MACHINE
form cutting

RADIAL DRILL
drilling and tapping

BORING MILL
hole truing

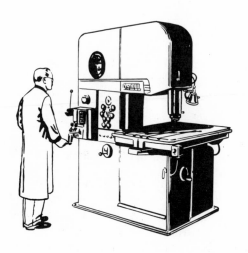

BAND MACHINE
sawing, slicing, filing

PRECISION GRINDER
surface finishing

## TOOLS

The lowest mechanism in the rank of production terms is the *tool*. It is the implement by which the unfinished product is held, cut, shaped, or formed.

Everyone has used hand tools such as a saw, hammer, or screwdriver. Other common hand tools are chisel, punch, sandpaper, drill, clamp, file, torch, and grindstone.

Basically, machines are mechanized versions of such hand tools. Most machines for fabrication use cutting tools including drills, taps, reamers, single point turning tool bits, milling cutters, saw blades, broaches, and grinding wheels. Noncutting forming tools include extrusion dies, punches, and molds.

*Tools* also include work holders and tool holders, guides, jigs and fixtures. They are critical to automation because in an entire manufacturing process tools are most liable to wear and breakage. For automation, tool holders must permit ready cutter replacement. It is also good practice to have spare tools (such as drills) right on hand for fast change. Holding jigs and fixtures must work fast but surely, as a workpiece out of place may damage the part and the cutter.

The application of tools is the role of *tool engineering*, a specialized branch of mechanical engineering. The field has become so complex that *specialists among specialists* are necessary. Some factories have separate tool engineering teams for machining steel, for cast iron, for press dies, for jigs and fixtures, and for grinding wheels.

A *new model* product requires extensive retooling of an automatic production system. That is, much of the basic machinery can often be reused, but all cutters, tool holders, work holders and dies must be changed and speeds adjusted to accommodate the new product. Manual work with simple power tools doesn't have this restriction to model change. This points out that high productivity is commonly the antithesis of flexibility.

Measuring tools and instruments are also important to production. Common examples of measuring tools are rules, scales, calipers, micrometers, gages, and precision devices that use electronic amplifiers and optics. Deserving special notice are air gages, which depend on escaping air as the measuring medium, thus greatly reducing gage wear problems. Measuring tools and their use are the responsibility of *inspection engineering*, another production specialty.

This brief discussion of tools must not obscure noncutting production operations. The medium of action on the product can be air, heat, magnetic fields, chemicals, or electric currents. In fact, *chipless* methods of manufacture, such as cold forming, die casting, or molding, may often be superior for automation. Many manufacturing methods and types of tooling are evaluated in the following chapter, "Methods, Tooling, and Operations."

## WORK

*Work* is the action or effort expended in production and refers to the use of machine power and manpower or brainpower, to create useful goods and services. The Rank of Production Terms, Chart 3-2, does not include *work* because this is a general term which is sometimes used to mean the same as job, operation, or treatment.

In another sense, *work* refers to the unfinished product, as workpiece, work-in-process, stock, or semi-finished goods. Work is defined in Chart 7-3.

## SUMMARY OF PRODUCTION TERMS

The relationship of the terms covered in Chart 3-2, Rank of Production Terms, is best summarized by analyzing a food preparation process that transforms raw peanuts into snacks attractively packed in transparent bags for sale by vending machines and in supermarkets.

Figure 7-2 (see Chapter 7) represents the process as a functional block diagram. Briefly, the basic *process* includes those functions which directly affect the product. In this case (A) raw material, (B) self-loading, (C) shell and screen,

(D) cooking, in oil, (E) packaging, by weight, (F) packaging, by count, (G) finished product. The process also includes the conveyors between machines.

Items (U) to (Z) are subsystems, as they do not directly affect the product. Items (U) to (Y) are simple process controllers, independent *local* control systems, which regulate temperature, speed, and count automatically. Item (Z), the control panel, integrates the action of the several sections of the process. The control panel functions include motor starting, sequencing of operations, and interlock protection. A production tally counter is also included.

Items (B) to (F) are functional *sections*, as are the automatic conveyors between machine sections. Sections (E) and (F) are combined as one *machine*. Section (B) is a *feeder* machine specially designed to load machine (C).

The *job* at each machine consists of several operations or treatments, such as machine (D), which cooks, drains, and salts the peanuts continuously. Machine (EF) includes weighing, sealing, packing, and unloading *stations*.

The Peanut Packing Process is fully automatic. However, an operator is required at intervals. His job is mainly surveillance. He sees that the hopper is filled, that the supply of bags is replenished, and that the finished peanuts have the desired color and taste, very difficult to instrument automatically.

Because the product is processed rather than fabricated, there is no shaping of a workpiece and, consequently, few tools are needed. Friction husking rollers and bag sealing clamps are the tools in this particular process.

The *systems* approach to the development of the Peanut Packing Process considers more than the physical treatment of the peanuts and the control subsystems. Other factors are:

  a. raw materials (peanuts, oil)
  b. supplies (bags, cartons)
  c. outlets (vending machines, supermarkets)
  d. perishability and storage
  e. sanitation and health laws
  f. package style, size and price
  g. maintenance and waste disposal
  h. process flexibility

Unexpected advantages may be revealed by a systems study preceding equipment design. In the process just described, an Automation Feasibility Study may reveal that the machines should be capable of handling several sizes of bags, and they should also be able to treat and pack varied nut meats other than peanuts. Perhaps the Automation Feasibility Study would also advise that the process be able to prepare and pack *shoestring potatoes,* using an alternate form of machine (C).

This example shows that a systems study can sometimes increase the value of a process at little additional cost, by suggesting how the mechanisms can be made more versatile. Adaptability to varied products and packages reduces the risk of obsolescence.

## FUNDAMENTAL MANUFACTURING OPERATIONS

Manufacturing a product entails six fundamental manufacturing operations, as shown in Chart 3-3. These operations are distinct and separate for ordinary methods of producing goods. Oftentimes, the separate machines performing these operations can be linked by use of automatic devices which transfer the workpiece from machine to machine, accomplishing automatic continuous production. Joining existing standard production machines in this manner makes possible *progressive* automation with a minimum expenditure for new equipment.

The fundamental operations can occur several times in a manufacturing process or not at all. After discussing each fundamental manufacturing operation, an industrial process will be explained which summarizes the different terms and compares them in their functional, operational, and physical aspects.

### MATERIALS HANDLING OPERATIONS

*Materials handling* is defined as transporting unfinished goods, workpieces, and supplies to and from, between, and during manufacturing operations. Loading, positioning, unloading, and storing are also materials handling operations.

Chart 3-3. Fundamental Manufacturing Operations

| OPERATION | EXAMPLES |
|---|---|
| MATERIALS HANDLING | Manual effort: lift, carry, push, wheelbarrow, roller conveyor. Mechanized: belt conveyor, industrial truck, hopper feed, bucket conveyor, transfer shuttle, power and free conveyor, Archimedes screw, endless chain, pneumatic tubes. |
| WORKING | Turning, grinding, milling; stamping, spinning, bending; welding, riveting; polishing, plating, painting; annealing, degreasing, baking. |
| INSPECTING | Go-not go; thread gages, air gages; magnaflux, X ray; optical comparators; micrometers, surface plate layout; laboratory analysis; photoelectric sorting, segregating; ultra-sonic probing. |
| ASSEMBLING | Putting together an engine, typewriter, binoculars, watch, vacuum cleaner, panel board, fluorescent fixture, carburetor, automobile, fuel pump, shaver or compressor. |
| TESTING | Functional testing of fluorescent lamp starters, engine idling speed, transistor characteristics, generator loading, dynamometer response. Also pressure, leakage, high voltage breakdown, hardness and rupture testing. |
| PACKAGING | Toothpaste in tubes; cement in bags; cigarettes in packs, cartons, and shipping cartons; bearings in wraps; milk in paper cartons; appliances in crates; wire on spools; cloth on bolts. |

*Transportation,* by truck or train, is materials handling between factories. Materials handling can be reduced by careful plant layout and can be mechanized in countless ways.

Automatic materials handling is the most important step to continuous automatic manufacture. Until automatic machines could be loaded and unloaded without the constant need for human attention, continuous automatic production was limited.

Materials handling as a fundamental operation means not only conveyors and loaders but includes positioning the workpiece within the machine by indexing, shuttle bars, slides, and clamps. The manufacture of automobile doors is described as an example.

An automatic press line forms the door from sheet metal. The material is drawn, flanged, pierced, and folded on successive stamping presses. The material is fed into the first press and successively to the others by specially designed conveyors and positioners. A mechanized grab device called the *iron hand* removes the stamping from the dies.

Meanwhile, another stamping line is forming the inner door panel. Both inner and outer door panels are then automatically transferred to a resistance welding press which joins the two sections. Without automatic materials handling, these noisy and hazardous presses had to be loaded and unloaded by men.

Waste removal, too, has been mechanized. This is not as easy as it appears. Removing trimmings and cutoffs can be more difficult than materials handling of the product. This must be done, though, for a tangle of scrap leads to damaged tooling and defective work.

## WORKING OPERATIONS

The *working* operations are those which create a product by alteration or treatment of a workpiece or goods in process, as by machining, forming, joining, finishing, or heating. *Working* is synonymous with *making*. Processing and fabricating are forms of working.

Whereas working a part most generally means removing metal or cutting, *chipless methods* such as cold forming, electric arc erosion, electro-polishing, die casting, chemical milling, powder metallurgy and extrusion, are gaining ground, as discussed in the next chapter.

The manufacture of automobile doors, previously described from the materials handling

Materials handling

aspect, is also illustrative of forming a product by progressive stamping. Cutting and bending steel wire to form refrigerator shelves is also working, as is machining refrigeration fittings from bar stock on an automatic turret lathe.

Working (or making) by processing is exemplified by rayon cord (for tires) which passes through dipping, stretching, drying, coating with rubber, cooling, and winding operations. Electric adjustable speed drives at each section of the process automatically control proper speed and tension of the rayon cord.

Many working operations already perform as fast as existing tools and knowledge permit. Even with automatic materials handling to and from machine stations, the workpiece is actually being worked upon only a brief time. The search for faster and cheaper manufacturing methods must lead to radical product redesign which will simplify the product and eliminate most cutting operations.

## INSPECTION OPERATIONS

*Inspection* is the examination of a workpiece, both visually and with instruments, to determine defects, errors, and flaws of material or manufacture. Inspection can be based on measurements (length, diameter, weight, depth, viscosity) or attributes (color, freshness, appearance, lumber grades).

The traditional purpose of inspection is to cull out unsatisfactory materials, parts, subassemblies, and assemblies. A more advanced attitude of inspection is to *prevent* the production of unsatisfactory items, not merely to discard them after they have been made. Unsatisfactory quality trends should be detected and corrected promptly to minimize production of defective parts.

Mass production depends on the assembly of complex products from standardized interchangeable parts. Inspection assures that the parts being manufactured and the materials used conform to drawings and specifications so that the parts will be truly interchangeable.

Manufacture of precise products may demand constant inspection, manual or automatic. Some products may require only *spot checking*, once the machines have been accurately adjusted.

The Peanut Packing Process previously discussed requires only occasional surveillance, for example. However, all manufacturing processes depend on some form of information feedback to insure that the products being manufactured continue to be acceptable. The feedback link is usually man. Less frequently, it is accomplished automatically.

Complex parts can be inspected automatically by combining numerous gaging units into a gaging fixture. One such automatic inspection machine gages 80 dimensions on automotive crankshafts. These include diameters, alignment, eccentricity, bores, and filet radii. The machine

41

is self-loading and unloading. Dimensions are marked on record cards to facilitate adjustment of the machining operations when a trend for the dimensions to go out of the acceptable limits is noted by the operator.

## ASSEMBLY OPERATIONS

Assembly is the fitting together of individual parts to make up a fabricated product. The parts may first be combined into smaller groups, known as *assemblies* and *subassemblies*. Assembly by hand is very common even in industries which are otherwise highly mechanized. Automatic assembly is complex and costly, yet great opportunities for automation lie here. Automation of assembly operations has succeeded in the manufacture of TV chassis, electric switches, clock motors, valves, locks and motor windings.

Assembly line

The ideal solution to automatic assembly problems is to redesign the product radically, to simplify manufacturing and assembly operations as illustrated in Figure 2-8.

Trying to assemble automatically products which were originally intended to be put together by hand results in needlessly complex and costly machines. The linotype machine, for example, does not pick individual pieces of type out of a case as a human compositor does. To

eliminate direct manual labor, particularly hand assembly, both product and production system should be designed concurrently, to be compatible.

Automatic assembly of television chassis is an example of product design to accommodate production. Use of circuit boards with etched wiring is the basis of automatizing electronic manufacture. The various resistors and capacitors must be supplied to the inserting mechanisms properly positioned, either on belts or in magazines. Dip soldering completes the connections. Thus, manual wiring, parts insertion, and soldering are eliminated, as well as human error and omissions. However, many operations in television manufacturing are still manual, such as installing the picture tube and loudspeaker.

## TEST OPERATIONS

Testing is the trial of a product by actual function or operation, or by subjecting the item to external effects. Although tests are a form of inspection, it is helpful to consider them separately. For manufacturing purposes, *inspection* is the examination of parts and materials for conformance with dimensional and physical requirements. *Testing* determines the acceptability of a completed mechanism.

Testing simulates the maximum demands to be made on a product after it is placed in service. Test and adjustment often occur together, such as *hot test* of engines, or *cut-in* adjustment of voltage regulators.

Fluorescent lamp starters are manufactured, inspected, and tested automatically. The two main components are a capacitor and a sealed thermal switch. After these parts are manufactured, they are inspected for defects by simple electrical instruments. After automatic assembly, the completed fluorescent lamp starters are tested in a machine which connects them to actual lamps. The starters which do not light a tube are automatically rejected.

Complex processes may require many tests and inspections. Testing includes life tests, destructive tests, analysis, wind tunnel tests, road tests, and over-load tests. Many of these are needed for product development experiments. Tests cannot be considered as fundamental manufacturing operations unless they can be performed without interrupting the *flow* of the work in process.

The normal sequence of the fundamental manufacturing operations is listed in Chart 3-3. The sequence is: working, inspecting parts, assembling, and finally testing the assemblies.

## PACKAGING OPERATIONS

Packaging consists of preparing the product for delivery to the user. It varies from filling ampules with antibiotics to steel strapping aluminum ingots into palletized loads. A product may require several packaging operations. For example, vitamin capsules are individual packages themselves. However, they are dispensed in bottles, which fit into boxes, which in turn fit into shipping cartons.

Weighing, filling, sealing, and labeling are a part of packaging, which is highly automatic in many industries. When possible, the cartons or wraps are formed from material on rolls right in the packaging machine.

Packaging is a specialty which overlaps product design (styling) and materials handling. Some packages cost more than the contents (cosmetics). Some packages are omitted entirely (bulk shipment of liquid sugar), an obvious saving when permissible.

Packing must consider appearance, protection, and costs. Cans and bottles and cardboard packages are well known. Use of soft plastic containers and wrappings became common in a short time. Lined boxes are now used for chemicals where fragile glass bottles were necessary before. Cheese slices, apples, screws, and lamp bulbs are now merchandized in direct sale packages, to stimulate sales in convenient quantities. Thus, packaging is becoming a fundamental manufacturing operation. This is important for automation, as such packaging can almost always be done automatically.

The six fundamental manufacturing operations, materials handling, working (making), inspecting, assembling, testing, and packaging are covered by Chart 3-6, Development of L.P. Gas Container.

## PRODUCT ELEMENTS

It was previously shown that production (useful work) depends on the use of both energy and information. These are sufficient for production of services (data processing, computing, record keeping), but production of useful goods (manufacturing) requires a third ingredient, materials. Product elements are the workpieces, materials, and parts which go into the make-up of useful goods. They are discussed in their order of completeness, in Chart 3-4. End products, semi-products, goods-in-process, and miscellaneous parts are described and compared therein.

*Products* are the outcome of manufacture. The meanings of manufacturing, fabricating, processing, machining, and treatment, have already been explained. Products vary from simple one-piece items, such as a spoon, to complex devices made up of many parts and pieces, such as cash registers. A spoon and a cash register are both end products. Whereas the spoon is not made up of parts, the cash register contains many.

A radio, another end product, includes a loud speaker (a semi-product); permeability tuner (unit); station selector (assembly); filter (component); and a line cord (piece part). The cabinet and circuit board are goods-in-process during their fabrication and assembly. Miscellaneous brackets, clamps, insulators, and connectors are needed, also. Thus, a radio is a product made up of products.

Whereas a rectifier is only a part of a radio, it is the end product of another production system in the specialty component manufacturer's plant. The distinction between end products and semi-products depends on the viewpoint of the user.

## MODULAR ELEMENTS

*Building block* units and *modular* units deserve special notice. These are semi-products deliberately designed to permit flexible arrangement to suit requirements.

For example, ready-made kitchen cabinets are

Chart 3-4.  Product Elements

| | |
|---|---|
| **END PRODUCT** | The completed goods produced by manufacturing. Continuous goods are produced by processing; discrete products by fabrication. An outboard engine, a hi-fi, a book, can opener, mattress, shirt, freight car, frozen goods, and sardines are typical end products. The end product of one production system may be a part or component of another product, as sparkplugs, tires and batteries are units of an automobile; or as sugar, flour and milk are ingredients of bakery products. |
| **SEMI PRODUCTS**<br><br>UNIT<br>ASSEMBLY<br>COMPONENT<br>PIECE PART | Unit: A portion of a product that is complete in itself and is probably the product of a collateral manufacturing system. By means of interchangeable units, it is possible to make up many models of a line of products, to suit different needs. Typical are electric sub-station apparatus, office intercommunication systems and transfer machine unit stations. The magneto and carburetor are units of an outboard motor; turntable and amplifier are units of a hi-fi; and a multispindle station and hydraulic power unit are "building block" units of an automatic in-line transfer machine. |
| | Assembly: A group of related parts and components joined together to make up a convenient major portion of a product. When fastened by welding, rivets or other permanent means, an assembly may be thought of as a component of a unit or product.<br>Automobile instrument panel; cylinder head assembly; piston (with rings, wristpin, and connecting rod) assembly; window lift mechanism; TV tuners; washing machine gearbox; refrigerator handle assembly; typewriter carriage assembly; headlamp subassembly; brake cylinder subassembly. |
| | Component: A manufactured device or preassembly used as a functional portion of an assembly.<br>For example: condensers, transformers, tubes, transistors, sockets, focusing coil are components of a TV set.<br>Typical automotive components are bearings, oil seals, pulley, tie rod ends, timing chain, thermostat, radiator, shock absorbers, brake cylinder, engine mounts, and hose clamps. |
| | Piece part: A separate finished part of a product that cannot be further disassembled.<br>Piece parts are discrete (separate) items, not continuous goods.<br>Camshaft, poppet valves, tappets, rocker arm shaft, wristpin, piston, intake manifold, and timing gears are engine parts. Typical typewriter piece parts are margin lever, paper support, type bar, segment plate, and key arm. |
| **GOODS-IN-PROCESS** | The object receiving the manufacturing action may be referred to as the workpiece, semi-finished goods, work-in-process, stock or blank; or by its finished name, such as housing, frame, shaft, elbow. For fabricated goods the goods-in-process may be rough castings, stock cut off from bars or tubes, forgings, sheet goods, plastic pellets, or raw materials. For continuous processing the material (goods) in-process "flows" and may be liquid, crude oil, solutions, beverages; in strip form, as wire, paper, cloth, steel; or bulk, as flour, sulphur, cement. Common names are strip, web, "stuff," mix, flow, stream, crude, "soup" and "juice." |
| **PRODUCT ELEMENTS**<br><br>STOCK<br>HARDWARE<br>MATERIALS<br>INGREDIENTS | Stock: The substances from which piece parts are made.  Also, supplies, materials, hardware, and ingredients, collectively. For example, hex rod, steel strip, boiler plate, extruded sections, bar stock, plastics beads, wood stock, laminated sheets, brass tubing, billets, stamped blanks, rough castings.<br>General stock consists of lengths, sheets or pieces of semifinished goods, from which the material needed for a piece part is cut. "Raw" materials such as plastics beads or sintering powders are also stock.<br>Rough castings and aluminum ingots, which are products from the foundry and smelting point of view are stock for machine finishing operations. |
| | Hardware: The standardized fasteners, retainers, clips and fittings readily available in quantity. Bolts, lockwashers, screws, cable clamps, lugs, hose connectors, grease fittings, pins, seals, staples, rivets, brackets, wingnuts. |
| | Materials:  The substances applied to the product in process as a part of manufacturing. Paint, glue, insulation, plating, grease, wrapping, undercoating, sealer, ink, solder, welding rod. Note that "raw" materials, such as ore, petroleum, and pigiron are basically stock. |
| | Ingredients:  The substances which go into a mixed or compounded product or treatment. Ingredients imply a mixture of things. That is, materials-in-process which is bulk or liquid not solid. Typical processes which use ingredients are papermaking, dyeing, pharmaceuticals, and glassmaking. Products made up with ingredients are: gasoline, with octane and ignition control additives; paints, with oils, dryers, and pigments; and food products, with fruit, vegetables, spices, flour, cocoa, etc. Degreasing is a treatment which uses soaps, alkalies, and solvents as ingredients. |

available in many widths. These can be joined together to make up wall or base cabinets to suit any size and shape kitchen without the need for on-the-site cutting or building. The same idea of interchangeable standardized units is used by manufacturers of pre-engineered and matched process control panels, electronic computer sections, and of automation transfer machines. This trend to unitized semi-products is very important, as it permits great variation in end product without sacrifice of standardization and the advantages of high volume production.

Optional features of automobiles, such as power steering, automatic transmission, radio, and choice-of-engine also depend on unitized semi-products. Clever planning permits *different* engines to be manufactured with the same automated production line, by taking advantage of interchangeable standardized assemblies and units.

For example, the same engine which is used for the highest priced luxury automobile is also used for heavy duty trucks, with slight variation. The truck engine is assembled with different carburetor, generator, manifold, and valve lifters. Otherwise, it is the same engine block, head, pistons, and crankshaft as the *deluxe* automobile engine.

To summarize, a complex product or process can be a composite of related semi-products or sub-units, and thus be both standardized and *special* at the same time.

## VIEW POINTS: FUNCTIONAL– OPERATIONAL–PHYSICAL

Manufacturing even a simple product requires decisions at all management levels and by many specialists. One man may have considerable overall responsibility as *project engineer*. It is his job to coordinate investigation, planning, and design. However, he cannot develop a new product or production system by himself. He depends on engineering specialists and on the advice of executives, consultants, and production people.

Consider a manufacturing company which is interested in producing a discardable flashlight. Their new product file shows that this idea was first suggested in 1911 and has been brought up almost yearly since then, but the short shelf-life of batteries, unreliable lamps, and fabrication costs were unsurmountable problems. However, improved cell structure, durable plastic materials, miniature sealed-beam lamps, and automation economies now make this idea feasible, as a hermetically sealed all-in-one unit.

Three main interlocking problems exist:

    a. product design
    b. manufacturing process
    c. sales and purchasing.

Here are a few of the specialties which must be considered before the discardable flashlight can finally be placed on the market:

Management: finances, patents, plant.
Product design: styling, metallurgy, materials, production methods, electrochemistry, lamps and reflectors, switch.
Manufacturing process: fabricating case, processing ingredients, quality control, materials handling, plant layout, tool engineering, automatic control, machine design, induction heating.
Sales: market analysis, pricing, transportation, advertising, foreign, military, perishability, competition.

These considerations are not of equal importance. Many can be handled routinely by the manufacturers' staff, whereas others may require that specialists be consulted.

How can these many details be coordinated without confusion or delay? How can development be planned so it is capable of being understood by both executives and by technical specialists? The answer is, "Use the functional approach."

In studying or discussing any phase of design or development, it is important from what *direction* the system or process is viewed. The particular *viewpoint* taken in discussion is termed the *aspect*. The three general aspects on which discussions and studies can be based are the *functional*, the *operational*, and the *physical*, as shown on Chart 3-5.

These terms are relative and range from the

Chart 3-5. Viewpoints: Functional–Operational–Physical

| TERM | EXPLANATION | EXAMPLES |
|---|---|---|
| FUNCTIONAL VIEWPOINT (executive) | The purpose of an action or device, viewed in the broadest and most general aspect. Considers fundamentals only. Operational and physical considerations are expressly excluded. Answers: "What is our aim or goal?" | Join; cut-off; shape, form; compute; thrust; initiate. (Examples below correspond to these general functions.) |
| OPERATIONAL VIEWPOINT (generalist) | The manner or mode in which the desired function can be accomplished. Compares alternate processes. Evaluates factors pro and con. Answers: "What are the optimum methods?" | Weld, rivet; saw, burn; roll, spin; forge, cast, stamp; average-optimize-equate; solenoid, hydraulic cylinder, linkage; push-button, limit switch, proximity switch. |
| PHYSICAL VIEWPOINT (specialist) | Concerns the actual apparatus needed to accomplish the operation. Considers: buy or build? made-to-order or ready-made machines? What kind? Answers: "What equipment is needed?" | Spotweld, gasweld, electrode weld; circular saw, band saw, hack saw; sand cast, shell cast, injection cast; analog, digital, logical. |

general to the specific. The operational aspect from the general manager's point of view may be the functional aspect to the production planner.

## FUNCTIONAL ASPECT

The functional aspect is the *black-box* approach. The machine or system being examined is viewed only by what it does, or what it is to do. What is in the black-box, how this is done, and by what means it is accomplished, are not considered when a problem is viewed functionally. The principle of operation and the physical mechanism do not matter to the users of refrigerators, for example. It is only the function of the machine that counts to them.

## OPERATIONAL ASPECT

The *operational* aspect concerns *how* a particular manufacturing or control function is accomplished, the method or mode of its operation. If forming a hole in a workpiece is the function, the operational aspect decides how this hole is to be formed, that is, should it be drilled, punched, stamped, burned, bored, or molded?

From the functional aspect, the purpose of a refrigerator is to produce cold. Operationally, the ways in which this could be done include ice chest, evaporation cooler, motor-compressor-evaporator, absorption system, or thermoelectric

effect. Further operational development would consider type of refrigerant gases, that is, flame or electric heat for absorption system; air-cooled, water-cooled or earth-cooled condenser; and many types of electrical and fluid controls.

## PHYSICAL VIEWPOINT

The *physical* aspect is the actual equipment, the *hardware* required to accomplish the desired function in the manner determined operationally. The physical aspect of design includes the mechanism, switches, wiring, controls, and instruments which are required for the desired purpose.

The refrigerator, previously discussed functionally and operationally, is viewed in terms of components from the physical aspect. The details of motor, compressor, case, controls, shelves, size, and materials are developed after the functional and operational aspects are decided.

## THE DESIGN TEAM

Few machines or control systems are designed by one man. Usually a design team is required. A typical design team includes mechanical engineers, electrical engineers, and draftsmen. For convenience, the *team* of specialists is sometimes referred to as *the machine designer.*

There was a time when a machine proper

| MANUFACTURING OPERATIONS: | MATERIALS HANDLING: | WORKING (MAKING): | INSPECTING: | ASSEMBLING: | TESTING: | PACKAGING: |
|---|---|---|---|---|---|---|
| FUNCTIONAL considerations | 11. loading materials<br>12. between stations<br>17. scrap removal<br>19. unloading work | 21. tank body<br>23. nozzle fitting<br>25. charging check valve | 31. dimensions<br>33. alignment<br>37. threads & fits | 41. make up shell<br>44. attach nozzle fitting<br>47. insert charging valve | 51. leakage<br>53. bursting<br>55. valve | 61. fill with gas<br>63. finish coating<br>65. marking<br>67. protection |
| preliminary OPERATIONAL development | 11. coils? sheets? tubing?<br>12. gravity chutes? belt conveyors?<br>17. scraper? vibration? manual?<br>19. roller conveyor? pallet loads? | 21. spin? stamp? deep draw? joined lengthwise? around?<br>23. machined? die cast? roll threaded?<br>25. tamper proof? reliability? | 31-33. visual? automatic? plastics gage? electro-gage? airgage?<br>37. pre-inspection? manual? by sampling? | 41. position? braze? weld? resistance-arc-gas? cement?<br>44-47. position? braze? weld? | 51. air? gas? water?<br>53. hydraulic? gas?<br>55. pre-assembly? | 61. fire hazard?<br>63. paint? spray? dip?<br>65. label? stamp?<br>67. threads? shipping cartons? |
| secondary OPERATIONAL development | 11. use steel of proper width in long coils<br>12. to suit machines<br>17. vibration chute to belt, to baler<br>19. roller conveyor to shipping department | 21. redesign product to use longitudinally joined hemi-cylinders, both alike<br>23-25. invite bids from job shops do not specify method of manufacture | 31-33. combine inspection with assembly fixture, visual surveillance required.<br>35. check parts from suppliers manually, 3 pieces per 1000 | 41. automatically position two half-shells in welding fixture. Use microswitches to signal misfits. Arc weld longitudinal joint.<br>44-47. place and resistance weld fittings | 51-53-55. test and fill all at once. Charge with L.P. gas at test pressure. check for leaks with "sniffer", reduce gas to normal pressure. protect from flame. | 61. combine charging with testing.<br>63. dip paint, dry with I-R lamp bank.<br>65. stamp production code, attach label<br>67. attach thread protector or hood, provide for multiple packages. |

**final OPERATIONAL development**

FITTINGS

STAMP AND FORM — A — T

SCRAP TO BALER — U

v → ASSEMBLE AND WELD — B — W

X PNEUMATIC TUBE CONVEYOR → TEST AND CHARGE — C

FIREWALL

Y → DIP AND DRY — D

CHAIN CONVEYOR — Y → LABELS AND CARTONS — E — Z

**PHYSICAL equipment**

MACHINES

A. DONALD #60 PRESS (STANDARD)
B. WELD-O-MATIC (SPECIAL)
C. DESIGNED AND BUILT BY USER (SPECIAL)
D. OTIS ENAMELING CO. #200 (STANDARD)
E. WRAPRITE PACKAGER TYPE NY (MODIFIED)

MATERIALS HANDLING

T. PUNCHPRESS EQUIP. CO. 5 IN. (STANDARD)
U. V. VARIOUS PRODUCERS - GET BIDS
W. WELD-O-MATIC PARTS FEEDERS (STANDARD)
X. PNEUMATIC CONVEYOR CORP. (SPECIAL)
Y. OTIS ENAMELING CO. (ASSEMBLED)
Z. MECHANIZED MOTION CORP. (ASSEMBLED)

Chart 3-6. Development of L.P. Gas Container Manufacturing Process

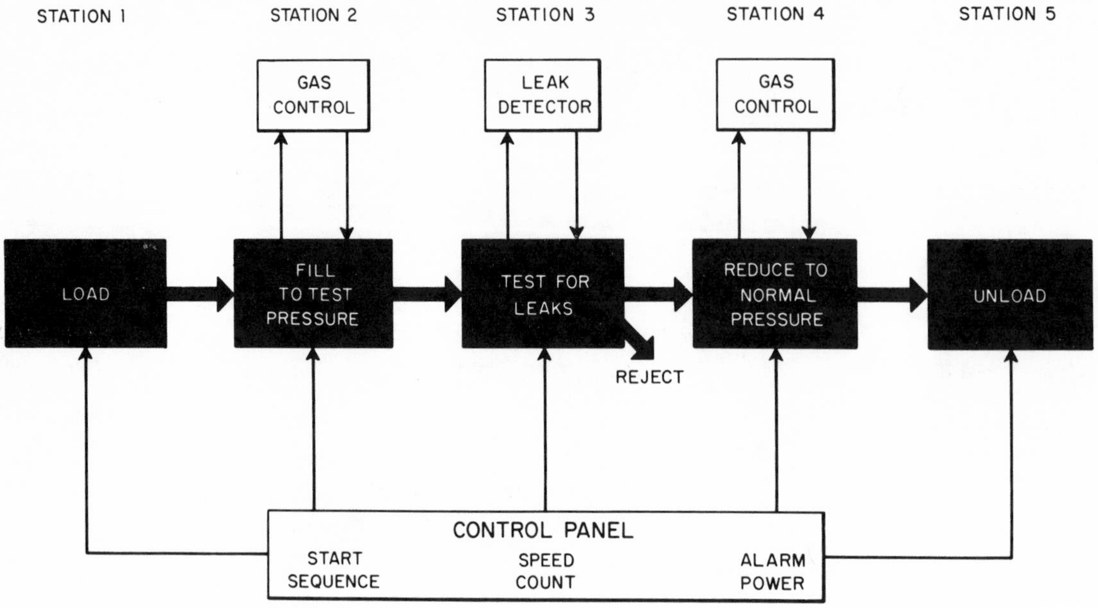

STATION 1          STATION 2          STATION 3          STATION 4          STATION 5

**Figure 3-7.** Functional block diagram, charge and test machine.

(that is, the mechanisms) would be designed, and even built, before the control designers or production men were called on the scene. This practice *froze* the design without the advantages of using the most suitable control system, or without considering manufacturing methods. Nowadays, machines must be designed concurrently with their measuring, actuating, and control systems, or the Basic Principles of Mass and Flow Production, Chart 3-8, cannot be complied with.

A problem encountered by team action is that electrical engineers may know controls, motors, solenoids, and amplifiers, but do not have an intimate knowledge of machine mechanisms, lubrication, friction, inertia, and wear. In contrast, mechanical specialists are not usually aware of the improved capabilities of automatic control. They may not be able to properly evaluate electric-motor servo drive, as compared to hydraulic-motor servo drives. Therefore, they are apt to consider needlessly restricted traditional solutions to their design problems.

The functional approach makes it possible for the machine and its controls to be conceived and considered as a coordinated unified system at early stages of development. The various mem-

bers of the design team and necessary consultants merely exchange their functional concepts, verbally and on paper. This is commonly done in the form of block diagrams (as shown on Figure 3-6, Development of L.P. Gas Container Manufacturing Process) supported by rudimentary sketches and symbols.

The machine design starts simply with functional blocks, on paper. These preliminary steps by the functional approach do not require extensive study or computations. Once it has been provisionally determined what each element in the machine or process is to do (its function), then the members of the design team determine the modes of operation best suited for production. Ultimately, they consider the physical design of the machine-control combination.

Each member of the design team contributes his particular specialties to the development of the machine design. The interim and final designs are a blend of all specialties, including stress analysis, circuitry, servomechanisms, hydraulics, quality control, and production engineering.

Needless to say, a single tour from functional to operational to physical aspects will not suffice.

Chart 3-8. Basic Principles of Mass and Flow Production

1. (a) Mass production requires mass consumption.
   (b) Full production requires continual demand.

2. Mass production products must be specialized.

3. Mass production products must be standardized.

4. Mass production products must be simplified, both in general and in detail.

5. All production materials and supplies must conform to specifications.

6. All production materials and supplies must be delivered where needed to a precise time table.

7. Production machines must be fed sound materials without interruptions.

8. Processing must be progressive and continuous.

9. An operational time cycle must be set and maintained.

10. Operations must be based on motion analysis and time study.

11. Work quality and accuracy must be strictly maintained.

12. Mass production system must be planned on a long-term basis.

13. Maintenance must be by anticipation—never by default.

14. Every mechanical aid must be adopted, both for man and machine.

15. Every production activity must be studied for the possible economic application of power and mechanization.

16. Cost information must be available promptly and continually.

17. Production, including materials handling, should be designed to suit the task.

18. The mass production system employed, be it manual, mechanical, or automatic, must benefit everyone—customers, workers, and owners.

from Frank G. Woollard
London

For any machine (or product) design, a number of solutions and tentative proposals will be advanced. Furthermore, operational problems will reflect back into the functional, requiring a reframing of the functional approach. Likewise, physical problems encountered may demand a reappraisal of both the functional and operational aspects.

The functional approach to development is a powerful technique. By considering function only at first, and by making use of block diagrams and other *models*, complex manufacturing process and control systems can be worked out to an appreciable degree without any need to take specialized engineering details into account. Functional thinking and planning also prevent the existing way of doing things from dominating new methods. Functional thinking is an attitude of mind which avoids prejudgment and makes possible novel solutions to attain the desired

results. The functional approach is less costly too, for the further a development can proceed before detailed designs are prepared and machines built, the less is the risk of wasted effort.

If a specific type of physical equipment is immediately considered for a particular function, it may certainly do the job but possibly on an inefficient basis, or at the sacrifice of desired flexibility of production. This does not mean that *catalog* machines are not to be used, but that functional and operational aspects should first be analyzed before a physical choice is made.

Special machines for production should include ready-made and perfected components whenever they are available. Unique systems are best built by assembling suitable off-the-shelf equipment. This is the modular method of design. Even though components are available, it takes the skill and experience of design and production specialists to determine which physical equipment to select for a job of automatic manufacturing.

## EXAMPLE OF FUNCTIONAL APPROACH
## TO DESIGN

Chart 3-6, Development of L.P. Gas Container, Manufacturing Process, is an example of the functional approach. It also compares the six Fundamental Manufacturing Operations by developing an automatic process for the manufacture of steel tanks (bottles) for propane, a liquefied petroleum (LP) gas. Such disposable tanks are widely used for blowtorches, soldering, cooking, and lanterns.

Referring to the chart, the product design (size, shape, material) had previously been decided. Management policy set the production requirements, but these production requirements were subject to reconsideration if production economies could result.

The chart does not complete the design of the production process. The different machines and material handling devices must be designed or bought, installed, and interconnected to work as one system. The *functional approach* is applicable for perfecting each succeeding stage of development.

Considering machine (C) of the process as an example, the design team responsible for it would start with a functional block diagram, such as Figure 3-7, Charge and Test Machine. In this way, the product, mechanisms, controls, and instruments are coordinated by the specialists on the team. Each block on the diagram is further expanded and detailed through functional, operational, and physical design stages until a finalized machine is achieved.

# Methods, Tooling, and Operations

4

Charts 4-1 through 4-8 cover fabrication, the manufacturing operations associated with the production of piece parts, and their assembly into a product.

Chart 4-1 explains tools and tooling. It shows that there is much more to tools than the mere cutting devices. Guiding, holding, clamping, and checking devices of all sorts are also tools.

Machines are the powered agencies by which tools are applied to the workpiece to bring about the desired conformation. In many cases, tools work by a cutting action. Fabrication by cutting is the method best known and will always play an important role in producing goods. However, it introduces many problems to automation and is wasteful of materials and energy. This is why nonchip making methods are stressed again and again.

Chart 4-1. Tools and Tooling

| TERM | DEFINITION | EXAMPLES |
|---|---|---|
| TOOLING | All devices that come in active contact with the workpiece during fabrication. | Includes all of the items listed on this chart. |
| TOOLS | Devices that alter the shape of the workpiece, commonly by cutting action. | Drills, broaches, mills, saw blades, reamers, grinding wheels; also power wrenches, power screw drivers, power hammers. |
| MACHINE TOOLS | Machines that apply tools to workpiece for fabrication, especially for cutting or removing metal. | Lathes, shapers, honers, grinders; milling, drilling, boring, broaching, and contouring. |
| JIGS | Devices that guide the position of the tool with respect to the workpiece. | Drilling jigs, boring jigs, routing jigs, engraving jigs, depth stops, saw guides. |
| FIXTURES | Devices that hold the workpieces in the correct positions and locations during fabrication. | Welding fixtures, positioners, assembly fixtures, clamping fixtures, chucks, magnetic fixtures, pallet fixture for transfer machine. |
| PATTERNS | A model of a workpiece used for forming molds. Also a guide, usually of sheet metal for determining layout or outline of a workpiece. | Wooden foundry mold patterns, core patterns, sheet metal layout patterns, photoelectric torch cutting from pattern drawn on paper. |
| TEMPLATES | Devices used to form a workpiece by directing and restraining a tool. | Metal spinning templates, metal turning (of motor shaft) template, band saw template, tracer flame cutting from template. |
| DIES AND PUNCHES | Devices used to form the shape of a workpiece by use of pressure, also thread forming cutters. Male punch commonly forms metal against female die. | Casting dies, extruding dies, wire drawing dies, pipe forming dies, plastics molding dies, forging dies, stamping dies, punch press dies, pipe threading dies, sintering dies, cold forming dies, perforation punch, extrusion punch. |
| MOLDS | Devices used to form objects of desired shape by confining fluid materials until solidified. | Foundry molds for cast iron, aluminum, copper; molds for casting plastics, vacuum forming molds (plastic refrigerator panels); glass blowing molds (bottles). |
| GAGES | Devices used to check sizes and dimensions. | Plug gages, ring gages, snap gages, go-no go gages, air gages, indicating gages, electrical gages, automatic inspection gages and instruments. |

*(Note, between JIGS and FIXTURES: "Commonly a combined jig-fixture." Between PATTERNS and TEMPLATES: "These terms are commonly interchanged.")*

*Tooling* is expensive and represents a major cost whenever a new product is to be manufactured. It is highly desirable to be able to use a machine with a wide variety of tooling so that it can be used for many products. This means that the machine should be made for as general a purpose as possible, whereas the tooling that is used by the machine can be as specialized as necessary for the job.

In any production arrangement then, the tooling is usually worthless, so far as its future use to make other products is concerned. In fact, tools must be considered expendable, for they wear out. The machine tools proper are ordinarily useful for future applications, after suitable readjustments and retooling.

Automation has in some cases restricted the potential future use of machines by assembling the machine stations in a special purpose configuration. This is justified in the case of specialized high production items, such as lamp sockets, or hinges, but every effort should be exerted to make use of standard unit stations as part of automatic machines so they can be re-used even if the product changes.

Returning to consideration of the high cost and unrecoverability of tooling, automatic methods can be of big help here. For example, use of precision positioning and orientating devices, such as numerical control, can reduce the need for some holding and positioning fixtures. Use of nonchip fabrication methods can lessen the cutting tool cost. Automatic wide-range inspecting devices and automatic measuring devices can reduce the unrecoverable cost of work-checking gages. Further, program-following machines can reduce the cost of tooling fixtures, patterns, templates, and dies, by working directly from paper without requiring the direct guidance of an operator.

## CHIP GENERATING OPERATIONS

It must be admitted that the chip-making is a very important manufacturing operation. Over the years, they have become highly perfected, and most of our existing production technology is associated with them. However, we should not continue to use them blindly. Better, we should understand their capabilities and limitations and try to avoid them whenever we see that automaticity will be better served by the use of nonchip methods.

As an analogy, let us consider sculpture. There are two approaches to this art form. In one, the artist starts with a solid block and chips away to *release the image* of what he is creating. The other method is to start with a framework and to add material as needed to develop the desired figure. No one is criticizing one sculptor for wasting marble and commending the other for being economical with clay. The inference drawn here is that it is possible to work from the inside to the finished form, as well as to work from an outside position to the finished form.

When one stops to consider, it is amazing how much manufacturing depends on producing holes in solid objects. Every hole represents the

consumption of energy and material. Furthermore, the chips and heat generated in hole-cutting are a nuisance. Fortunately, techniques have developed to overcome the problems of chip-generating operations and radically new nonchip methods are being perfected.

It is convenient to classify cutting tools into three classes, as shown in Chart 4-2, Chip Generating Operations. As a general rule, the more cutting points on the cutting tool, the easier it is to introduce feedback control, as the individual cutting increments are smaller. It is not that the number of cutting points are important by themselves, but the less amount of metal removed by each distinct cutting action, the easier it is to control the cuts by feedback methods.

Abrasive cutters (grinding wheels for example) can be considered to have a very large number of individual cutting points. Therefore, it is possible to interrupt the cutting as soon as the proper size is reached, as in the case of automatic centerless grinding of engine valve stems. When single point tools are used, as in the case of a lathe, the amount of metal removed is in large increments, so feedback control is limited, for it is not practical to stop action during a *cut*.

The operations that disintegrate metal, such as plasma jet and electro-erosion (see Chart 4-7), are equivalent to having a large number of small cutting edges, so that they can be closely controlled, especially in the case of the electro-erosion methods.

In summing up, use cutting tools having few cutting points if it is desirable to remove metal rapidly at a narrow zone, and if coarse surface finish (smoothness) can be tolerated and power efficiency is important. Use multipoint cutters for finer work where better control is needed. Use grinding methods for precision finishing, especially where feedback control is desired.

To combine precision work with speed, it may be necessary to mix operations, as by roughing with cutters and finishing with grinders. Nonchip disintegrators can be used to remove metal, either by copying the shape of the electrode (electric discharge machining), or according to program control (electron beam machining).

Chart 4-2.  Chip Generating Operations

| | TERM | DEFINITION | EXAMPLES |
|---|---|---|---|
| **SINGLE POINT CUTTING TOOLS** | TURNING | Rotating workpiece against a cutting tool; tool moving along workpiece axis for straight cut, radially to workpiece axis for facing cut, both axially and radially for taper cut. | Motor shafts, screws, RR wheels, hydraulic fittings, pistons, flanges, knobs, by lathes of many types; can be follower (duplicating) controlled. |
| | BORING | Rotating a cutting tool within an existing hole, to enlarge or true the hole. | Cylinders, bearings, pump housings, dies, drilling jigs, trueing weldments. |
| | SHAPING | Straight line motion of a workpiece against cutting tool, withdrawal of tool during return strokes; workpiece advancing for each cutting pass of tool. | Gears, cams, slots, grooves, slides, dovetails, key-ways, die profiles. |
| | PLANING | Straight line motion of tool over workpiece, withdrawal of tool during return strokes; tool advancing over workpiece for each cutting pass. | Machine beds, slides, surface tables, precision rails, measuring scales. |
| | SLICING | Use of long single cutting edge, straight or on edge of a disk, to part objects when applied with motion and pressure. | Cloth, paper, shaving wood, fiber, any soft materials, soap, boxes, rubber, plastics. |
| **MULTIPLE POINT CUTTING TOOLS** | DRILLING | Use of a cylindrical cutting tool, having two cutting points on its end, rotating about its axis, and feeding it into the workpiece along its axis, to form a hole. | Any holes, exact size and location not critical; castings, steel fabrications, by single and multiple spindle drill presses of many types. |
| | REAMING | Use of a cylindrical cutting tool having a number of cutters about its surface, rotating it about its axis and feeding it into an existing hole, along its axis, to enlarge or true the hole. | Of drilled holes for size, truing punched holes, correcting misaligned holes, removing burrs. |
| | MILLING | Use of tools rotating about their axis, usually disks having cutting teeth about circumference; moving workpiece against rotating cutter to remove metal. | Removing metal for dies, flattening surfaces of castings, keyway slots, end milling cavities, recesses, facing, edging. Can be tracer controlled. |
| | ROUTING | Side milling, "a drill that cuts sideways," use of thin cylindrical tool having cutters around end; rotating it at high speed and moving it radially into work piece to remove metal. | Engraving, grooving, copying from master part, especially soft metals and materials and wood. |
| | HOBBING | Use of milling cutter, usually cylindrical, having special shaped teeth, to form special profiles in workpiece; used to cut gear teeth or threads. | Spur gears, helical gears, screw threads, racks, slots. Similar to milling. |
| | BROACHING | Use of a straight cutting tool having a series of teeth in a line, teeth increasing in size; tool is pulled or pushed axially through an existing pilot hole to develop a nonround hole of specific shape. Similar to filing action. | Square holes, internal gears, cutting splines, cores, fast smoothing of engine block. Similar to file action. |
| | SAWING | Use of tool having equally spaced teeth, in a straight line, or about the circumference of a disk; used to cut slots or to part materials. | Steels or any softer materials; wood, structural iron, sheet metal, bars, plastics; by hacksaw, bandsaw, or circular saw. |
| | TAPPING | Use of long cylindrical cutter having many teeth helically positioned around the surface, fed and turned into a hole, to develop a female (I.D.) thread. | Bolt holes, pipe threads; all internal threads, nuts, for engine studs. Dies develop male (O.D.) threads. |

Chart 4-2. Chip Generating Operations (Continued)

| | TERM | DEFINITION | EXAMPLES |
|---|---|---|---|
| ABRASIVE CUTTING | GRINDING | Use of rotating abrasive wheel, disk, or belt, to remove metal; abrasive material being part of or bonded to the wheel, disk, or belt. | Round or flat; rough or precise internal or external, "centerless" of valve plunger, "surface" of pump housing. |
| | BUFFING | Use of rotating wheel, disk, or belt, to improve the surface of workpiece; abrasive material being applied to the workpiece or to the moving surface. | Handles, hinges, bumpers, electric iron sole plates, kitchenware, bright metals. |
| | LAPPING | Use of fine abrasives loaded into metals softer than the workpiece to bring workpiece to true flat, cylindrical or mating form. | Machinists surface plates: machine slides: gages, valve seats. |
| | HONING | Use of fine abrasive stones to remove tooling marks from workpieces and for precise size control, especially of internal cylindrical surfaces. | Hydraulic cylinders, engine cylinders, slide bearing faces. |
| | SUPERFINISHING | A form of honing by oscillatory action of fine abrasives, for the purpose of removing undesirable fragmentation metal above solid crystalline base of metal. | Bearing races and balls, transmission gear teeth, rear axle bearings, shafts. |
| | BRUSHING | Use of brushes, usually wire, to prepare surfaces, and for appearance. | Metal for plating, removing insulation from wire, for soldering aluminum. |

## MOLD FORMED OPERATIONS

Chart 4-3 lists the more common Mold Formed Operations. Such manufacturing operations are especially desirable for automatic fabrication. Mold forming operations (principally molding, casting, and blowing) permit solid objects to be made from fluid materials. This makes possible piece parts of considerable complexity without the need for cutting. This is economical of materials, machinery, and energy. Hence, mold forming operations should always be considered when an automatic line is being planned.

Shell molds, plaster molds, lost wax patterns, and centrifugal casting are improved versions of the traditional process, that is, casting in sand molds.

*Die-casting* is the process of forcing molten metal alloy of fairly low melting point into metal dies. A familiar example is line casting of type for printing. Automotive door handles and trim are often made this way. Casting into metal dies rather than sand permits high rates and can be readily automated. Whereas casting and blowing generally apply to metals and to glass respectively, some modern plastics can be die cast

(termed *injection molding*) and blown into molds. This broadens the applicability of mold forming production operations.

Concrete can be considered as a plastic material suitable for massive products. New techniques with concrete, that is, high strength, prestressed, and light aggregates, make it ever more suitable for precision casting and mold forming by automatic manufacturing. Furthermore, epoxy resin plastic adhesives permit concrete sections to be glued together, the joint becoming stronger than the concrete.

Concrete is usually cast, but stiff concrete mixes are suitable for being power tamped into solid forms and can then be steam or dielectric heat rapid cured. Products suitable for being manufactured from concrete are pleasure boats, earth moving machinery, military tanks, indoor and outdoor furniture for the home and the office, machinery bases, steam radiators, piping, and plumbing fixtures.

An example of a fairly complex molded product is a garden hose nozzle. The nozzle is assembled from but four parts, all made of butyrate plastic, injection molded in one operation. The manufacturing process consists of molding the

Chart 4-3. Mold Forming Operations

| TERM | EXPLANATION | EXAMPLES |
|---|---|---|
| CASTING AND MOLDING | Pouring molten material into a mold cavity to form a solid object having the configuration of the mold; or a shell by centrifical or slush molding. | Engine blocks, flywheels, skillets, aluminium bars in induction motor rotors, radio cabinets (injection molding), plastics toys. |
| BLOWING | Blowing a hollow globule of material in the plastic state within a mold cavity, to form an object having the configuration of the mold, in the form of a thin walled shell. | Glass bottles and jars, plastic bottles, lamp bulbs, radio tube envelopes, TV tubes. |
| VACUUM FORMING | Drawing a sheet or globule of material in the plastic state onto a mold to form an object having the configuration of the mold relief and depressions. | Plastics aircraft windows, skylight domes, refrigerator door liners, plastic shelves, drawers, and containers. |
| DIE CASTING | Injecting molten or plastic material (metal, alloy, or plastics) into a permanent cavity die for high speed production of intricately shaped parts. | Carburetor bodies, zipper teeth, automobile door handles, lamp housings, lock barrels, electric boxes, toys. |

four parts and then their assembly. No metal parts are used. There are no castings, no forgings, and no machining, even for the threads.

SINTERING AND FORGING

Closely allied to mold forming are *sintering*, and *forging*, which are considered force operations, as well as mold forming operations. *Sintering* is the pressing of a mixture of metal powder and binder into a mold, usually while hot. Functionally, it is equivalent to the casting of noncastable mixtures.

*Forging* is the forming between dies of metal slugs heated to the plastic state. The heated metal takes the shape of the die cavities, thus forging resembles a mold form forming operation, for the forging dies are analogous to molds. Forging usually requires several separate force operations, in sequence. If great ductility and toughness are needed (as for a surgical forceps), then forging is called for rather than casting, as many cast materials are ordinarily somewhat brittle.

COLD FORMING CHIPLESS OPERATIONS

*Cold forming* is the permanent plastic deformation of metal at or near room temperature. Whereas conventional machine tool practice is to cut metal by various chip generating operations, cold forming is chipless and *conforms* the metal to the desired form. In a sense, cold forming *moves* metal instead of cutting it.

The expression *cold forming* is not descriptive of a way to produce a part, for it includes *upsetting, extrusion, swaging, rolling, hammering,*

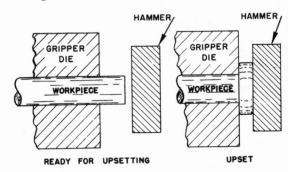

Figure 4-4. Cold forming by upsetting.

*splitting, bending, ironing, drawing, spinning, shearing,* and so on. These methods should be considered as being metal working techniques comparable to *drilling, milling, grinding,* and so on. The cold forming operations can be used solo or combined with conventional metal working operations.

Though drawing, swaging, bending, rolling, and so on, are all cold forming operations, heading, upsetting, and extrusion, essentially cold forging operations, are what is usually meant by the term *cold forming*.

*Upsetting*, Figure 4-4, thickens a part to a greater diameter by mashing it down axially, either unconfined as in a nailmaker, or within a die as in a bolt maker. Upsetting the end of an object constitutes *heading*.

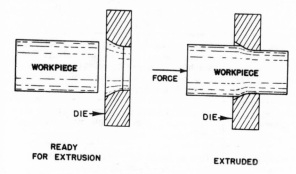

Figure 4-5. Cold forming by forward extrusion.

*Extrusion*, Figures 4-5 and 4-6, is the process by which hot or cold metal is forced through tooling gaps and orifices to shape a long or short part. Because high forces may be needed over a considerable length of travel, extrusion is usually performed on vertical hydraulic or mechanical presses. However, the newer *heading* machines (*nut makers, parts formers,* and *bolt makers*) have longer strokes than the older headers so they, too, can extrude parts. This is especially desirable for the many parts which require

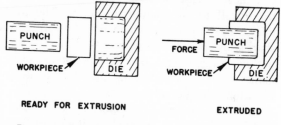

Figure 4-6. Cold forming by backward extrusion.

heading, as well as forward and backward extrusion. Hereafter, the term *parts former* will be used when referring to automatic multiple die machines that can make a variety of parts from wire.

Large parts formers can handle wire up to 1¼

inch diameter, which can be upset (thickened) to form parts having almost twice this diameter. Until recently, parts much over this range have had to be made on presses, for parts more than two inches or so in diameter are simply too big for parts formers. However, there is no sharp dividing line between what can or should be made on a press or on a header type of machine. Many smaller parts which are well within the range of header work are press formed rather

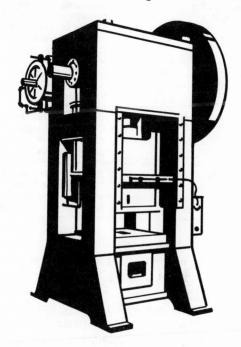

Forming press

than headed. Automatic progressive multidie parts formers are being used to forward and backward extrude parts weighing one half pound or more. Most cold formed parts, whether they require heading, upsetting, or extrusion, can be made on *either* a parts former or a press.

Cold forming seems to have evolved from two directions, nail making and sheet metal pressing. Nails, soon followed by screws and bolts, were the first steel items made automatically on a big scale. The machine used was termed a *header*, for heading nails was its principal function. As better metals became available and larger machines were developed, the sizes of the *fasteners*

Chart 4-7.  Electro and Chemical Operations

| TERM | EXPLANATION | EXAMPLES |
|---|---|---|
| FLAME CUTTING | Heating metal to the point where it burns when oxygen is played on the hot spot, as by an oxyacetylene torch. | Cut-off, scarfing, trimming off defects, deep flame "boring," shaping boilerplate. |
| ELECTRIC DISCHARGE EROSION | Using the erosive effect of electric sparks to form holes of precise shape, in very hard metals and tool alloys. | Holes in nondrillable hard metals and alloys, extrusion holes in dies, shaping hardened cutting tools, removing broken tools from workpieces. |
| PLASMA JET EROSION | Removing large amounts of metal rapidly by impinging ionic plasma jets; the plasma jet being a high power, high intensity electric arc created by electronic means. | Experimental: forming massive forgings, steel plate fabrications, or castings into machine members by point to point disintegration of metal by three-dimensional numerical control. |
| ELECTROPLATING AND POLISHING | Depositing metals on base metals, or surface treating metals or conductors by electrolytic methods. | Electrolytic plating, copper, chrome, silver, gold, electric polishing, anodizing aluminum. |
| CHEMICAL MILLING | Use of chemical methods for removing metal from rough workpieces, rather than use of chip generating machine tool processes; a gross version of etching. | Turbine blades, pump cavities, photo etching, name plates, engraving. |
| ELECTROLYTIC MACHINING | High intensity "reverse electroplating" for removing metal, attaining high current densities by using moving electrodes and flowing electrolytes. | Gas turbine "buckets" (blades) formed to exact warped shapes by rotating forming anodes. |

manufactured increased. Before long, all sorts of parts which could be cold formed out of wire by upsetting and heading began to be made on headers. Today, a parts former, which is basically a jumbo nail maker having multiple progressive dies, can produce parts having very complex shapes not resembling at all a nail, nut or bolt.

While cold forming was growing out of nail manufacture, another branch evolved from sheet metal stamping and press work. The gage of sheet metal worked became increasingly thicker until blanks over one inch thick were subjected to cold bending and forming. Eventually, small billets and slugs having no resemblance to sheet metal stampings were used. Because cold forged parts have some properties not possessed by hot forgings, *cold forging* too has increased. It is sometimes used for truing up malleable iron and die castings.

In summing up, any operation that permits a solid object of the exact desired form to be made without cutting, from fluids, powders, or plastic materials, is desirable for automation. Such methods include all forms of casting, blowing, and sintering, and especially cold forming.

## ELECTRO AND CHEMICAL MACHINING

Not all *machining* involves the use of a metal cutting tool, as shown by Chart 4-7, Electro and Chemical Operations. Gas flame cutting lends itself well to automation machines. The automatic tracer follower which cuts out structural shapes by photoelectrically following a paper outline is a good example. Besides the use of gas flames, electric arc burning also has some applications for separating metal.

Somewhat different is electric arc erosion, which does not *cut* as much as it erodes holes. This process is also called EDM (electric discharge machining). The outstanding attributes are that EDM can cut the hardest metallic materials, even tungsten carbide, into precise shapes. EDM is especially advantageous for shaping very hard materials, and irregular die cavities.

Electroshaping is a recent development which

permits three dimensional shapes to be made directly in any conductive material, regardless of its hardness. The process is somewhat similar to electric discharge machining, for electric current does the work, but it doesn't involve arcs, sparks, or high temperatures. The process is also called Electro Chemical Milling, ECM.

Electroshaping works on the reverse electroplating principle. That is, instead of using an electric current to deposit metal on a workpiece, the electrolytic action is used to remove metal from the workpiece. The concept is old but was impractical until recent developments overcame limitations which made the metal removal rate impractically low.

Only about three amperes per square inch of metal was formerly permissible with metal removal rates of about .0002 inches per minute, due to the depletion of the electrolyte. The new technique pumps fresh electrolyte (acid conductive solution) against the workpiece and rotates or oscillates the forming electrode tool to raise the current density to 1500 amperes per square inch, increasing the metal removal rate to about 1/10 of an inch per minute, considerably faster than EDM. By use of these techniques, hard jet engine turbine blades of complex curved form can be readily *machined* at low cost.

Not listed in the chart are *ultrasonic machining* and *airblast cutting*. Ultrasonic vibration cutting produces results similar to that of electro-arc erosion machining, by an entirely different method. It is not confined to metals but can be used on ceramics and glass as well. This technique places a cutting tool in contact with the work, wetted by a slurry of fine abrasives. The tool (commonly a piece of copper or brass having the desired cross-sectional form), is vibrated at ultrasonic frequency, causing the abrasive particles to cut through the material.

Precision abrasive air blasting is a technique developed from modern dental practice. Abrasives are blasted by a small blast gun against the material to be cut or machined. This permits cavitating or cutting metals, glass, and ceramics, also. As in electric erosion and ultrasonic vibration machining, the precision air blast technique is slow for most production applications.

These three cutting techniques can be used where no other fabrication operation will work. As examples, the electric erosion technique can cut steel extrusion dies and the hardest cutting tools. The ultrasonic vibration method can actually shape quartz crystals and synthetic gems and glass. The air blast technique can cut inside threads in quartz or glass tubing.

## PLASMA JET EROSION

A new tool for industry is the plasma jet. This is an electric arc consisting of a beam of electrons and ions with a temperature of 30,000°F., produced by a magneto-hydrodynamic generator. Its industrial applications have hardly been investigated as yet, but it seems to offer great possibilities. The plasma jet cuts steel by actually vaporizing the metal instantly, whereas the familiar oxy-acetylene flame must first heat the steel red hot, then supply excess oxygen to burn the steel. The plasma jet makes it possible to fuse and shape ceramics and to bond ceramics and metals together.

The plasma jet seems unusually suitable for point machining. This means moving the plasma jet through *three* dimensional space, as directed by an automatic control. It is not difficult to visualize producing a machine section of complex shape and contour from a solid block of metal or ceramic, almost to finished form.

Let us say we want ceramic blades for a heat turbine. The plasma jet might be able to give us *rough* blades from solid blocks, so that only a bit of ultrasonic machining would be necessary to bring them to finished form. Rough machining an entire engine block by one machine may be possible.

The scientists have made possible the plasma jet. It is now the development engineers' job to make use of this new power tool for industry. At present, plasma jet shaping and cutting does not seem to be suited for high production but for short run job shop work, and for one-of-a-kind tool room work. This remains to be seen. It may prove to machine so rapidly that it supersedes conventional machining operations to some extent. The plasma jet may revolutionize manufac-

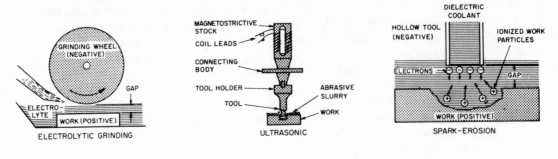

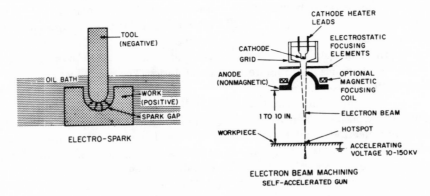

Figure 4-8. Machining the "unmachineable."

turing as much as did the introduction of electric arc welding years ago.

Figure 4-8 illustrates methods for accomplishing fabrication operations considered impossible until recently. Electric or electronic control is at the heart of all of the new machining technique listed.

### ELECTROPLATING

Electroplating and its variations, *anodizing* and *electric polishing*, are proven production operations. Until quite recently, it required that skilled personnel control the plating process, to judge results, and to make changes to compensate for temperature, acidity, current, and temperature variations. Now much of this can be done by automatic controls which make electrolytic methods suitable for automation.

Electroplating while the work is in continuous motion is possible. Whenever it is desired to

build up thickness of material, apply protective coatings, etch, anodize, or polish large amounts of metal or even of nonconductors, electroplating may be the answer.

Not listed in the chart is *vacuum plating*, whereby the objects to be plated (plastic toys, for example) are placed in an evacuated chamber where metal is vaporized onto the articles. Commonly, aluminum is used to coat plastics objects in this way, and silver is used to coat glass. This results in a thin metallic covering. It is fast and cheap but is a batch process and does not as readily lend itself to continuous automatic manufacturing, as does electroplating.

### CHEMICAL MILLING

Whereas electroplating etches and builds up material by the action of electric currents, chemical milling works by the use of acids and caustics to etch metals. The process is quite simple, con-

60

sisting of merely masking the areas that are not to be etched and etching the unprotected surfaces to the required depth.

In practice, this simple theory is complicated by practical problems of masking techniques, undercutting, etching mordants, and control. This has been fairly well solved by the aircraft industries, and chemical milling seems to have a future in automation, to produce complex parts with a minimum of machinery.

Because chemical milling uses simple vats and trays, this is a saving that equates the rather high cost for the chemicals used. Chemical milling uses conventional process controllers to regulate the variables of temperature, acid or caustic concentration, and agitation of the liquid. Furthermore, chemical milling shows signs of being adaptable to feedback control by use of supersonic thickness instrumentation to measure the thickness of the metal as it is being etched.

The object of chemical milling, unlike ordinary electropolishing, or etching, is to remove large amounts of metal over rather wide areas. As much as one-half inch of metal has been removed in one milling operation. Chemical milling has been proved especially satisfactory for working aluminum but can also be used for steel, magnesium, and titanium.

A secondary benefit is that a high surface finish results, mirrorlike in character. This surface finish indicates freedom from lines of weakness and simplifies inspection. There is some evidence that a piece of metal chemically milled has a higher fatigue strength than the one milled by a machine tool. Even *rough* chemical milling cuts are rounded, whereas tool cutting marks are sharp and tend to concentrate stresses.

## FORCE OPERATIONS

In fabricating parts, it is frequently necessary to apply forces to the workpieces as part of the process to conform them to the desired shape. Chart 4-9, Force Operations, lists and explains the more familiar force operations.

There is no sharp line dividing *pressing* from *stamping*. Both shape sheet materials by the use of high forces. Pressing usually refers to the use of sustained forces, whereas stamping usually refers to the use of impulsive forces. In either case, many conformations can be performed concurrently to a single workpiece, such as a sheet or flat piece of metal.

Automation is a series of operations performed successively, and force operations can fit into an automation line. Small presses can be used to accomplish single operations as part of an automation line, such as staking lugs on cables, forming electrical connectors or contact springs, piercing, and so on.

Large presses permit an interesting variation. They are capable of what can be termed *parallel* automation. With one stroke of the press, a number of bending, cutting, and forming operations can be accomplished simultaneously.

*Progressive stamping* permits the one machine and set of dies to form an entire part, such as an automotive generator pulley and fan, by advancing the part one position with each stroke of the press. A six-stage arrangement would work six pieces at progressive stages of completion. For the automation system designer, this means that if he is to use small presses, he should strive to make each one as simple as possible, using unit machine stations. If he can use large presses, he will try to introduce as many workpiece forming operations as possible into each single press stroke.

Stamping and pressing operations include the suboperations of *bending, shearing, punching,* and *embossing* (coining).

Punching is the term applied to the use of the shearing principle to form holes in sheet material. An interesting variation of punching is *nibbling.*

Nibbling is valuable because it permits cutting irregular shapes in sheet materials with a simple low-power tool. Thus, it applies largely to short-run manufacturing operations. Rather than use special tooling to shear sheet metal to the desired shape, a nibbling tool is made to traverse the outline of the desired form. Powered hand-tool nibblers are useful and inexpensive. However, there is no reason why a tracer-follower nibbler machine can't be used to follow an outline traced on paper, as flame cutting tracers do. This

Chart 4-9.  Force Operations

| TERM | DEFINITION | EXAMPLES |
|------|-----------|----------|
| PRESSING | Applying large forces with or without impact, for forming a workpiece, or to force one piece into another; or to hold workpieces under compression while undergoing heating, cementing, or laminating. | Pots and pans, lamp reflectors, automotive fenders, typewriter covers, refrigerator or furnace panels; pressing electric motor shaft into laminations, handles into hammer heads, bearings into recesses; also "deep drawing." |
| STAMPING | Applying large forces to the workpiece, by impact; for forming or punching sheet metal. | Washers, motor laminations, slots in laminations, container covers, switch plates, thumb tacks; electrical hardware-connectors, lugs, terminals; razor blades, speed nuts. |
| SHEARING | Parting sheet metal or rods or bar stock by placing material in the acute angle formed between two dies sliding across each other. | Sheet metal shears, rod and bolt cutters, wire nippers, bar cropping, plate notching, angle shearing, cutting sheet to size, trimming off surplus, paper cutting. |
| PUNCHING | Causing die to pass into or onto another die, to form the metal or to cause a hole to be formed in the intervening sheet metal material. | Bolt holes in channels, beams, and angles; socket holes for electronic chassis, business machine cards, perforating sheets for ornamentation or expansion, holes in leather, paper, fiber. |
| NIBBLING | Cutting sheet metal by making a series of overlapping small punchings at high speed. | Trimming sheets to size or line, cutting circles, cutting sheet metal to contours, notching. |
| COINING | Embossing or imprinting a surface pattern on cold metal or forcing a part to size by applying dies at high pressures. | Medallions, name plates, scale markings, knobs, buttons, trim, electrical contacts, welding projections. |
| HAMMERING | Repeated blows, for heavy vibration, for rough forging, or for crushing. | Forging, nailing, shaking out parts or cores, swaging (forming end on workpiece), upsetting (shortening and thickening workpiece), heading nail and bolt heads. |
| FORGING | Stamping, pressing, or hammering metal, usually while hot, between dies, to form rough workpieces for finishing. | Crankshafts, connecting rods, hammers, socket wrenches, axles, rough balls (for ball bearings), gears, axes, knives, forks, pry-bars. |
| SINTERING | High pressure pressing of metal powders combined with binders, into dies or molds to form solid piece parts. | Porous sleeve bearings, magnets, electrical contacts, motor brushes, pump rotors, pressure seals, cutting tools; all derivatives of "powdered metallurgy." |
| EXTRUDING | Forcing hot or cold metals or plastics through dies to develop long materials of desired cross-sectional form. | Aluminum window channels, shaving cream tubes, seamless tubing, plastic garden hose, synthetic fibers, moldings and trims, insulation around wire, steel bars. Also cold extruded steel valve lifters, ball studs. |
| DRAWING | Pulling ribbons of metal (skelp) through dies to form tubes; pulling rods or wires through dies for sizing and for reduction of diameter. | Tubing, pipe, wire, through dies; metal strip through rolls. |
| STRETCHING | Elongating materials, to remove kinks, harden, reduce thickness, or to stretch form over dies. | Stretching rods, wire, tubes, strip, for straightening; tension winding of wire and strip on-and-off of reels and coils; tensioning rods and wires for prestress of concrete. |
| ROLLING | Reducing thickness or imparting specific cross section to sheets or bars, by passing them between pairs of rollers. | Rolling shapes round, hex, square; rolling rails; roll forming chair legs, window channels, automobile frame members, radiator sections; slitting steel strip into ribbons (by shearing rolls). |

achieves simplicity and flexibility without the need of special tooling; however, nibbling is slow as compared to completely tooled press operations.

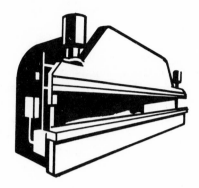

Bending brake

Two-dimensional shaping of sheet metal by nibbling can furthermore be done by light equipment and does not strain the material, which can be lightly held. Nibbling is a chip-making operation, but the chips are in the form of coarse small punchings of regular size, comparatively easy to dispose of.

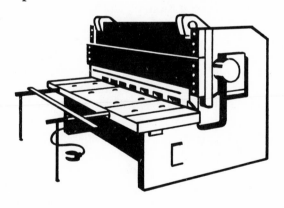

Shear

Coining is the generic term applied to cold embossing between dies, where flow of the metal results. Coining is really shallow cold forging, using precision dies and an exact-sized blank. Deep cold forging involving considerable plastic flow is *cold forming*, previously discussed.

Embossing and knurling and thread rolling are best done by means of rolls under pressure, as this permits handling long workpieces, simplifying the automaticity of the operation.

Roll forming

Sintering (pressure compacting of powders) has the virtue of making a complete finished part without machining. Almost as good is *extrusion*. This is not to say that, operationally, sintering and extrusion are comparable processes, for they are not. Functionally, though, they are similar, for both result in goods that require little additional work to bring them to finished form.

Rolling

Extrusion is the forcing of material through shaped dies. This can develop long objects that need only be cut to size and lightly worked (such as for screw holes) to make them usable. Aluminum drawer handles are an example. A variation of pressure extrusion is impact extrusion, the process by which collapsible tubes for

Rolled products

toothpaste and shaving cream have been made for years. Impact extrusion is also suitable for cans and plastic objects.

Originally, extrusion was only suited for fairly soft metals. Its range of application is very wide now, including steels and plastics. Because extrusion provides materials in a highly prefinished form, and extrusion can result in long, easy to manage pieces, it offers good opportunity for inclusion into automation processes. What is more likely than including the extrusion process into an automatic manufacturing line is to design the automation line to make use of extruded materials, greatly reducing the machining necessary to produce the product. Being chipless processes, both sintering and extrusion eliminate waste and chip handling.

Drawing, as used for forming wire and tubing, is an old process but well suited for automatic methods because it results in long continuous material. *Stretching* is similar to drawing but is used mainly for dekinking, and for work-hardening long sheets and wires. Drawing and stretching can be readily combined.

Rolling to reduce thickness and to shape bars and sheet metal is conventional practice for forming rails and strip. Sheet metal can be formed in continuous shapes by passing between rollers which bend, fold, curve and seam the metal, such as for the production of steel door jambs and metal decking. This constitutes *roll forming*. The roll forming process is naturally automatic, as long coils of metal can be shaped into semi-finished formed sections in an automatic continuous manner.

Perforated metal sheets, the production of expanded metal from penetrated sheets, and patterned metal are examples of common press forming and roll forming work.

The following example illustrates why it is so advisable to design a product with the manufacturing process in mind.

A new office desk, as first sketched may have *high style* but may not be amenable to production by automation methods. If the product designer consults the production engineers, he can modify the design, without compromising style, to facilitate economical manufacture.

The desk could be made up entirely from flat pieces stamped from sheet stock (sides, top, drawer ends); from extrusions (moldings, slides, channels); and roll formed sections (legs, braces, drawers). By use of efficient production operations, stamping, shearing, extrusion, and roll forming, very little metal is wasted, few machine operations are needed, and joining problems are minimized. The entire product can then be readily produced by automation. This example applies to many products, such as household appliances and modern furniture.

*Forging* imparts valuable metallurgical characteristics to piece parts, but multistage forging is costly and not easy to automate. Not so with cold forming, essentially cold forging, previously discussed under mold forming operation. Whereas hot forging is accomplished above the critical range of a metal where the crystals are not fixed, *cold* operations are done below the crystallization temperature, for specific production and metallurgical advantages.

The widespread use of tubing has led to the development of operations similar to heading and upsetting specially suited for pipe and tubing. Two such operations (basically working on the hot and cold forging principle) are termed *metal gathering* and *cold drawing*. These revolutionary techniques for increasing the thickness and for forming the ends of tubes can be used singly or together. They are used for producing irregular-shaped parts (usually symmetrical axially) from metal tubing.

In both metal gathering and cold drawing, parts can be produced as one piece from end to end without the need for couplings, fittings, or welding. The processes were developed with automation in mind and are suited for integration into continuous manufacturing systems.

*Metal gathering* is a process by which a portion of the parent tube (or a solid rod) is gathered into a heavy mass at either or both ends or even midpoint. This is accomplished by heating and pressing simultaneously, the heat being generated in the part by conduction of high electric currents. The gathered metal thickens the tube, affecting both the ID and OD. The gathered metal is then shaped by forging to form a head, flange, or a coupling.

As the part is hot when it leaves the metal gathering operation, it can be forged without further heating. Some machining is usually needed to obtain the desired end configuration of the tubular workpiece.

As previously mentioned, sintering, the forming of complex small solid objects from metallic powder mixtures, is suitable for automatic manufacturing methods. It permits easily handled powdered bulk materials to be converted into precise parts. In most cases, sintering is done mainly to develop materials having special properties, such as magnets, electrical contacts, motor brushes, and bearings.

The advantages of sintering, sometimes termed powder metallurgy, have not been adequately exploited. Alert designers will take advantage of the fabrication ease of sintering metallic powders, even when the special properties that can be acquired by sintering are not especially needed by the parts. This will make possible an assembled product made up largely from sintered parts, an advantage being that a single machine could be used to produce many items merely by changing tooling (dies mainly) and the assembly devices.

Here is an example. Let us say it is desired to manufacture steam valves in large quantity. A machine can be developed to make *every* part from powdered metal and binder. The precision parts can be made and assembled automatically as needed by the same machine. The desirability of having *instantaneous castings* will be appreciated by production men. Sintering not only provides the equivalent of instantaneous castings but eliminates finishing operations. So sintering, along with the other two principal chipless machining methods, die casting and cold forming, are destined to play an active part in automation for the piece part industries. This is even more so now that ductile and flexible parts can be produced by sintering powdered metal.

Figure 4-10 illustrates two recent methods for cold forming sheet metals into deep concave configurations. These techniques have proved to be especially useful for forming missile nose cones and aircraft sections of tough alloys.

## BENDING OPERATIONS

The main advantage of bending operations, from the automation standpoint, is that they permit making up rather complex forms from simple continuous materials. Roll forming, a variation of pressure rolling, has already been discussed. The other operations that bend the workpiece are covered in Chart 4-11, Bending Operations.

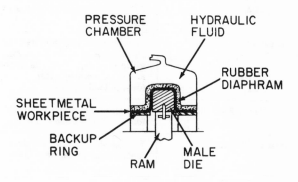

A. HYDROFORMING

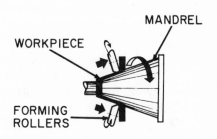

B. HYDROSPINNING

Figure 4-10. Hydraulic forming methods.

*Spinning* is a bending operation with high automation potential. This is as much stretching as bending, but no matter how it is classified, spinning permits making up a variety of deep sections from sheet metal with relatively light equipment, compared to successive stage deep-drawing presses. The tooling is simpler too.

One handicap of metal spinning is that it requires continual speed adjustment, for the turning speed must be changed depending on the hardness, thickness, and radius of the material. These variables can now be automatically controlled by a limited purpose control computer (mentor) that reconciles the several variables

Chart 4-11.  Bending Operations

| TERM | EXPLANATION | EXAMPLES |
|------|-------------|----------|
| **BENDING** | Deflecting materials beyond the elastic limit for the purpose of causing a permanent change of shape or form. | Pipe, steel plates, rails, ornamental iron, angles, reinforcing iron, brackets, structural members. |
| **BRAKING** | Bending sheet metal over straight dies for sharp folds. | Cabinet panels, furnace covers, fiber and metal boxes, heat ducts. |
| **SPINNING** | Developing a "form of revolution" from a sheet metal disk by stretching and bending it while rotating. Force is applied at progressively increasing radii, causing disk to conform to backing form. | Access covers, hoppers, mixing tubs, body panels, aircraft sections, food machine pans, processing vessels. |
| **SEAMING-FLANGING** | Joining or attaching by pressing together folded edges of sheet metal. | Drums, boxes, cans, heating ducts, flexible pipe. |
| **ROLL FORMING** | Rolling sheets into cylinders; or making longitudinal folds, bends, and seams, in long strip. | Drums, boilers, tanks; decking, concrete forms; corrugated roofing, gutter pipe; steel furniture members. |
| **WINDING** | Coiling or wrapping wire or strip to form the desired configuration. | Pencils, coils, springs, metal cylinders, shafts, plywoods, laminations; nose cones, jet tail sections, helical formed pipe. |

and adjusts turning speed as a function of the position of the spinning tool.

Spinning is the only operation on the list that cannot use continuous materials. The other bending operations work directly from coils of strip and wire, or from long rods or tubes, whenever possible.

*Winding* is a little-used technique for making up piece parts that deserves consideration. Rather than cut up solid stock, shapes can be wound from strip, then brazed, glued, or otherwise bonded into solid form. This is an advantage when it is desired to have one machine serve for a variety of sizes. Some missile parts are made in this way. Ribbon and brazing metal is wound to form, then fused into a solid piece.

Examples of forming materials by winding are paper tubes, containers, cans, edge wound induction motor stators and rotor cores, and transformer cores. It is obvious that making up electric cores from strip is far easier and more efficient concerning material than is use of separate lamination pieces. A similar technique could be used to automate the production of cylinders, pistons, and other tubular items.

It might be asked "why not just use tubing of the desired size?" The point is that it is especially desirable to be able to use one basic machine to make up a wide variety of objects, starting with a single material that is in continuous form. This is why sintering, die casting, cold forming, and so on, are so attractive for automatic production.

Making up metal parts by winding is a step beyond special purpose machines. The next generation of automatic production machines will display a wide range of operation and be able to produce a wide variety of work, too. The last chapter discusses other automation trends.

## FABRICATION TREATMENTS

A number of *treatments*, commonly applied to workpieces, are listed in Chart 4-12, Fabrication Treatments. A common characteristic of treatments is that their effect on the workpiece or material does not change its form or shape. The objective here is to see how readily these treatments can be accomplished automatically.

### VIBRATING

Of the several treatments listed, *vacuum depositing* has already been discussed. *Vibrating* is as much a materials handling activity as it is a treatment. By means of vibrations, materials

Chart 4-12.  Fabrication Treatments

| TERM | EXPLANATION | EXAMPLES |
|---|---|---|
| COOLING | Reducing temperature of an object to aid in its subsequent processing. | Shrink fitting bearings, changing crystaline structure of metals; increasing machinability of soft material-rubber, lead, plastics. |
| HEATING | Subjecting the workpiece to an elevated temperature, to make it more suitable for subsequent operations, or to change its surface or internal characteristics. | Welding, soldering, brazing; stress relieving, annealing; for quenching; for forging; to bake, dry, or harden. |
| QUENCHING | Sudden chilling of a hot object, to change its surface or internal condition; by air, water, or in oil or molten metal. | Quench hardening, scale removal, pickling hot pipe, case hardening. |
| PAINTING | Applying liquids to the surface of the workpiece, which harden and finish the object, or prepare it for subsequent operations. | Dip, printing, rolling, spraying, electro static field paint dispersal; enameling refrigerators, appliances, automobile bodies. |
| BLASTING | Hurling particles onto the workpiece to change surface condition, or to prepare for subsequent finishing operations. | Etching, scale removal, surface work hardening, sand blast, grit blast, shot peening. |
| VIBRATING | Subjecting workpieces to vibration to reduce friction, to compact ingredients within the workpiece, or to allow bulk handling of objects in a fluid-like manner. | Concrete and plastic casting and molding; moving small parts in pipes, chutes, ramps; emptying by gravity. |
| VACUUM DEPOSITING | Coating metallic or plastic objects with a thin veneer of finish metal in a vacuum chamber. | Metallizing plastic toys, coating lenses for anti-reflection, silvering mirrors. |

can be well compacted. Furthermore, vibrations reduce the effects of interparticle friction, allowing granular and powdered materials to be handled as fluids. And, high intensity vibrations reduce the forces required to press form work pieces.

The most dramatic use of vibrations for automation is for orienting parts and for uphill flow. By means of vibratory part feeders, small parts (screws, rivets, lugs) can be dropped in a hopper, then the vibrating device causes the pieces to *flow* up a spiral incline and be loaded into the machine, proper end forward.

The use of controlled vibration is being applied to machine actions also, to overcome unavoidable static friction and backlash effects. The control engineers term this use of vibration to fluidize control system behavior *dithering*, a trick learned from gun control designers.

COOLING

Occasionally, cooling is needed as part of a manufacturing process, as for shrink fitting or metallurgical transformation. This is ordinarily done by means of the conventional mechanical compressor-expansion-refrigeration cycle. It is not especially difficult but does not allow localized cooling. The recently developed improvement of the long-known Peltier effect makes possible direct cooling at the desired point by electricity. Thus, *electronics cooling* may be as easy to accomplish as electric heating. By *Peltier effect* is meant the action of an electric current flowing through a junction of two dissimilar substances to remove heat from the space surrounding the junction. This is the complementary action to the *Seeback effect* of thermo-electric generation, more commonly known.

The design engineer can now circuit heat and cold as well as electric power, without the need for any nonelectrical equipment. Where he wants heat, he specifies electric resistors. Where he wants cold, he specifies cooling junctions. Where he wants force, he specifies a motor or uses heat expansion of a strut to generate the force.

Electric actions have always been easier and cheaper to design and to install than mechanical ones. Thus, electric cooling further permits electrical control to simplify the mechanical design of industrial machines.

Here is an example of how electrical cooling could aid an industrial process. Let us say we must maintain an extremely accurate temperature for fast growing semiconductor crystals. Heat can be fast via electric elements. If the material becomes too hot because of reaction conditions, it must be cooled. However, air cooling is too slow, and a refrigerated cooling coil has a long lag. By means of Peltier junctions, both positive heat and negative heat (cooling) can be added as needed, determined by an automatic control system.

*Quenching, painting* and *blasting* are all treatments readily accomplished by automatic methods. Especially suitable for automation is the electrostatic paint spray technique. This takes advantage of the fact that unlike electrical charges attract each other. Hence, the paint automatically sprayed onto the work (such as a washing machine cabinet) passing by on a conveyor is charged with one polarity, while the object painted is oppositely charged. This causes paint leaving the gun or paint slinger to fly directly onto the contra-charged workpiece. Thus, the paint is more uniformly applied and very little paint stays in the air or is wasted.

### HEATING

The most common fabrication treatment is *heating*. The purpose here is not to show the need of heat for processing but to point out some methods of applying heat that are especially applicable to automation. One way is to heat the entire object by keeping it in a hot atmosphere (oven). This is done for brazing, for example, where objects are passed through a hot hydrogen atmosphere which deoxidizes the workpiece and permits the brazing (or silver soldering) metal to flow readily.

Heat treating oven

It is not always desirable to heat the entire object, so local heating is called for. Far better, in most cases, than the open flame (as from a torch) are electric *conduction heating* methods. Passing electric current directly through the material to be heated is fast and efficient. This is done by electric welding and metal gathering but demands an intimate contact with the workpiece.

*Induction heating* allows local heating by the eddy currents which are generated within a metal piece by induction from a high frequency generator. As no contact is needed, it speeds up manufacturing operations. Induction heating offers the advantage of controlling the depth of heating. It is not necessary to heat the entire workpiece. Low frequency currents cause the entire object to be heated, as desirable for forging or for strain relieving. High frequencies heat only the outer skin of a workpiece so that objects such as gears can be surface hardened with a minimum of distortion.

Whenever heat is required quickly at a specific point during an automation process, induction heat or electric resistance heat (called *ohmic heating*) is probably the answer. Typical applications are annealing, melting, brazing, and chill-hardening. However, electric heat is not confined to metals.

Poor conductors and nonconductors can be

heated too. *Radar* ranges, for example, can cook foods even when wrapped, by means of induced high frequency currents. As another example, dielectric heating uses radio frequency waves to generate heat within stacks of plywood sheets to bond the glue.

*Infrared heating* (radiation heating) has been used successfully to dry and bake paint. A variation of this proven production technique is to use focused IR. This means that reflectors are used to focus high intensity infrared heat to a comparatively sharp zone that can be directed to inner portions of radiation-translucent materials, such as wood, plastics, or liquids.

### Nuclear Radiations

Nuclear radiations, which are not heating processes, offer some advantages for automation. Atomic radiation toughens some plastics and can be used in lieu of heat in some cases to set materials such as glues.

Nuclear radiations permit treating materials while in motion and without contact, always desirable for automation. Exactly what nuclear radiations can offer industrial automation is little known, as it is a new field. Among proven applications are: changing the physical properties of polyethylene plastics; sterilizing foods for extended storage; radiographic photography; tracer element control; and thickness instrumentation. Potential automation applications of some nuclear radiations are: bonding glues in plywood; sterilizing materials (such as padding for mattresses); separating materials by selective absorption; and changing metallurgical characteristics of tools and materials. Some tests indicate that metals being bombarded by neutrons require much less force to cold form to the desired shape.

In not all cases are radiations beneficial though, for radiation damages some materials.

### ASSEMBLY OPERATIONS

Fabrication consists of two principal production activities:

1. Manufacturing individual piece parts.
2. Assembling the various parts into a complete product.

The term *fabrication*, therefore, refers both to the *making* of the parts and to their assembly into a product.

It is possible to be a manufacturer and even to use automation without producing any piece parts by merely confining operations to the assembly of piece parts purchased from specialty manufacturers. This can be a sound practice at times. For example, some farm tractors are manufactured entirely by assembling purchased piece parts. The point here is that assembly is what finally forms a usable product from pieces that are not usable in themselves. Also, practically every manufacturer has some assembly operations, using his own fabricated parts or purchased ones.

So far as automation is concerned, the automatic manufacture of individual parts has been in existence for many years, but automatic assembly is rather new. Chart 4-13, Assembly Operations, lists operations suited for automatic assembly.

*Inserting* implies that there must be a major part into which a smaller part can be inserted. The automatic process designer must select one part to be the carrier of the other parts. This is not always obvious. In the case of a television set, the electronic chassis acts as the carrier and is made to travel through the assembly process to receive the parts assembled onto it. In the case of a bicycle coaster brake, the housing is the carrier onto which the parts are *loaded*.

On some products, there is no *natural* piece to act as the carrier. In such cases, one part must be specially designed as the carrier to permit ease of handling during automatic assembly. An example follows.

When it was desired to automate electric clock motor assembly, the round case was not suited for use as the main carrier of the subordinate parts. The lower cover was therefore made rectangular so it could be firmly held by a fixture, with a positive positioning during automatic assembly operations. All of the necessary parts were then assembled onto the lower cover, which acted somewhat as a chassis. The upper cover was merely the last of the assembly operations. This was easier than assembling parts onto both

Chart 4-13.  Assembly Operations

| | TERM | EXPLANATION | EXAMPLES |
|---|---|---|---|
| **ASSEMBLY OPERATIONS** | INSERTING | Fixing or placing one part or component into a hole or recess of a larger part; loose or force fit. | Pistons into cylinders, bearings into recesses, disks and shafts into bicycle coaster brake housing. |
| | JOINING | Connecting a part or workpiece to a like part or workpiece, sometimes called "splicing." | Steel strip, wire, steel plates, structural steel, rolled sections, coupling pipe. |
| | FASTENING | Attaching a part or component onto a larger part; or securing one part onto another one by some device. | Screw fasteners, cementing, keying, welding, friction force fitting, riveting (see following terms). |
| | ASSEMBLY | Putting together the piece parts and components of a fabricated product. | Electronic: radio, computer unit; Mechanical: engines, gear boxes; washing machines, dryers, stoves; Composite: record player, alternator. |
| **JOINING AND FASTENING OPERATIONS** | CRIMPING | An extension of the parent material of a piece part is bent to secure a part or component or to join the material. | Seaming can tops, sheet metal joints; bending tabs on toys, metal trims, capacitor cans. |
| | TORQUEING | Applying torque to treaded fastening devices; a twisting action. | Nuts and bolts; speed nuts; self-tapping screws; studs, bottle caps, threaded shafts, pipe assemblies. |
| | RIVETING | Joining or fastening by use of a headed pin passing through bolt objects to be joined or fastened, the unheaded end being set (thickened and shortened) to secure the pieces. | Eyeletting for electronics, leather, sheet metal, fiber; structural members, beams, girders; also stapling and wire stitching. |
| | WELDING | Joining or fastening by fusing like materials with molten metal cohesion by intense local heat. Also heat fusing plastics, raincoat seams. | Brazing; gas, electric arc, spot, resistance, pressure, welding (see following terms). |
| | KEYING | Fastening or retaining a piece part onto or into a larger object by the use of keys; pins, bars, spring clips, friction grips, "C" rings. | Wheel to shaft: taper keying, spring pins, spring "U" clips, "grasshopper" clips, "hair pins," split washers, cotter keys; also nailing and pinning. |
| **WELDING OPERATIONS** | SOLDERING AND BRAZING | Joining or fastening by the use of molten material of a lower melting point than the material being joined or fastened, usually by use of lead-tin or silver-brass mixtures. | Soft: soldering iron, electronic chassis by dip; hard: furnace silver soldering or brazing tubing, fittings; making up "solid" parts from laminations or ribbon windings. |
| | ARC WELD | Use of an electric arc for melting and depositing molten iron onto joint locations. | Steel girders, beams, channels, automotive frames, ornamental iron, machinery fabrications, tanks. |
| | RESISTANCE WELD | Passing controlled high currents through two metals held firmly together, so that welding results from heat developed at their interface. | Studs to plates, wires to lugs, brackets to housings; washer drums, pipe seams, cabinets, metal boxes. |
| | PRESSURE WELD | Forcing two prepared surfaces together under very high local pressures, so that the metals bond by molecular forces. | Wires into lugs; foils and thin metals; replaces some resistance spot welding applications. |

body and upper cover as had been done manually.

The product designers and the automation process designers must therefore work together to assure that parts can be assembled onto some frame or *carrier* piece. Then they must be sure that the subassemblies can be readily joined together.

The automobile is a familiar example of using a major part as the carrier to facilitate assembly operations. The engine block is the carrier for assembling the engine components. The transmission housing is the carrier for the assembly of the internal gears. The chassis is the carrier for the assembly of the engine, wheels, differential, and body to form the automobile. In some instances, the part which serves as the carrier requires special brackets or orienting lugs to facilitate automatic assembly and materials handling.

*Automatic assembly* requires automatic insertion of the parts onto or into the carrier part, after which they must somehow be joined or fastened. The problem here is that manual methods for fastening and joining are not especially suitable for automation. However, machine fastening and joining must not preclude the possibility of manual disassembly and reassembly in the future for repair purposes.

### Joining and Fastening Operations

Of the several joining and fastening operations listed, the torquing of threaded fasteners is ordinarily easier for a man to accomplish. Machines can be made to use bolts and screws but they can do crimping, riveting, and welding faster and better. The designer must therefore use nontorque methods as much as possible to make best use of the machine, but he must use enough screws and bolts to permit manual overhaul.

A good compromise at times is the use of spring fasteners, such as a machine assembling a cylinder lock which forces a spring-clip onto a prepared groove to unite the assembly. It is easy for the machine to do this, yet a locksmith can remove the core for rekeying.

Welding and riveting are specially amenable to automation. Rather than attempt to rivet through prepared holes, it is good practice to punch holes and rivet concurrently.

The welding operations listed all pertain to metals, but operations analogous to these are suitable for nonmetals. Some plastics can be *welded* by use of heat, or by first wetting the two pieces with a solvent.

Spot welder

New fast-setting cements and glues permit mixed assemblies of metals, wood, fabrics, and plastics. The use of glues and cements to replace conventional joining practices has long been attempted. Often, though, the glue must be applied just before the materials are to be joined; else the joint must be heated or otherwise cured or accelerated. This would be difficult to control if the process was to be done manually. By means of automation, however, the use of glues for assembly is practical because the automatic machine for assembling by glueing can readily control the variables of pressure, spreading, temperature, and curing. Thus, we can expect considerable simplification of automatic assembly by the use of industrial adhesives, such as epoxy resins, in automatically controlled machines.

Metals can be glued together and laminated with wood, plastic, or fiber fillers. Just as brake facings are bonded to brake shoes without rivets, adhesive fastening is in many cases displacing sewing, welding, and other modes of fastening.

## MACHINE TOOLS

Logically, any devices that apply powered tools to workpieces are machine tools. However usage restricts the term to the seven basic $A_2$ metal cutting machines shown on pages 36 and 37, whose evolution is developed on the front "endpaper." So though they are powered tools, welders, presses, assembly machines, etc. are not machine tools.

Some machine tools are not the single purpose machines that their names imply. For example, a lathe can be used for boring and a drill press can be used for spot milling. Therefore, it is necessary to know the operations of which the machines are capable, for their common name tells little of their capabilities. Only the informed would know that a *jig boring machine* is useful for drilling, boring, reaming, threading, milling, and even turning, at times.

Manufacturing still depends very much on machine tools. Some ordinary machine tools, such as automatic lathes and grinders, are quite self-acting. In fact, one version of automation is to use a number of automatic machine tools in series, with suitable intermediate materials handling and storage devices. The trend, though, is to consider the manufacturing operations required, apart from any particular machine. This permits use of a composite machine or system made up from *units* that perform the desired operations. For example, cast iron radiator sections could be finished on separate drilling, milling, and tapping machines. Milling, drilling and tapping stations can also be assembled from standardized units to form a transfer type automation line.

This again stresses the advisability of first conceiving an automation system from the *functional* aspect, that is, what is to be accomplished. Then after functions have been established, the possible *operational* methods for accomplishing the functions can be considered. Only when the type of production methods have been established should the *physical* (equipment) aspect of the process be considered.

Instead of considering machine tools *per se*, which is an equipment orientation, consider the functions and operations desired. Then decide what tooling and machines can be used to accomplish the necessary operations.

It is always far easier to produce round holes and round parts than other shapes. As much as possible, rotating operations are favored: the lathe (turning) for producing round external shapes, and drilling and boring to produce round internal holes. Whenever nonround shapes or holes are needed, shaping, electric discharge machining, broaching, and milling operations are called for.

*Turning* is done on a lathe, of which there are a great variety. Most lathes are horizontal, but some very large ones, as for turbine housings, are vertical. The automatic lathe (screw machine) has been highly developed and was the first automation many a factory has had, starting decades ago.

*Boring* is the operation of improving the characteristics of a hole which already exists. It implies precision and is usually done by a precision boring machine. Boring is the converse operation of lathe turning. In lathe work, the material turns against a nonrotating cutting tool. In boring, the work is fixed, and the tool rotates in the rough hole. Boring machines, milling machines, and drilling machines are quite similar in principle but differ in their construction, applicability, and ease of control.

*Shaping* and *planing* means cutting successive shavings from a flat surface by straight reciprocating strokes of the tool or workpiece. Shapers and planers are not especially suitable for automation because their work is so discontinuous in nature. It is difficult to integrate such operations into an automation line.

*Slicing* is fast and positive. It can be considered a form of shearing. The slicing operation can be done by a press or by special equipment, as by the flying shear, or by rotating discs (for *slitting*).

*Drilling* is possibly the most common automation operation. It is especially suited for transfer line machines. Use of drilling implies that the shape of the hole and its location are not extremely critical. It is ordinarily accomplished by a drill press or drill head, which may include power feed, and sometimes fast return. In the case of large drills, a separate electric motor is provided for each drill. More commonly, multiple spindle drill heads are used. This means that one motor, by means of gearing, powers a number of drills, all of which are fed into the workpiece (such as an engine block) at the same time.

*Drill Head* is the term applied to standardized self-contained machine units that can be used as stations comprising part of a transfer line for automation. The drill head, which is also suitable for reaming, milling, and tapping, is a basic automation component. Some work is being done by leading automation machinery manufacturers to incorporate dull drill detecting devices.

*Broaching* requires any of several types of tension or compression presses. For light work, a drill head mechanism (not rotating) can be used to force a broach into the workpiece. Essentially, broaching uses a linear series of teeth increasing in size to shape a specific form, such as a key way, square hole, splines, rifling, and so on, driven by an axially applied force.

*Reaming* and *tapping*, too, are done by a drilling, boring, or milling machine. It is possible to drill, ream, and tap with one tool. Tapping demands a fast, reversal rotation mechanism.

*Milling* can be done by means of drill heads, milling machines, or boring machines. The milling machine is primarily intended for rotating milling cutters (like thick circular saw blades), as the work passes under the cutter in a straight line motion. The milling machine therefore has three-dimension workpiece feeding actions.

The most versatile machine tool in a typical tool room is the precision boring machine. It is provided with power assists to help the operator position the work precisely under the cutting tool. Accurate measuring devices are built in to locate the position of the workpiece. The table bearing the workpiece can also be used to feed the work along any axis.

Some boring machines are adapted so that the precise positioning of the workpiece with respect to the cutting tool can be accomplished by a servo drive, in accordance to programmed instructions on cards, tapes, or dial settings. This is discussed in later chapters. The boring machine can be used for drilling, milling, or boring. It is sometimes referred to as a jig boring machine because it is capable of boring tool guiding jigs to the necessary high accuracy.

The drilling machine is the least expensive of the hole generating machines. A drill press is used whenever fast hole drilling is needed, and the exact size of the hole is not critical, which is the case when a subsequent machining operation will control the exact position of the hole, or a subsequent reaming operation will develop the desired diameter, roundness, and straightness of the hole. A limitation of the drilling machine is that it does not have a precise method for positioning the work under the drill point.

Drilling can be done on a lathe too, by turning the work onto a stationary drill. Boring can be done on a lathe by rotating either the work or the boring tool.

*Grinding* can be done on a milling machine but ordinarily requires a grinding machine, of which there are many types, such as internal, external, centerless, and disk grinders. Grinders are particularly suitable to automatic size control (self-measurement and adjustment).

Grinding, welding and press forming are seldom incorporated into transfer machines but can be integrated into automation lines.

*Sawing* is an old machining operation that has made a strong comeback due to innovations in sawing machines. In a sense, sawing is similar to milling, for a toothed cutter removes stock from the workpiece. A saw of course removes material from the kerf, to cut off, or to form the material to a desired profile.

Modern saws are capable of cutting thicknesses of metal equal to the wood cutting capabilities of former days. Metal cutting band saws can cut steel a foot or more thick, and aluminum several times as thick, to close tolerances. The outstanding characteristic of the modern metal cutting band saw is not its high level of automaticity, it is usually only $A_1$ or $A_2$, but its great versatility.

Band saws of late design can cut off or miter large pipe, or cut thick slabs of steel to any desired shape. To accommodate inside holes and shapes, such saws feature devices for welding and tempering the saw blade after it has been threaded through a pilot hole in the part to be shaped internally.

## AUTOMATE OR NOT?

Whether the manufacturing methods, tooling, and operations discussed should be used in the form of automation depends on many factors, discussed in the following chapters. Unlike the automation efforts of the 1950's, we now have actual experience to guide us. We can look back on the successes and failures of others and profit from their mistakes. Our choices are, full automation, partial automation, or no automation, gradual or rapid changeover.

Possibly the greatest advantage in the use of automation is that it forces a more efficient regime onto a production process. Automation is doomed to failure unless applied to a well-organized manufacturing process that is already efficient and follows good industrial engineering practice. Automation is not a panacea to apply as a *quick-fix* to a troubled process, unless that process is to be discarded entirely and replaced by a completely new automatic system. Radical changeover is a costly move which should not be decided upon hastily.

In many cases, practices that are compatible with the eventual introduction of automation and which render the conventional production system more effective, offer a far greater incremental improvement than does the introduction of the actual automation equipment. This suggests that the industrial engineer and manufacturing executive might organize their plant along the lines of automation but *not* actually commit themselves to the last step of adopting automation. They would thereby reap much of the advantage of automatic production without its great cost and without the great risks involved.

This same line of reasoning applies to big scale data processing, where automatic digital computer equipment is used to simplify and reduce a mass of paperwork, as in the case of a mortgage loan and life insurance operation. Here, too, with *office automation* as is the case with *industrial automation*, automatic equipment cannot be applied unless the manual procedures to be automated are already direct and efficient. If the non-automatic practices are upgraded to higher efficiency, the consequent improvement and productivity noted may approach the improvement that might be obtained from the final step of automating.

The chapter following, Pre-Automation Activities, discusses many preliminaries and practices for improving industrial production which are rewarding in their own right and make the eventual introduction of a more embracing automation system more certain of success, with the least possible shock to the manufacturing organization.

# Pre-Automation Activities

5

The adoption of automation is one way to improve production, but it certainly is not the only way nor is it the only one that should be considered. Other production improving methods must be investigated and adopted first because they not only aid production directly but pave the way for maximum automation benefits.

CHECK-OFF LIST: PRELIMINARIES FOR IMPROVING PRODUCTION

1. Product design
2. Work simplification
3. Production planning
4. Flow arrangement

VALUE ANALYSIS

A redesign of the product for the sake of simplifying production is always advisable, as deficiencies and *temporary* measures have a way of being perpetuated. For example, one plant had a spotweld problem. Their temporary expedient was to design rivets into the product to bolster the joint where welding trouble was experienced. This emergency measure was never revised so the product continued to employ both welds and rivets at the same point. For automation, the use of welding was preferable. Therefore, the welding problems should have been overcome not side-stepped by a quick-fix solution.

Other simplifications are not always so obvious. The intensified search for simplification is referred to as *value analysis.* The objective of value analysis is to determine whether a product can be produced in a simpler, cheaper, or more readily manufactured form.

Examples of deficiencies discovered by value analysis are: use of higher grade materials than required; excessively restrictive specifications; nonstandard hardware; making parts which can be purchased at less cost. Excessive model variations, mediocre designs which do not adequately optimize production methods, inadequate reliability, lack of standardization, and so on, are typical indications that value analysis could help to "get the most for the money."

Simplifications of the product and its parts are not an automation activity, but simplification is always desirable. Conventional production deserves it. Automatic production demands it. Figure 5-1 shows that products can be simplified greatly if the effort is made.

### METHODS STUDY

Restudying the product for possible simplification and reduction of cost cannot be separated from re-evaluation of the process, termed *methods study.*

A methods study may reveal that automation is desirable by showing that processing techniques having a natural automatic content (such as chemical milling or electric discharge machining) are applicable.

The early automobile industry perfected the principle of orienting the production layout to the product. They departed from the then customary practice of arranging machines in groups according to their operations. The mass production practice of lining up ordinary manually controlled machines so the workpieces could be readily brought from machine to machine was a radical move in the 1920's.

This is still very sound practice today. Any planning toward the attainment of flow production is worthwhile, for this concept is even more necessary when automation is used. This means that production planning and industrial engineering, for conventional mass production, are steps toward automation, too. When automation is introduced, it is just good sense to have the production process already oriented by flow lines, the proper flow arrangements worked out, and the product and methods as simplified as possible.

## SUB-AUTOMATION IMPROVEMENTS

### CHECK-OFF LIST

1. Use of prepared materials
2. Use of central lubrication system
3. Use of chip removal system
4. Use of dynamic maintenance program
5. Use of variable speed control
6. Use of variable position control
7. Use of human engineered controls
8. Use of defective tool detection system
9. Use of machine load indicators
10. Use of automatic surveillance system
11. Use of automatic measurement system
12. Use of semi-automation

There are a number of auxiliary production practices that do not directly affect the product but have a positive bearing on the efficiency of the process. The major ones are listed above in the check-off list. These auxiliary production practices are considered to be *sub-automation* practices, for they do not in themselves permit production without human intervention, though they do contribute toward this goal.

Several of the practices listed can be considered to be local automation systems in their own right. These are the bricks from which much of the automation structure is built.

The practices listed above apply mainly to fabrication by metal-cutting. It is implied that they embody automatic or a semi-automatic features. The point to keep in mind here is that the adaptation of such practices is usually a good move from the production engineering viewpoint and has the added advantage that each constitutes a step toward full automation. Their gradual adaptation by an existing plant can lessen the *automation shock* that might result if a fast radical changeover is made. A further ad-

**ORIGINAL**

**CURRENT**

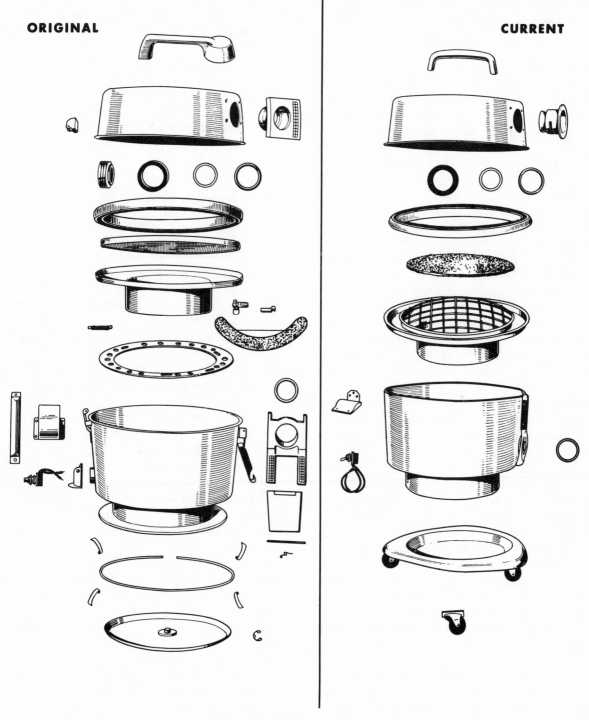

Figure 5-1. Product simplification.

vantage is that these practices pay off right away and are, for the most part, suitable for short run shops as well as for high quantity production.

## USE OF PREPARED MATERIALS

Any procedure which permits a product to be manufactured in fewer operations is of definite benefit. In other words, it is frequently desirable from the standpoint of both cost and process simplicity to make use of materials that have already undergone substantial preworking. Typical examples of preworked materials are pre-enamelled sheets, preshaped stock, and small items (fasteners, electronics parts, hardware) packed in continuous rolls or coils. Ordinarily, the use of material that is merely precut into short pieces is a disadvantage, not a saving, for it complicates holding the piece parts while they are being processed.

All materials have been preworked to some extent but usually only in forms traditional to trade practice. The user may benefit by demanding that purchased materials comply to the needs of his process. The packaging of electronic resistors in paper bands for use in automatic assembly machines is a case in point.

A viewpoint that helps here is to consider the materials supplier's factory as being a part of the total production process. Many suppliers provide applications engineering service to help customers make best use of the vended materials. The supplier's sales and applications representatives can work with the user's production engineers to have the materials delivered in the form most suited for the manufacturing process.

For example, production of a thermometer was simplified by redesign to use extruded brass of specially shaped cross section for the thermometer case. Purchasing extruded bars that were already of proper form eliminated a number of costly machining operations and waste of material.

## USE OF CENTRAL LUBRICATION SYSTEM

Lubrication has been a nuisance to production men ever since machines existed. The risks of under-lubrication are matched by the losses caused by over-lubrication, a common fault. The day can be anticipated when lubrication will not be necessary for most mechanisms. Thus far, though, it is needed, so it must be accomplished without interference to the manufacturing process.

An automatically controlled lubrication system for each machine is worthwhile, for it replaces the man with the oil can and grease gun. This assures proper attention to prevent wear or breakdown due to burned out motors and seized bearings. Damage to the product by excess grease is also eliminated.

## CHIP REMOVAL SYSTEM

Chip-making operations, the use of cutting tools, still predominate in the fabrication industries. Press operations such as stamping and forging also leave scrap, swarf, and offal. Even though nonchip methods are finding increasing use in industry, some chip-making operations will always be necessary.

Chip making not only consumes great amounts of power and materials, but the chips themselves seriously interfere with the normal operation of the machine or process. With ordinary production methods, the operator keeps the machine clear of chips and scraps. However, with modern high speed metal removal practices, chip removal is a difficult job and slows down production.

Steel shavings and turnings present the biggest problems. A sharp tool working at optimum feed and speed (such as a lathe cutter or a drill) throws out long spirals of metal which whip around and lash everything within range. These turnings may inadvertently actuate switches or interlocks. More commonly, they jam loaders and interfere with the fit of workpieces in the holding fixtures, so necessary for accurate production. Chip breaker attachments help to control this hazard. Cast iron does not present as much a problem as does steel, for cast iron chips are small and granular, not long ribbons of material.

A battery of multispindle drilling machines develops chips so fast that only an automatic chip removal system can cope with them. Even then, some men are needed to police chips which may elude the automatic chip collectors.

What to do with the chips is a big materials handling problem. Dropping the scraps into conveyors below the machines is often the most practical solution. Chips of different materials such as brass, aluminum, magnesium or plastics must be handled separately to preserve reclaim value.

An example of producing more chips than parts occurs in the spark plug industry. Before cold forming spark plug shells was common practice, they were turned out on batteries of automatic screw machines. Many spark plug shells are still turned out rather than cold formed, especially for the replacement market and for special models such as marine and aircraft spark plugs. When turning out a typical automotive plug of the 1960's, two out of three pounds of expensive free machining steel was converted into chips. These were such a big problem that bricketting machines compacted the chips to ease their handling and to increase their reclaim value which, however, was always far less than their cost.

The long stringy chips also retained up to seven gallons of expensive cutting oil per cubic yard of chips, which had to be recovered as it was too costly to discard.

Conversion of any big scale chip producing fabrication process to an automatic chipless machining process often provides big secondary payoffs, as well as saving metal and time. The conversion, however, is not necessarily painless, for unexpected tooling failures may embarrass production when changing over from screw machines to cold headers, for example.

### Use of Dynamic Maintenance Program

Maintenance does not result in production, but the absence of proper maintenance can stop it. Many plants perform maintenance in an extemporaneous manner, "putting out fires," living from one emergency to another. This is almost good enough when ordinary machines are used with which the service men are familiar. Ordinarily, one independent machine out of action is of minor consequence; but in the case of an integrated automation line, one machine down affects all production.

New automatic production equipment is more complex than are conventional machine tools. Repairmen of greater skills are required, and a better organized repair procedure is needed. However, the role of electronics in industrial automation has been exaggerated. Most problems are still the commonplace ones, such as the jammed interlock, the grounded conductor, the burned out motor, or a hydraulic line smashed by a truck.

Electronics fail too, but the service man should not be expected to measure transistor junction voltages or study oscilloscope patterns while production is waiting. Plug-in units standardized to reduce spares facilitate quick replacement. Finding the troublesome unit is all that should be necessary, not the making of repairs within the unit.

Maintenance procedures that are good practice in general and mandatory for automation, include the use of standardized units and components, such as motors, contactors, valves, amplifiers, servos, and machine units. As much as possible, the controls for each section or station should be localized at that location. Simplified trouble-shooting diagrams, sequence of operation lists, fault detectors, test measurement points, and tables of normal readings should be provided at each machine or section.

Automation demands that maintenance be a dynamic program, including training, ease-of-maintenance-design and well-rehearsed trouble-shooting procedures. Written-out general orders, routine duties, and special responsibilities are advisable. Simulated failures can drill the maintenance crew in coordinated quick action. In many ways, maintenance must resemble a military organization in that possible contingencies are anticipated and plans made to cover all eventualities.

### Variable Speed Control

Many industrial machines can be operated at various speeds. The speed is selected according to tool engineering practice, taking into account the machinability of the metal, tooling, the surface finish desired, and the amount of power available. If these factors on which cutting speed is based are fairly constant, then the speed selected need not be altered, but the factors that contribute to the selection of the optimum cutting speed may vary. In this case, it is good practice to have the cutting speed also vary, to keep it at the optimum level.

An example is a taper cut or a facing cut on a lathe. The cutting speed is affected by the revolutions per minute and by the radius of the cut. As the tool travels toward the center, the peripheral cutting speed reduces because the radius becomes smaller. Ideally, the revolutions per minute should then be increased to develop the desired cutting speed. This can be accomplished automatically by use of a machinability mentor (limited purpose computer).

The object here is to reduce the need for having an operator continually select the desired speeds. The mentor method is one way to do this. With program controlled automatic machines, it is possible to include cutting speed information with the program.

### Variable Position Control

Most fabrication machining operations require that the cutting tool be brought to the work or that the work be brought to the tool. The resulting accuracy of the machining operation is only as good as is the relative tool-work position during the machining operation. In the case of manually controlled machines, workpiece or tool positioning is the main job of the operator. On repetitive work, such as various sizes of electric motor shafts, he may be aided by a template.

On large machines (such as the giant lathes and milling machines used to manufacture turbines and locomotives), the operator must have a power assist to help him bring the work and tool together properly. In the case of precision boring machines, for example, he may have a servo and a precise optical measurement device to aid him. This is a great help even if he must make only one or two pieces.

When the job to be done is very complicated, and when several workpieces are required, automatic positioning is advisable. In its basic form, the operator sets dials to the positions he wants,

and the automatic control system does the rest. When the proper tool-workpiece position exists, the operator initiates the actual machining operations.

This method can be further automatized by using preprogrammed tapes or cards to select the worktool positions, improving accuracy and set-up time.

Automatic positioning is ideal for small lot production operations such as in the aircraft, earthmover, and marine industries. This amounts to semi-automation, as an operator is still required, but his responsibility, efforts, and chance for error are greatly reduced.

The ultimate form of automatic positioning system is the complete external program, such as numerical control, or record-playback. Here, the exact positions of the tool-workpiece, as well as the proper operations, sequences, and tooling data, are recorded so that any number of parts can be made without requiring the constant attention and skill of the operator. With such job-shop automation, the part must ordinarily be set onto the machine by an operator and removed when completed. However, this is of minor importance for small quantity runs.

Fully automatic positioning is not always justified. Lesser forms of automaticity are a big help too, such as servo power assists. Even simple refinements of the arrangement and form of control handles and levers can be a big help. The easier it is for the operator to physically adjust the machine mechanisms (bed, head, gearing, speed controller), the more precise and faster will be his use of the machine.

A skilled operator may spend many hours carefully machining the housing for a huge air compressor. Then one slip-up may ruin all of the previous work. The longer and more detailed the job, the greater is the possibility that an operator may ultimately commit a costly error. Automatic positioning control eliminates human errors by relieving the operator of the need to make critical decisions and adjustments.

### Human Engineering

The policy of recognizing man's limitations and assuring that his abilities are not exceeded

Chart 5-2. Industrial Production Equipment

| | | |
|---|---|---|
| **MACHINES** | **HAND TOOLS AND POWER TOOLS** assist man | Drills, nut tighteners, saws, grinders: all $A_0$ and $A_1$ devices. |
| | **SEMI-AUTOMATICS** partly self-acting | Drill press, milling machine, cut-off band saw; all $A_2$ (single cycle) machines. |
| | **AUTOMATIC MACHINES** continuously self-acting | Centerless grinders, packaging machines, specific product machines; all $A_3$ machines, also feedback and mentor controlled machines $A_4$ and $A_5$. |
| **MATERIALS HANDLING** | **CONVEYORS** | Belt, chain, pneumatic tube, bucket, vibrating, drag, monorail, transfer, station-selector systems. |
| | **HOISTS** | Chainfalls, elevators, winches, overhead cranes, lift trucks. |
| | **POSITIONERS** | Orienters, indexers, manipulators, servopositioners, roll-overs. |
| | **LOAD AND UNLOAD** | Gravity chute; shuttle, magazine feed; transfer arms, cross slides, vibrating feeders. |
| **ARRANGEMENTS** | **JOB-SHOP AUTOMATION** for small lots and prototypes | Production machines not restricted to specific products. Such semi-automatic machines help the operator do a better job but do not work unaided. Examples are jig boring machine, turret lathe, OD grinder. |
| | **ISLANDS OF AUTOMATION** localized automaticity | Groups of machines, within a conventional production line or department, are arranged to produce automatically a high volume part, such as engine valves, or lamp sockets, or a machine for automatic assembly. |
| | **CONTINUOUS AUTOMATIC MANUFACTURING** self-acting | Automatic machining and assembling of a product, from basic materials to completion; electrical connectors, gas valves, locks, wheels, engine manifolds, door handles. Popular "automation." |

by the job requirements is termed *human engineering.* Any easing of man's tasks, even if within his range of capability, usually results in better work. The ultimate in human engineering, though this is not widely recognized, is automation, where he is relieved of *all* direct tasks.

It is not always practical or desirable to go all the way to full man-replacing automation, but it is always desirable to help him do his job better. The use of automatic speed controls and position controls previously mentioned are examples. This also applies to improved control handles and layout, and to automatic measurement *readout* indicators.

Man seems to work best as a simple amplifier. This means that if all of the necessary information is easy for him to read, the control devices he must manipulate are of good form, and he is given power assists, he can do the best job. If he must actively seek out the necessary information (as by stopping the machine to measure the parts in process), or if he must use finesse to adjust the controls, or if he must reconcile many variables and act somewhat as a computer, his work is certain to be compromised.

TOOL REPLACEMENT AND DEFECTIVE TOOL DETECTION

The hardest working parts of any industrial machine are the tools, the devices that actually come into contact with the workpiece and conform it to the desired shape, such as the metal cutting mills, drills, and saws. A significant part of production cost is for expendable tools. Besides their direct cost, the damage that can result to the work in process or to the machine if a tool should break during operation is something to consider. The problem is to get the most life from the cutting tools, yet to avoid failures.

Ideally, a tool is used until dullness begins, then it is replaced. However, this is not always practical (on multispindle drilling machines and transfer machines, for example), so tools are ordinarily changed according to a count of the number of their machining cycles. They do not all wear at the same rate, though, and tool dullness exhibits wide variability. A tool changing schedule that is safe enough to prevent tool failure shutdowns wastes much tool life.

A dull tool detection instrumentation system

would be of value here to detect impending tool dullness. An automatic dull tool detection system coordinated with a program for changing drills by duty count can result in maximum tool usage with a minimum of shutdowns, either for routine replacement or for tool failures. Automatic dull tool detection is further discussed in Chapter 14, Automation Trends.

Although dull tool detection is desirable, lesser techniques are valuable, too. One of these is automatic tool breakage detection. A sensor (such as a feeler type switch or proximity switch) senses when a tool (such as drill or reamer) is broken. It also senses that a hole is not clear, implying a defective tool or inoperative machine station exists. Both automatic dull tool detection and automatic broken tool detection are forms of *automatic surveillance,* to be discussed shortly.

### Load Indication

A load indicator is another useful adjunct to many industrial machines. Every machine has a particular capacity. Not only is it uneconomical to underwork a machine, but some machines (such as mixers, or ball grinders) work best when loaded somewhat near capacity. Underloaded motors are apt to have a poor power factor, increasing power company penalty charges. Thus, underloading increases production costs, and overloading may damage the machine or process. A load indicator (usually easily instrumented) allows a machine to be used safely up to its full capacity.

Worth special attention is the use of load indicators on large conveyor systems which use several drive motors. Load indicators tell whether or not each section or motor is carrying a normal share of the load and indicate where binding or an obstruction is occurring.

### Automatic Surveillance

An automatic machine is one that accomplishes many of its operations without human intervention, but it can only do what is anticipated. The unexpected is not routine so it cannot be handled by the machine. Therefore, a man is in attend-

ance even upon automatic machines. He acts as an overseer instead of as an operator.

A machine overseer exercises surveillance over the machine, a job in itself. We must have him, but it behooves us to make his job as easy as possible so that he can look after the largest number of machines or machine operations. This is where automatic surveillance comes on the scene.

Along with its manufacturing functions, the machine is made capable to oversee some of its operations. That is, the machine is devised to detect and indicate whenever some abnormal conditions occur. In this way, the man patrolling the machines can take remedial action. This concept is not new, but it is especially valuable now because so many machine operating factors (such as temperature, pressure, electric current, load, force) cannot even be seen.

A machine can monitor its operations by calling attention to abnormal conditions, as a ringing bell indicates lack of materials, or a flashing light indicates machine drift. The machine may turn off when abnormal conditions exist, as when a tool is broken or the workpiece is not in the proper position.

It is good automation practice to design automatic surveillance to accompany the automatic control system. This makes it possible to make use of automatic operation as long as conditions are suitable, then to assist the machine with human aid when necessary. In this way, we get the advantages of both automation and human resourcefulness.

Self-correcting feedback control can be considered as being an advanced form of surveillance, whereby the machine monitors its own actions, and even makes some of the necessary corrections.

Airliners are an example of the extensive use of automatic surveillance devices. The pilot depends on signals and alarms to remind him of wheels down, fuel level, excessive engine temperature, closed doors, fire alarms, and collision alarms. The indicators, instruments, and controls in an airliner have been human engineered to make the pilot's reactions as error-free and natural as possible.

## AUTOMATIC MEASUREMENTS

Automatic measurements, a great aid to a machine operator, are absolutely essential for feedback machine control and for automatic inspection and classifying machines.

The only way a machine operator knows how well he is accomplishing his work is by means of measurements. In the case of an ordinary lathe, he stops the machine and measures the work as necessary. This reduces his productivity. If the machine would indicate to the operator directly the measurement of the work in process, he could make the necessary adjustments while the machine is running.

If a machine is to be self-correcting, then its control system must be aware of the size of the workpiece, so that by feedback action it can compare the measurement of work accomplished to a standard and then make the necessary correction.

Measurements are absolutely necessary if any manufacturing process is to be corrected. In the case of manual operation, the machinist must have the measurements. He ordinarily performs the measurements himself but benefits if it is done automatically. The machine which is to be automatic and capable of self-correction must have the measurement information. For automatic self-correction, only automatic methods of measurement will do. Hence, automatic measurement is *desirable* for the machinist and *essential* for the automatic feedback machine.

Until recently, size-sensing transducers had to be in physical contact with the objects being measured. This presents a number of problems, for the measurement devices are subject to mechanical wear and to damage. The relation of the workpiece to the transducer must not vary if the measurement is to have any value. Such *contact* transducers find a wide range of use.

*Proximity* measurements are introducing new advances to automatic measurements and automatic feedback control. These utilize transducers that develop a signal proportional to the dimension, without physical contact.

Foremost among noncontact devices are air gages. These depend upon the metered escape of air between the part being measured and measuring jaws or rings. Because the measuring unit is not in direct contact with the workpiece, wear and damage are minimized. In fact, air gages can be successfully applied while the part is in motion. Another important advantage is that suitably designed air gages give a magnification of measurements without recourse to electronic amplifiers or to mechanical linkages. The output measurements can be in the form of easily read markings on an indicator, or can easily be adapted for automatic signaling of high and low values, if desired.

The miniaturized photoelectric cell offers interesting potentialities for noncontact automatic measurements. These cells develop a signal proportional to the area receiving light. An optical system is used to project a shadowgraph of the object being machined onto a screen, as with the familiar comparator used for inspection purposes. The wafer-type photocells are fastened over the edges of the projected image at key locations, so that size variations result in variable signals from the photocell. This permits accurate measurements, while grinding or turning parts, for example, without physical contact.

As discussed elsewhere, automatic measurements are but a step away from fully automatic $A_4$ self-correcting machines. If the operator makes simple adjustments to a semi-automatic machine in response to indications from automatic measurements signals, he is but the human *servo-actuator* in the control system of the process. The man-machine combination can be considered to be semi-automatic feedback control.

## AUTOMATIC STATISTICAL QUALITY CONTROL

Automatic measurements are valuable, but even more so are functions (computations) of the measurements. For example, the *average* of a sample of measurements gives the centerline of machine performance. The *range* or *standard deviation* of a sample of measurements is an index of the dispersion of the machine and indicates the capabilities of the machine.

The machine-mean (the arithmetical average of measurements), $\overline{X}$, is used as the basis for

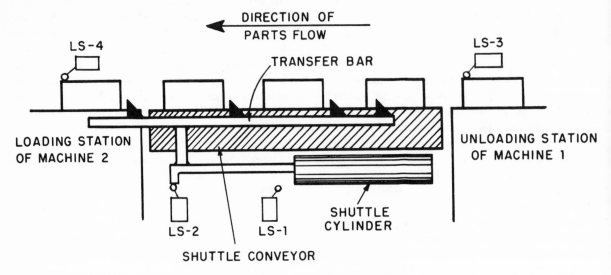

Figure 5-3. Basic automotive automation.

feedback machine control. The standard deviation of measurements $\sigma$ (sigma) can be used as an indication of machine capability, or that a machine is tending to perform abnormally.

Manual methods of statistical quality control (SQC) have proved of great value in industry. They assure consistency of performance and make the maximum precision from machines possible. They also make possible quick detection of malfunctions, such as drift or defects. The main shortcoming is that manual statistical quality controls demand human effort in plotting and analyzing the data. Automatic quality control (auto-QC) provides the advantages of statistical quality control without the need for men doing the routine measurement and data plotting work.

Auto-QC, whereby the machine-mean $\overline{X}$ (average) and the standard deviation $\sigma$ ("center of gravity" of the measurements relative to the average) are displayed on meters and recording instruments, is a great aid to machinists and production men. Further, auto-QC provides information of the centerline of machine performance, so valuable for automatic feedback control. Thus, auto-QC helps the machinist do the best job and get the most precision and fewest rejects

from the machine. It is also a necessary step for some self-correcting automation.

SEMI-AUTOMATION

This concludes the items in the check-off list at the beginning of this chapter. All of the improvements discussed have some automaticity. They best exemplify semi-automation practices rather than automation. In many cases, the answer is to introduce some automatic aids to production, as those listed, but to continue to make use of machine operators. Replacing the operator entirely is not always warranted by circumstances.

In this light, semi-automation is a worthwhile goal. The purpose for providing the operator with automatic aids (such as automatic speed control, positioning, and measurements) is that he will accomplish much more work in a day, and more important, will commit far fewer errors.

Another advantage for adapting semi-automation is that its introduction can be adapted in easy stages. Furthermore, the use of sub-automation production aiding practices (semi-automation) is not lost when full automation is adopted, for they are needed for machines without men even more than for operator-controlled machines.

84

## INFORMATION HANDLING FOR IMPROVING PRODUCTION

### CHECK-OFF LIST

1. Counting
2. Classifying
3. Inspecting
4. Testing
5. Measuring
6. Displaying
7. Processing
8. Programming
9. Centralizing

The automatization of information as an aid to improving production was not mentioned in the previous discussion because it deserves to be singled out. One of the easiest ways to gain improvements and cost savings is by use of automatic and semi-automatic methods for handling the information associated with operations on the factory floor. The preceding check-off list lists a number of ways by which information can be mechanized to aid production. Most of these involve comparatively simple techniques.

The information treating activities listed are not ordinarily used separately. That is, *display* of information implies that the information had to be obtained and processed. *Classifying* implies counting, too, but considering these nine items separately in the following discussion helps reveal their potentialities.

Counting is about the simplest information process there is. Many machines, such as printing presses, make free use of simple counters. The policy is sound, and increasing use is made in industry of operation counters, also of machine running-time meters. However, their use is not as widespread as is desirable. All too often the machine operator is expected to keep a tally on the output of his machine and to record machine on-and-off time.

In the case of conventional mass production using independent machines (cold headers, grinders, stamping presses, screw machines), it is not expensive to have counters and timers installed at each machine. What is more important, each counter and timer can have a duplicate at a central data control console. The production supervisor can thereby monitor the outputs of a large number of machines and assign work to machines that are nearing the end of their run.

In this sense, he acts as a digital computer, but he can use his experience and judgment as no computer can. Furthermore, a typical Master Counter-Timer installation with a central display console is not expensive and does not require specially trained personnel as programmers.

### CLASSIFYING, INSPECTING, TESTING, MEASURING

Not much need be said about *classifying, inspecting, testing,* and *measuring,* as they are treated elsewhere. The object here is to remind one that they can contribute valuable information for localized application, as well as for a completely automatic manufacturing system. All of these information operations require transducer measurement devices which need not be complex or costly.

### DISPLAY

Assuming information is being made available to an operator to help him control a machine, somehow the information must be presented to him. This is termed *display,* usually accomplished by dials, recording charts, or digital (numerical) indicators.

### PROCESSING INFORMATION

Ordinary information is good. Processed information is better. Discussed previously were the averages and dispersions of measurement information, which are more meaningful to an operator than are the measurements themselves. This is a form of information processing. It has been established that the simpler the tasks imposed on the human operator of a control system, the more precise and less variable become his responses. So if at all possible, the information presented to him should be in a form that he can use without effort.

Two ways by which an operator can be relieved from complex mental control tasks that lead to error are *unburdening* and *quickening.* In the case of unburdening, the information is processed so that the operator need not pay attention to values of inconsequential disturbances,

Chart 5-4. Automatic Machine Loading Devices

| MACHINE | LOADING DEVICE | TYPICAL PART |
|---|---|---|
| Assembly | Conveyor<br>Barrel Hopper<br>Tumble Hopper<br>Magazine<br>Vibratory Feeder | Toilet Seat Posts<br>Pins, Rivets, Screws<br>Balls for Bearings<br>Capacitors, Resistors<br>Bushings, Fasteners |
| Boring,    Horizontal<br>            Precision | Magazine<br>Loading Arm | Pipe Fittings, Connectors<br>Gear Blanks, Pulleys |
| Broaching | Elevator and Shuttle<br>Vibratory Hopper | Flanged Parts<br>Hanger Studs, Keys |
| Burring | Barrel Hopper | Shoulder Pins, Sleeves |
| Chamfering | Barrel Hopper | Brake Pistons, Dowels |
| Cut-Off (Saw) | Hopper and Elevator | Shock Absorber Tubes |
| Drilling,   Gun Type<br>            Upright<br>            Indexing | Magazine<br>Magazine and Dial<br>Feed Tunnel and Disk | Gun Tubes<br>Carburetor Bodies<br>Screw Machine Parts |
| Gear Cutting Machines,<br>        Hobbing Type<br><br>        Gear Finishing | <br>Vibratory Hopper<br>Vertical Conveyor<br>Gravity Chute | <br>Helical Pinions<br>Distributor Spindles<br>Geared Shafts |
| Grinders, Double-Disk | Barrel Hopper<br>Distribution Conveyors | Seals, Washers<br>Bearing Races |
| Grinders, Surface<br><br>        Centerless<br><br><br><br>        Cylindrical | Vibratory Hopper<br>Transfer Arm<br>Elevator Hopper<br>Chain Conveyor<br>Transfer Conveyor<br>Automatic Lifter<br>Magazine Feeder<br>Gravity Feed | Pump Vanes on Magnetic Chucks<br>Bearing Races<br>Tappet Bodies<br>Pitman Shafts<br>Transmission Parts<br>Crankshafts<br>Turbine Shaft<br>Motor Shafts |
| Inspection Machine | Magazine Feeder | Finished Gears, Cartridges |
| Honing Machines | Magazine Feeder | Gear Bores, Cylinders |
| Induction Hardening | Removal Elevator | Piston Rods, Gears |
| Lapping Machines | Barrel Hopper | Bearing Races |
| Lathes | Conveyor Units<br>Loading Chute<br>Transfer Arms<br>Magnetic Loader | Pistons, Power Brake Housings<br>Motorshafts, Pulleys<br>Axle Parts<br>Stator Cores |
| Milling Machines | Chain Fixture | Diesel Valves to Length |
| Punching Machines | Vacuum Sheet Lifter | Door Panels, TV Panels |
| Presses, Open-Back<br><br>        Straight-Side<br><br><br><br><br>        Dial-Feed<br><br>        Bench Type | Chute<br>Vibratory Feeder<br>Tool Slide<br>Conveyor Unit, Loading<br>Transfer Feeder, Loading<br>Coil Handlers, Loading<br>Iron Hands, Unloading<br>Storage Hopper<br>Vibratory Hopper<br>Barrel Hopper | Drawn Cups, Caps<br>Washers, Clips<br>Cartridge Cases<br>Cabinets, End Bells<br>Stampings, Grills, Wheels<br>Strip<br>Auto Roofs<br>Drawn Cups<br>Washers, Lugs<br>Clips, Rivets |

Chart 5-4. Automatic Machine Loading Devices (Continued)

| MACHINE | LOADING DEVICE | TYPICAL PART |
|---|---|---|
| Punching Machines | Vacuum Sheet Lifter | Door Panels |
| Screw Driving | Barrel Hopper | Screws, Studs, Nuts, Washers, Pins |
| Screw Machines | Magazine Feeder<br>Vibratory Feeder | Hydraulic Fitting Shells<br>Electrical Nuts |
| Straightening Machines | Shaft Hopper | Hydraulic Control Valves |
| Threading Machines, Rolling<br><br>Grinders | Vibratory Feeder<br>Magazine<br>Barrel Hopper | Stud Blanks<br>Shafts<br>Blanks |
| Transfer Machines | Turn-Over<br>Walking Beam<br>Vibratory Feeder<br>Dial Table | Pump Body<br>Powersteering Body<br>Welch Plugs, Transistor Discs<br>Hub Caps, Pulleys |

but he is alerted when abnormal trends occur. Quickening provides the operator with immediate knowledge of the effects of his action on the machine. This compensates for machine or process lag time, and avoids over-corrections.

PROGRAMMING

Programming ordinarily means devising the step-by-step operations necessary for automatic control. These are the *instructions to the machine*. However, programming nonautomatic jobs is valuable, too. This is especially true for job shop and tool room work, where often a skilled mechanic is expected to program the work himself. He is given a drawing and told, "Make up two of these."

This is not an efficient procedure. Machine time is wasted while he makes the decisions, and the decisions must be remade every time that the part is duplicated. A program of preplanned instructions eliminates decisions and delays on the factory floor. Tell the machinist what to do; which machine, tool, speed, and cut to use; and step-by-step operations. Make his decisions for him, and he will be able to do more and better work.

*Centralizing* refers to collecting data from all the units in a system at one information center. Centralized indicators can conveniently show the productivity counts, defect counts, material on hand, machine stoppages, and inspection reports

so that management can supervise the manufacturing system efficiently.

This policy is already well accepted in highly automatized continuous processes such as the petro-chemical plants. However, the fabricating industry is slow to take advantage of the potential benefits of collecting process information at one location. The benefits are valuable for non-automated fabrication as well as with full automated systems.

Summing up the points in the check-off list, automatic information handling devices (counters, warning lights, measurements) are worthwhile aids to production. Centralize the indicators for maximum benefits. This helps management to keep each machine fully utilized and to correct deficiencies before loss or damage occurs.

## INDUSTRIAL PRODUCTION EQUIPMENT

Chart 5-2, Industrial Production Equipment, lists equipment and arrangements as used by the fabrication industries. Examples and a brief discussion of the most common arrangements of the equipment are compared.

The six fundamental manufacturing operations were discussed in Chart 3-3. These are:

1. Materials handling    4. Assembling
2. Working               5. Testing
3. Inspecting            6. Packaging

Mechanization of industry transformed these from manual to machine operations, then to semi-automatic operations, finally to fully self-acting operations. Industrial automation consists of uniting fully automatic manufacturing operations with intermachine automatic mechanical handling devices, all interrelated by automatic control.

In the most familiar version of automation, the machine elements themselves are arranged in the most direct manner so that the product can *flow* directly from one machine operation to the subsubsequent one. As remarked earlier, the arrangement of operations for automation is not much different that that for the efficient production by conventional flow-line manufacture. Figure 5-3 illustrates how continuous automatic manufacturing evolved from machine tools.

The earliest attempt toward automation was automatizing machine loading and the intermachine transportation of the workpieces. Conventional machine tools did not especially lend themselves to the use of automatic loading and unloading. So newer machines were developed that contained features suitable for use with automatic materials handling. At the present time, both *ordinary* machine tools and models specially intended for intermachine automaticity are in wide use. Chart 5-4 lists loading mechanisms suitable for machine tools.

Installing automatic materials handling equipment between machines proved successful. The advantages were that it permitted use of machines already on hand and permitted *easy* introduction of automation into existing production systems.

However, this did not apply to new factories, for they did not already have machines on hand. Rather than buy conventional machines and then be obligated to develop suitable intermachine materials handling equipment, it was more sensible to make use of machines that already had the materials handling functions integrated into their design. If such machines did not exist, there was strong incentive to design them. This led to the development of the transfer machine, which is a composite of many separate machines and intermachine handling devices. The result is a multistation *supermachine* which integrates workpiece forming and handling, saving time, money and floor space. Figure 5-5 illustrates varieties of automation transfer machines.

Fabrication entails both machining (working) and materials handling. In the case of job-shop automation, automatic materials handling between machines is not used because short runs involved do not justify this.

Full-scale automation of a complete or major section of a product is justified only by large volume. More often, certain key components within a family of products are of sufficient number to justify their manufacture by fully automatic methods. This leads to concentrating the production equipment for the automation of that particular high volume component. This may create an *island* of automation within a production line consisting mainly of semi-automation and even making use of manual assembly.

An island of automation can also develop by performing some intermachine materials handling functions automatically. The result is a focus of automation developments in an otherwise conventional factory. The island approach is the gradual way to automate.

A disadvantage is that separate islands tend to grow as automatic materials handling and machining is extended. Eventually, when two islands connect they may be difficult to coordinate. Also, an automated manufacturing process which *grows* in this way may not be as well integrated systemwise and may waste floor space, compared to an all-at-once system-engineered automation design.

The integration of materials handling and machining operations for *continuous automatic manufacturing* is the popular understanding of what *automation* represents. The materials handling and the machining for the entire process are intentionally coordinated. It was pointed out above that the usual case is for the materials handling to unite the machines. This is the case with the *transfer machine,* in which a number of more or less standardized machine units or segments are arranged as one, along with interstation transfer devices.

Another case is the *specific product machine,*

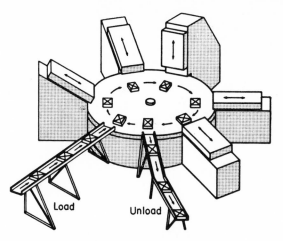

Dial Table Type

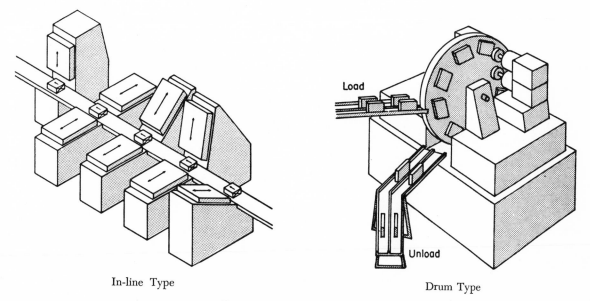

In-line Type

Drum Type

**Figure 5-5.** Transfer machines.

which also includes all of the interstation materials handling functions within the machine proper. Specific product machines are *custom designed* for a particular limited purpose, such as automatically assembling transistors. These machines may perform most or all of the six fundamental manufacturing operations.

An interesting variation of bringing the materials handling and the machining together is to bring the machine station to the materials handling conveyor. This is the practice used mainly by manufacturers of electrical and electronic equipment, though it appears that this version of automation is spreading. The trend here is to position individual machine stations at various positions about a chain conveyor line. The innate advantage of keying the machines to the conveyor rather than vice versa is the greater changeability of the production system attainable. However, conveyor-oriented lines require more space and have longer in-process time. The difficulty of precisely positioning the workpiece is increased, but this is offset by easier machine station location, for conveyor station automation is essentially an automatic version of a manual line.

Ideally, an automatic production system has the flexibility of the conveyor-station line and the compactness and intersection directness and precision of the transfer line. Indeed, this is the direction of developments in automatic production systems. Transfer machines are becoming increasingly *changeoverable*, and the precision and ruggedness of the conveyor-station system are increasing.

Activities that precede the adoption of automation have been discussed, and it was shown how automation evolved in a common sense way from conventional mass production machinery. The "how-to-do-it" aspects of introducing automation are covered in the following chapter.

# How-to-Do-It

6

The *approach* to automation is the major basic policy by which the equipment is selected. For example, if the management decides that it wants automation only to the extent that the existing machinery can be used, and that the introduction of new devices must be accomplished with a minimum of disturbance to production, then there is no need to consider elaborate specialized machines. However, if a new product is to be manufactured in a new plant and high production will be needed, the merits of individual automatic machine tools would not be considered.

The purpose of Chart 6-1 is to display the most prominent characteristics, advantages, and limitations of the various approaches to automation. These concern the minimum considerations that management must make on their own. They

Chart 6-1.  Approaches to Automation

| APPROACH | EXPLANATION | CHARACTERISTICS |
|---|---|---|
| EXISTING<br><br>Versus<br><br>NEW | The policy of using existing machine tool-type machinery and obtaining automation by concentrating on loading, unloading, and intermachine materials handling equipment. | Less outlay of money required for automation; permits progressive automation installation, compatible with partial automation.<br>Requires special loading and unloading equipment and does not allow standardization; not as efficient or effective as special automation machines.<br>Examples: gear hobbers, crankshaft grinders, piston lathes. |
| | The policy of using machines that are originally designed to facilitate the incorporation of automation, or the use of new fully automatic machines. | Standardized multi-operation equipment is available with built-in transfer mechanisms. These are more reliable and faster acting than converted machines.<br>Causes a more abrupt change to the production process, requires familiarity with new machines, and capital investment may be high. Example: size-controlled grinders, self-loading copying lathes. |
| PROGRESSIVE<br><br>Versus<br><br>ABRUPT | The policy of introducing automation to an existing production process, in easy incremental stages, whereby one or several machine stations are progressively automated. | Permits automation by easy stages, allowing gradual familiarity to new techniques and can be coordinated to existing machines. The policy of continual improvements. Limited automation means limited accomplishments, disrupts production more often; more difficult to integrate. |
| | The policy of automating an entire production process at a time, whereby all of the machines and stations, and the intermachine materials handling equipment, and control systems, are integrated and coordinated, in a single automation project. | Especially suitable for a new plant or new product, or new process. Makes possible a big improvement and high performance in a short time.<br>Stops production for a long time and may present big adjustment and shakedown problems. Requires familiarity with completely new mechanisms and processes. |
| OPERATIONAL ORIENTATION<br><br>Versus<br><br>PRODUCT ORIENTATION | The policy of organizing a factory into departments, based on the type of manufacturing operation performed at each department. A product being produced is moved from department to department, for the necessary manufacturing operations. | The "job-shop" approach, the most common method for general production. As scheduling is flexible, varied products are somewhat easier to produce. It is relatively easy to introduce automation this way.<br>Does not produce products as such, only operations. Demands extensive materials handling mechanisms for automation and is not compatible with continuous flow production. |
| | The policy of organizing a production process with respect to the product. The product being produced "flows" through the integrated manufacturing process. The necessary manufacturing operations to the product-in-process occur at successive machine stations. | Does not result in "departments" organized on type of operation basis; faster production, less floor space, capable of high speed and large production, reduced materials handling. Less flexible as to product changes and is more vulnerable to production stoppage from breakdown. Usually costs more for machinery. Mainly for high production and long runs. |
| ISLANDS<br><br>Versus<br><br>LINES | The policy of using both operationally oriented (conventional) machines, and product oriented automatic production lines to manufacture a product. Automation "islands" are used, to produce the high volume components of the product. | Permits progressive adaptation of automation, allowing most suitable operations to be automated first; makes possible compromises, whereby only some operations are automated. Can be used for volume parts of a family of products.<br>As "islands" of automation meet, conflict may result, for independent islands are seldom compatible with each other. Also, transfer of materials between islands is difficult. |
| | The policy of producing the entire product or major component, by means of a product oriented line, eliminating entirely the need for non-automatic materials handling between machines. | Providing that all equipment is compatible and that standardized machine stations and components can be used, the most effective production results.<br>Special equipment is expensive as much design and development time is needed, though price per item produced can be low. Not flexible for model changes. Small runs are not economical. |

Chart 6-1. Approaches to Automation (Continued)

| APPROACH | EXPLANATION | CHARACTERISTICS |
|---|---|---|
| SINGLE LINE<br><br>Versus<br><br>MULTIPLE LINES | Manufacturing in "series." The policy of performing manufacturing operations successively, in a single series. Using a single, relatively large production line, rather than a number of parallel lines. | Usually cheaper, simpler, and more readily installed. Tests by machine builders represent actual production.<br>Reduces materials handling.<br>Any breakdown stops all production. Does not allow introduction of automatic process by easy stages and does not produce "partial" products. |
| | Manufacturing in "parallel." The policy of performing manufacturing operations concurrently by an arrangement of production lines in parallel, each individual line being in a series arrangement. | One line can still be in production, even if others are stopped; tooling and model changes more readily made; over-all manufacturing time is reduced; use of identical parallel line protects against delays from shut-downs.<br>More expensive than a single line; presents problems in integrating several parallel lines; requires more materials handling. |
| INDEPENDENT MACHINE SYSTEM<br><br>Versus<br><br>TRANSFER SYSTEM | The policy of operating each machine or station in an automation process at full rate. The individual machines or stations accept work from, and deposit into, materials storage banks. Each machine stops when the input storage bank lacks work pieces, or when the output storage bank is full. | Can produce parts above immediate requirements, allowing reserve to cover time lost for retooling or for repairs.<br>Precise synchronization of machines is not necessary.<br>Existing machines can often be adapted.<br>Demands storage hoppers or banks. Increased manufacturing process time; position or orientation of part may be lost between machining stations; takes more space. |
| | The policy of adjusting the operating rates of the machines and stations in an automation process, so that all do their work currently. After each work cycle, the work piece is transferred directly to the successive operation, without resource to interoperation storage banks. | Reduces in-process inventory, machine stations have high duty cycle, saves floor space, more precise orientation of work is possible.<br>Rate is set by slowest station; if one station stops entire line must stop. Process can not be readily varied to meet product changes. No parts storage for emergency stoppages. |
| FIXED PROGRAM MACHINES<br><br>Versus<br><br>VARIABLE PROGRAM MACHINES | Machines which are set to accomplish a specific job only. Changes to do other jobs are possible but not readily made, for they necessitate changes to the machine proper, to the tooling, or to the sequencing. | Far cheaper and simpler. Most practical, proved reliability, easier to repair and to maintain. Inflexible; vulnerable to product changes, not good for short runs.<br>Examples: press operations and assembly machines. |
| | Machines which can be readily varied, by automatic or semi-automatic means, to suit any job within their range. External programming makes possible changing tooling, feeds, speeds, and work piece position, as necessary, to do the job. | Highly flexible, readily programmed, allows mixed runs of similar products, changes require no delays, single items or short runs possible.<br>High cost, requires costly auxiliary equipment, requires specially trained operators and set-up men, limited types of operations.<br>Examples: tracer follower machines, record-playback control. |
| SPECIFIC PRODUCT MACHINES<br><br>Versus<br><br>STANDARDIZED UNIT MACHINES | Machines with capabilities limited to a few special operations, or to the production of a narrow range of closely related products.<br>Special purpose machines and specific product machines depend on custom made mechanisms designed solely for the job. | Compact, no process dead time, high duty cycle, short manufacturing time. A good buy when available "ready made."<br>Not flexible, one product only. Tool changes and repairs stop product completely. Custom designed machines are costly and trouble prone.<br>Example: thermostat assembly machine. |
| | Machines potentially capable of a large number of types of operations, or to the production of a wide range of products, of varied types. Made up of standardized "building block" units which can be installed, exchanged or re-used to attain operations and product flexibility. | Versatile: a composite of interchangeable standardized units; tooling rates and feeds can be reduced for increased life.<br>Assembly and control must be adapted to the workpiece; installation is always "custom," useful mainly for large processes.<br>Example: transfer machine. |

cannot be delegated to anyone else. Not until the executives decide what approach is best for their company and for their product can the problem be assigned to engineers for attention to the technical details. The chart is therefore not technical but contains general information as to what can be expected from the various approaches to automaticity.

Each of the eight *approaches* listed is contrasted with a diametrically opposed version. The approaches are not distinctly separate but have many similarities. The chart is merely a convenient way to display various points for management's decisions, for the wrong start assures the wrong finish.

Not discussed in the chart is the matter of fixed program versus variable program machines. For the most part, flexible program machines find their greatest application in the job shop. They would be very desirable for a high production line also, to permit readjustment for product changes. However, the cost is greater, so for the usual high production automation more or less fixed programs must be resorted to. Adaptability is not stressed.

The chart describes mainly $A_3$ industrial automation rather than higher orders of automaticity. Most industrial automation will continue to be $A_3$. There is no need for cybernetic refinements for most routine industrial machine operations. Wherever the advantages of $A_4$ (feedback control) can result in a definite operational improvement, or the use of $A_5$ (mentor control based on automatic cognition) makes a process more stable and adaptable to changing conditions, such higher orders of automaticity should certainly be used.

## EXISTING MACHINES versus NEW MACHINES

It appears to be good sense to use existing machines as much and as long as possible. First cost, though, is not final cost. The only valid cost of a machine is its cost per item produced, including all maintenance, production labor, and indirect costs. In this light, old machines may be too expensive. Only a thorough cost analysis can tell the true story.

If the old machines are serviceable, they could certainly be continued in service. Specially built automatic loading, unloading, and transfer mechanisms make it possible for existing automatic cycle machine tools to work in an automation line. However, this adds cost and complexity and introduces potential troubles to a system. Thus, in considering *existing versus new*, the convertibility of the machines for automaticity must be considered. Newer models of industrial machine tools usually have features that make them more readily adaptable for use in an automation line.

Press lines (stamping, or forming) are especially likely spots for obtaining automation by interconnecting existing machines, for presses are large and expensive though relatively simple mechanically. Among the earliest forms of present-day automation was the automatization of press line loading and unloading by the Detroit automotive industry. The improvement was considerable because large sheets such as automobile door sections and refrigerator panels were very awkward for men to handle efficiently. Also, automatic materials handling and loading greatly reduced the hazards to workmen associated with press operation.

Presses are sure to be used even more now that we are in the cold-forming era of mass production, and many parts formerly machined from stock are pressed to the desired shape with no loss of material.

## PROGRESSIVE versus ABRUPT

The progressive introduction of automation is attractive for obvious reasons, but the biggest reward comes with the biggest improvement. If the product or the plant is new, or high production is anticipated, full-scale automation is advisable. If the budget is modest and business-as-usual must be the policy, then the progressive introduction of automation is the way.

Some firms have been progressing toward automation without being quite aware of it. All machinery is periodically replaced sooner or later. When a new machine is bought, it usually includes many self-acting features. The gradual purchase of ready-made automatic inspection devices and conveyors evolves into partial automation.

The policy of automating progressively is not criticized, but it should be pointed out that even for such an approach, which is· not much different from the normal replacement of industrial machines by more effective models, an over-all plan is desirable.

Many firms buy machines as needed but select each machine separately on the basis of its operational requirements alone. It is better to make up a long range plan or procedure so that all machines bought will be compatible as much as possible. Then when a portion of the factory is ripe for automation (either as a fully automatic line, or an island) the machines can be united effectively.

This can only be done if the long view is taken. The future automated production procedures should be laid out on paper *now*. The *ideal* machines for each position should be called out. Then purchases and replacements can be made which are compatible with the eventual automation system. *Planning* is the key to all successful automation systems.

## OPERATIONAL ORIENTATION versus PRODUCT ORIENTATION

The choice of equipment is directly affected by the nature of the work process. If the work consists largely of the job-shop sort of operations, mainly short runs, there is no need to consider automation lines. As a general rule, planners attempt to use a continuous in-line flow arrangement of the work, whether for automation or not. This is, however, possible only if there is an appreciable demand for one product or for a particular family of items that can be produced by the same process with comparatively minor changes.

The extreme conditions are easy to specify. For mass production, always use the product-oriented flow line, with transfer automation and specific product machines. For one-of-a-kind, or short runs only, use operation-oriented independent machines in a job-shop arrangement, such as numerical controlled machine tools.

Between these extremes, the answer is to isolate the few items of the various products manufactured that can be produced by a special machine or subsystem (such as metal legs for a furniture manufacturer) and to automate these; the rest of the plant can make use of semi-automatics and flexible program (tape or tracer) machines.

## ISLANDS versus LINES

There are three versions of automatic manufacturing. The most familiar is the use of a single machine that does all of the necessary operations to the piece part being machined. An automatic screw machine producing lubrication fittings is an example. The single machine may be of the special purpose or specific purpose type, to be discussed shortly. However, only in certain cases can a single machine be used, for if the product has appreciable complexity, several machines are needed.

If several machines are to be used, they can be arranged in the form of islands or lines. In the case of islands of automation, a local enclave of machines is arranged to produce a part or a group of operations. No attempt is made to accomplish automatic continuous production of a major item or product. Just as the automatic grinder and die casting machine are valuable by themselves, several machines grouped together, forming an island of automation in a factory which is not otherwise automated, can be highly beneficial, too.

If the automation is to be of the continuous automatic manufacturing type, then a line arrangement of machines is needed. This is the use of machines to do *all* of a series of manufacturing operations, the easy ones as well as the not so easy ones. When a line of automation is used, a definite effort is made to replace all manual operations. Even here, though, there is no need to go against good sense. Continue to use manpower where mechanization is economically unjustified.

## Manual Operations for Automation Lines

It commonly develops that some operations are just not worth automating. It can be done but the cost and complexity make it impractical. Most *automatic* factories continue to use men wherever it seems to be practical. A man here and there also provides surveillance over the machines, correcting stoppages and malfunctions (such as by a cigarette wrapper in a feeder or a broken drill).

Examples of where manual aids to *automatic* production lines may be advisable are manual assembly of automotive panel instruments into a cluster; hand placing of gears and shafts into an automotive transmission assembly machine; and attaching the generator, starting motor, fan belt, and distributor to an automatically assembled automobile engine. These operations could probably be done automatically, but it is just not worthwhile in dollars and cents.

An operation which has defied attempts at economic automatizing is insertion of large, curved glass windshields into the bodies of automobiles. This job, which requires both strength and dexterity (in sealing the rubber gasket around the window), is difficult for a workman but even more difficult for a machine. Merely saying that it is not practical to do an operation of this kind invariably challenges automation designers to prove that it can be done. Some automation designers are akin to mountain climbers. To them, the challenge of the task is quite enough reason for doing it. Such enthusiasm and enterprise toward their work is commendable, but they sometimes need restraining by less inspired but more dollar-conscious industrial executives.

## SINGLE LINES versus MULTIPLE LINES

There is an inherent risk in deciding on a single, high rate automated production line. Compare the situation to a power station which utilizes several boilers and turbines and generators instead of one or two larger units, permitting repairs to be made a unit at a time, without shutting down the entire system. In such a case, light loads (smaller production requirements) can be handled more efficiently by using part of the equipment at full capacity.

In contrast, splitting production capacity into parallel smaller lines is not always feasible. Printing plants for newspapers, for example, do not always install two high speed rotary presses. In fact, the trend is to use the same facilities to print competitive newspapers in the same city, for morning and evening editions. This makes most profitable use of a single costly automated system.

Arranging production in semi-independent complementary subsystems has advantages, too. Storing critical parts and assemblies prevents interruption of the whole system while local repairs or retooling is made. An example would be an automation line for bicycles. One subsystem manufactures the wheels, another the coaster brakes, and another the tubular frame. All three lines bring completed components to the area where the final assembly is done manually. Even though a line should fail or need retooling, the others could still be producing parts. If a storage bank of preassembled components is maintained prior to the final assembly, there need be no assembly loss due to routine shutdowns.

The use of stored materials kept in reserve is often a very practical safeguard. Isolating the automation into several small lines allows them to be somewhat independent so that a single stoppage does not affect the entire process. In the case of the line for producing bicycle brakes, one missing part stops subassembly operations.

Summing up *single line versus multiple line*, use more than one identical line in parallel if you can; break up the line into independent branch sections if possible; use redundant control system circuits and quickly replaceable elements in the most critical circuits for added reliability; do not hesitate to store parts as an insurance policy against costly stoppages.

All of these suggestions are especially important when a new type of automatic system is first being used. Later designs of similar systems will have greater reliability because trouble spots will have been found and corrected.

## INDEPENDENT MACHINES versus TRANSFER MACHINES

The comments made regarding single line versus multiple lines apply to some extent to the discussion of *direct transfer* versus *independent machine* automation. It would seem that independent automatic machines should be preferred over the direct transfer of parts from one machine to the succeeding one. This is so if the part being machined is suited for common or bulk handling. However, if the components must be held in a very particular way, then direct transfer is better.

The main distinction between the two methods is that direct transfer takes the part in process and, as directly as possible, *hands it over* to the next machine or station for its immediate use. The independent unit machine picks up the part from storage (or is given the part by a vibrating feeder for example) and when finished drops it into a bin for the next machine. Each independent unit machine obtains parts from one intermachine storage and deposits its work into another intermachine storage bank. Some transfer arrangements also use intermachine shuttles that store some parts, and other unit machines release the parts in an oriented manner, which permits a subsequent machine to grasp it.

Generally speaking, however, if the parts (such as washers or rivets) can be dropped in random manner and loaded as needed without difficulty, the independent machines are the ones to use. If the parts (such as resistors or transformer laminations) require specific positioning, then there is no justification in scrambling them in a bin or hopper, for this complicates the job of positioning at the following operation.

## FIXED PROGRAM MACHINES versus VARIABLE PROGRAM MACHINES

The comparative merits of fixed program and flexible program machines are discussed in greater detail in another chapter. It should be pointed out that flexible programming is always desirable, but that program following systems are expensive and usually justified only for short run, job-shop operations that call for high precision. However, external programming is not the only form. The fact that some machines can be physically taken apart and rearranged or even redesigned permits some variation in the internal program.

Composite machines, such as transfer machines, do allow limited flexibility because the unitized sections (segments) are standardized and re-usable, and they can be rearranged and retooled for different models. *Special purpose machines* may resemble transfer machines, as the workpiece advances to successive work stations, but the units and mechanisms are not standardized. So desired changes in the product may make the machinery obsolete.

## SPECIFIC PRODUCT MACHINES versus STANDARDIZED UNIT MACHINES

If there is high probability that product form and demand will not change appreciably for many years (such as electric switches, telephone relays, hinges), then a specific product machine may be a good buy; but if yearly styles and models are the rule, and evolutionary changes are to be expected, then use of composite machines made up of standardized sections may be advisable.

The adjectives *special* and *standard* are relative. The special machine may eventually become a standard catalog item. *General purpose* is relative to *specific purpose*. A standardized transfer machine may be capable of machining engine blocks and heads, transmission housings, or pump castings, when suitably tooled and programmed. However, it cannot turn pistons or grind crankshafts, whereas specific product machines may permit certain variations. A machine intended primarily to form only electrical switchboxes can be adjusted to make a wider variety of boxes by changeover of the machine units and tooling.

Chart 14-1, Mobile Factories, lists examples of special purpose specific product machines.

Chart 6-2.  Automation Step-by-Step

| PRELIMINARY PHASE | Evaluate automation possibilities and consider preliminary methods for improving production, as per the text. Build up an automation file pertaining to methods apparently applicable to your industry. Consider the ''Approaches to Automation,'' per Chart 6-1. Get ''free advice'' from automation machinery and equipment vendors. Discuss your tentative plans with independent consulting engineers and consider contracting a consultant to aid you in interpreting automation for your plant and to conduct an automation feasibility study. Evaluate your present and future products; compare ''Pro-Automation Factors,'' per Chart 6-3 and ''Contra-Automation Factors,'' per Chart 6-4. |
|---|---|
| CONCEPTUAL PHASE | Obtain multiple automation ideas, pertaining to the process under consideration, as per the text, and from reports from automation experts. Consider ''Man versus Machine,'' per Chart 12-2 and the ''Approaches to Automation,'' per Chart 6-1. Specify range of acceptable performance. Create two or more preliminary automation systems. Repeat and refine to a best functional system, specifically integrating machine and control. |
| DESIGN PHASE | Prepare drawings and specifications and decide what-to-design, what-to-buy, what-to-build, and what-to-assemble from available machines. Consider utilities (services, such as power, water, cooling, chip removal, drainage, and air) to the machines; future product changes, standardization, availability of components, reserve capacity of every machine operation, and maintenance. |
| BUILDING PHASE | Building the machinery starts with invitation for bids, from vendors and contractors, followed by awarding the contracts. Then it is necessary to supervise vendors and builders, to check progress and delivery schedules, and to compare the machine being manufactured with the purchase specifications. Problems and interferences are bound to occur, which must be reconciled and resolved. The work of several builders and vendors must be coordinated. When the machinery nears completion, as much try-out as possible should be done before delivery. A consultant may act as liaison between the user (buyer) of the automation equipment and machinery builders or equipment vendors. |
| INSTALLATION PHASE | Installation involves study and preparation of the factory where the machinery is to be used, and arrangements for all necessary utilities. Pre-installation arrangements are also necessary for transportation and the installers; the millwrights, welders, riggers, electricians, and pipe fitters. Foundations and machinery mounts must be prepared. When installed, the equipment must be tried out; first without materials, then actual experimental production runs with materials. A final inspection of the installed equipment, and point by point operational check comparing to specifications, precedes turning over the equipment to the production men. |
| ADJUSTMENT PHASE | Adjustment phase activities: actual operational try-out; synchronizing and balancing operating cycles; correcting mechanical problems; trimming-up control actions; redesigning and rebuilding portions, if necessary; organizing procedures for start-up, shut-down, stand-by service, tool sharpening and replacement service, maintenance, trouble shooting and repairs, spare parts, training operations, maintenance and repair men; compiling operating records, including records of the capability, ranges and rates, for each station, accuracy of each automatic measuring device; and operating cost records. |

## AUTOMATION, STEP-BY-STEP

Chart 6-2, Automation Step-by-Step, outlines the procedure for attaining automation in the fabrication industries. The incorporation of an automatic process by a manufacturer involves six progressive phases. These are the *preliminary, conceptual, design, building, installation* and *adjustment* stages of development.

## PRELIMINARY STAGE

This is the educational phase of an automation program, before any formal studies are made. Various general aspects of automation are considered at this time. It may be advisable to engage the services of an independent consultant to conduct formal investigations and report on the feasibility of various approaches toward automaticity. If the company is large enough, they can set up an automation study group with *no other responsibilities,* as their *captive* consultants. The consultant or automation group assists the user at each phase of the automation program, if the decision is to adopt automation.

### Conceptual Stage

At the conceptual stage of an automation program, the more ideas the better. In the beginning, the ideas should be confined to functional concepts, what *results* are to be accomplished. After the functional objectives are decided, the operational matters, what *methods* are to be used, can be evaluated. When the operational methods have been tentatively determined, the physical *equipment* can be considered.

At each step of the conceptual stage of development, *functional, operational, physical* (for an example see Figure 3-6), begin with many ideas. These ideas should be evaluated critically and the two best proposals selected. The conceptual stage of automation system design ends up with block and flow diagrams.

### Design Stage

Design consists of firmly specifying, by drawings, words, and figures, the actual equipment. Some design is based on scientific principles and can be truly engineered, but much of it is an art based on judgment and experience. Practical design considerations can be checked by referring to Automation Injunctions, Chart 6-5, and Automation Admonitions, Chart 6-6.

The *functional* and *operational* aspects of design are usually the direct problem of the automation *user,* assisted by his advisers. The detailed *equipment* design is most commonly left to the machine builder.

Automation design is a team operation. Mechanical designers and control engineers must work together on an equal basis. The user's engineers, the consulting engineers, the machine builders engineers, and the equipment vendors' application engineers, must all contribute to attain the optimum automation for the job. Chart 15-1, in the Appendix, points out the distinctions in the roles and responsibilities of the various engineers making up the automation design team.

### Building Stage

In the case of automating a *process,* the equipment is assembled at its permanent location, such as a refinery. However, most automation for *fabrication* is made by a machinery builder. More or less standard sections and major components are used, if suitable, to simplify building and design.

The building phase includes a limited trial of special features. This is especially important if the design has never been built before. Automation lines can seldom be tried out in their entirety at the machinery builders' factory, but specific product machines should be proven before delivery to the user.

### Installation Stage

Ideally, installation consists of merely uncrating the machine and connecting to a power source. Usually, though, many preparations must be made at the factory to accommodate the new automatic equipment. This requires active participation of the production engineers and plant engineers who must maintain existing production while activating the new automation. The installation phase includes limited tryouts, up to the point where a production run is attempted.

### Adjustment Stage

Some calibrations and adjustments of the new equipment will be required to get optimum results from the automation process. Possibly even some redesign and rebuilding of trouble spots will be necessary. *Debugging* is unavoidable, for not every factor can be anticipated, not every contingency foreseen. This corresponds to the *shakedown cruise* of a naval ship and the *smoke test* of new electronic equipment.

## AUTOMATION—PRO AND CON

### Pro-Automation Factors

Chart 6-3 lists a number of pro-automation factors. Just as the contra-automation factors are not ironclad, not all of these benefits necessarily

Chart 6-3.   Pro-Automation Factors

| | |
|---|---|
| **INCREASED PRODUCTION CAPACITY** | The ability to produce a larger volume of goods. |
| **INCREASED PRODUCTIVITY** | The amount of production for the manpower involved. |
| **REDUCED LEAD TIME** | The time from when production is first needed, until parts are produced, is less with an integrated system. |
| **INCREASED DUTY CYCLE** | The number of hours per day which the machines can be used; the percentage of time each station is actually in use. |
| **REDUCED IN-PROCESS INVENTORY** | The number of items within the process, "in the pipeline," is reduced. |
| **REDUCED CAPITAL COSTS** | An integrated machine or system can cost less than equivalent individual machines with interconnecting materials handling equipment. |
| **IMPROVED QUALITY** | Machines are more consistent than men; less variation in output. |
| **REDUCED PRODUCTION COSTS** | The costs per part are greatly reduced for large volume production. |
| **SIMPLIFY PRODUCT** | Automatic assembly permits simplification of the product. |
| **REDUCES SPACE REQUIREMENTS** | The production per square foot of factory is greater with an integrated automatic system. |
| **IMPROVE SAFETY** | Removing the operator from hazardous locations; faster responses to emergencies. |
| **SIMPLIFY MAINTENANCE** | Maintenance of a single integrated machine of standardized unit sections can be simpler than that of many individual machines. |

result. They do serve as a rough guide of what can be expected from the automation of fabrication manufacturing operations.

CONTRA-AUTOMATION FACTORS

Every manufacturing process is a compromise of cost, results, time, and resources. Automation probably involves even more compromises than do other design activities. Potentially adverse factors can be best countered by a full awareness of their limiting nature.

The *Contra-Automation Factors*, Chart 6-4, need not all be limitations. Sometimes they can be effectively balanced by clever design. For example, automation does not always cost more. Further, sometimes the operations can be even more flexible (as with numerical control) with automation than by manual control. A wider range and variety may be possible with automation than before, but the points listed are the adverse characteristics of automation which must generally be considered.

AUTOMATION POSSIBILITIES

CHECK-OFF LIST

1. stereotyped operations
2. high labor content
3. changeover problems
4. expensive materials
5. quality problems
6. inadequate production capacity
7. changes contemplated
8. high volume items
9. antedated methods
10. heavy paper work

Let us consider the typical manufacturer who is thinking of automation for his fabrication operations. He has been in business for years but is becoming aware that something must be done to reduce soaring production costs and to meet competition. Though he admits automation can help him, his firm cannot consider discarding their plant and starting anew with highly automatized equipment. He would like to get auto-

Chart 6-4. Contra-Automation Factors

| | |
|---|---|
| PROCUREMENT PROBLEMS | Automation is not easy to buy or to design, or to build. |
| ADJUSTMENT PROBLEMS | Having installed the automatic equipment, a painful adjustment and rebuild period may be necessary. |
| DOWN TIME VULNERABILITY | The more complex a system, the more vulnerable is the whole to a sectional failure. |
| REDUCED FLEXIBILITY OF OPERATIONS | Orienting the production system around specific products limits use of the machines for other purposes. |
| REDUCED FLEXIBILITY OF SCHEDULING | Short production runs or frequent model changeovers are very costly. Automation demands long runs at full capacity for maximum benefits. |
| REDUCED FLEXIBILITY OF PRODUCT | Redesign of the product requires rearrangement or redesign of the production process. |
| REDUCED FLEXIBILITY OF MATERIALS | Materials must continue to come without variations in pack, form, content or size, which limits sources for materials. |
| GREATER CAPITAL COSTS | Automation requires a large capital expenditure, whether bought or designed, and built. |
| GREATER EXECUTIVE DEMANDS | High speed operation, and high break-even costs demand long-range planning and intensify problems when they occur. |
| HIGHER MAINTENANCE SKILLS | Automatic control and measurements increase need for specialized skills. |

mation, at least cost and with a minimum of disturbance to his existing production operations. He also prefers to automate gradually over a number of years, using the existing equipment as much as possible.

The prescription for him is *semi-automation.* This is the policy of improving specific operations by the introduction of automatic methods, treating the most *sensitive* operations first and gradually evolving to a highly automated arrangement.

How is this automation prospect to decide what he should do? A good start is to make an objective *automation feasibility study,* including an inventory of *automation possibilities* as part of this feasibility study.

Experience is a big help in compiling an inventory of automation possibilities. A check-off list is a help here, too, for manufacturer and production analyst alike. A list of the automation possibilities in a manufacturing plant helps to interpret the need for automation methods. This list also serves as a good start for a comprehensive automation feasibility study.

STEREOTYPED OPERATIONS

Some production methods have been in use for a long time without much improvement. Long usage does not necessarily imply inefficiency of operations, but it does hint that there may be some room for improvement. Thus, traditional manufacturing methods are often ripe for changeover to automatically accomplished methods.

A further consideration here is that if an entire industry uses the same old procedures, a more powerful technique, such as automation, makes it possible to attain competitive supremacy.

What is radically new automation in one industry is established practice in another. Bottling, printing, flour milling, and textiles had been highly automated long before the automation age received popular notice. It is well worthwhile to look outside of a field for proven examples of applied automation that can be adopted.

Examples of traditional fabrication methods whose functions can be automated are:

1. nut and bolt fastening
2. chip-making fabrication
3. removing metal to shape a workpiece
4. use of metal
5. manual statistical quality control
6. routine tool replacement
7. conveyors
8. manual assembly

Automatic methods which might accomplish the same functions listed above more effectively are:

1. clinching, use of adhesives
2. electric arc erosion, plasma jet, chemical milling, cold forming steel
3. adding stock to form shape rather than removing it, as electric arc forming
4. use of plastics, glass, ceramics, wood, concrete for traditionally metal parts
5. automatic quality control, including machine capability meters
6. automatic dull tool detection
7. catapulting parts instead of physical conveying
8. automatic assembly machines

### High Labor Content

Labor is always costly, both in money and in the problems associated with the use of human labor. Hence, high labor costs suggest that large potential savings may be possible by use of automation, if the operations can be rendered a routine.

As a broad rule, every routine operation that is done manually is expensive, so machines had best be used for routine work, and men reserved for nonroutine tasks. Many jobs that appear nonroutine on the surface can be *routinized*, making them amenable to automatic methods.

Assembly is a common high labor operation which often shows large savings by use of automation. Further examples of high labor content operations that can be accomplished by automation are: selective parts-matching assembly, inspection, measuring, production recordkeeping, tool room and precision machine work.

Products assembled from *multiple combinations* of parts have usually demanded manual methods, but these too can often be assembled automatically.

### Changeover Problems

For some products (such as oil-well machinery), machine set-up time is comparable to the actual running time required to produce parts because requirements are for short runs. The main benefit of automation here is to greatly reduce set-up time by making use of built-in variable tooling and preprogrammed control.

Automatic machines designed for short runs and fast changeover are especially valuable for manufacturers who must meet spot demands. They are also suitable for the manufacturer who must meet demands for multiple variations. This stresses the desirability of using machines that are capable of mass producing parts automatically, yet allow each item or group of items to have some individual characteristics.

There has always been a conflict between the production man's preference for an unvarying product, and the customers' demand for *specials* and for custom treatment. For example, electric motors are manufactured by highly automated production processes, but some customers demand various shaft and mounting configurations to the basic motor, which adds a high nonautomated labor component to the motor.

Some special working of standard items will always be needed to satisfy customer demands. To a large extent, modern automatic control techniques make it possible to mechanize the assembly of *multiple combinations*. Modern automatic control also makes it practical to manufacture specific variations to produce *custom goods* on a mass-production basis.

Here are some examples of multiple combinations and of specific variations to products that ordinarily require manual work, but which can be accomplished automatically:

1. assembling typewriter keyboards for any language, including special symbols
2. producing water valves of varied sizes and end fittings
3. producing screws and bolts to a wide variety of sizes, finishes, threads, and head shapes
4. paper envelopes, various sizes and window locations

5. cylinder lock keying
6. electronic devices to suit 50 or 60 cycle, 130, 160, or 220 volt power
7. medicines, various combinations of ingredients
8. various arrangements of electrical connector pins
9. combinations of blends and colors as of paint
10. shaft variations on electric motors
11. filling varied orders from customers (by automatic warehouse)

The ideal automation machine or system should be capable of producing a wide variation of product styles and sizes, with quick and easy changeover.

The need for warehousing is reduced when nonstandard orders can be quickly filled on demand. Combining several small lot, semi-standard products permits automation, provided the machine can meet the range of variation of the product.

There is apt to be customer reaction against excessive face similarity of products. Hence, if the manufacturer can allow the customer to select trim, color, pattern, and optional extras, all sorts of "made-specially-for-you" products are possible. An example of this is the auto industry, which sells *custom* combinations of standardized engines, drives, colors, bodies, interiors, and accessories.

## EXPENSIVE MATERIALS

Automation can prevent waste and spoilage in three ways. Automatic assembly reduces waste or loss of hardware, paints, and small parts. Automation also prevents damage to finished surfaces resulting from intraplant handling. Most important, automation reduces the high cost of human errors.

Wastage of materials (spillage, loss, contamination) is undesirable and so is damage to simple parts; but worst of all is the damage to complex parts which already contain a large investment in labor and effort. A single human mistake can cause large losses. For example, some products, such as large turbine gears or intricate dies, require a great deal of precision machining. One slip late in the process can ruin the entire piece. Even a machinist who is correct 99 per cent of the time cannot be relied upon for such work, for superhuman dependability and accuracy is needed. Automation protects the equity of investment which accumulates in the workpiece being processed.

This is true even for common materials such as steel strip. Damage which occurs after many stages of rolling and treating is very wasteful because of the accumulative production costs. The point to keep in mind is that the consistency of automation results in less loss to intrinsically expensive materials and to materials containing a large work and effort content.

## QUALITY PROBLEMS

It was just pointed out that automation may be able to correct excessive scrap and irregular production quality by eliminating the highly variable human element. A further consideration is that automatic control makes it possible to work machines closer to their ultimate capability.

In the fabricating industries, the *quality* of parts usually refers to their dimensions, which determines how suitable they are for the intended purpose. Every dimension must fall between specified limits.

Every industrial machine has a definite *capability*, which is its greatest possible accuracy. Ideally, the capability of the machine is comparable to the dimensional quality required of the workpieces. If the machine has a capability much better than what is required (such as if a precision jig-boring machine is used to do routine drilling jobs), this is an uneconomical use of production equipment. If extreme precision is demanded from an ordinary production machine (as when hydraulic valve cylinders are machined on a turret lathe), a high percentage of rejects can be expected.

Statistical quality control evaluation of workpiece measurements indicates the centerline of machine performance and the machine capability, thus making it possible to obtain the maximum accuracy potential from machines. Automatic quality control has been discussed previously.

## Inadequate Production Capacity

An existing manufacturing process may not have the capacity to produce sufficient goods. Automation can provide high rates of production and also provide a margin of reserve capacity. This can produce more goods per square foot of factory floor, sometimes eliminating the need for a contemplated plant expansion.

When a small scale manufacturing process must suddenly turn out large quantities (such as expanded demand for electric can openers), merely scaling up existing operations is seldom satisfactory. Increased production requirements may justify investment in plant and machinery which were not at first warranted at the original rate of production. Oftentimes, a new product is first made with existing facilities, then if the product catches on, automated manufacture is indicated.

Electric hand drills are an example of a product whose demand outgrew production capacity. For years, they were made in limited numbers mainly for industrial use. Then the growth of home workshops multiplied the demand manyfold. Manufacture by automation reduced the price to less than one third, which further increased demand. Other examples of products which had to greatly increase production capacity are transistors, TV tubes, foam rubber, plastic pipe and fittings, synthesized diamonds, quartz radio crystals, and pharmaceuticals.

One point worth mentioning is the use of automation mainly for reserve purposes. In peace time, the military establishment must both continually develop improved equipment and supplies, and also assure a high volume source in case of emergency requirements. Automation can be used to produce the low quantity needed in peace time and provide high reserve capacity if needed.

## High Volume Items

Some factories produce only a few models and kinds of products, but within the products are similar components that can be standardized for production by automatic methods. Savings can be effected by automating the items that add up to large numbers and producing the rest by con- ventional methods. This demands more than merely checking parts lists of products seeking identical parts. It calls for a positive program of standardization of components used for production.

An example of this practice is the manufacture of boat engines. These are available as one, two, four, six, and eight cylinder types, high and low compression. Yet, the engines use standardized pistons, rods, valves, rocker arms, and other parts. Some of the parts were upgraded to better than what is actually required to achieve high volume by standardization. This is justified, as the cost per item is less at the greater volume manufactured.

Other examples show how this works out. Manufacturers of low volume specialized electrical equipment for power plants can standardize on terminals, insulators, contacts, connectors, and switch blades. In the toy business, items such as motors and wheels can be standardized. Truck and farm implement manufacturers standardize wheels, pumps, valves, and suspension gear. Track parts for crawler-type construction machines and military tanks use many identical parts in one machine, so that even low product production may have high component production. This is also true in the case of turbine blades, conveyor parts, and electronic computer units.

## Changes Contemplated

If changes are contemplated for any production process, for whatever reason, it is prudent to consider automation at that time. If the process is going to be interrupted anyhow, automation can then be introduced without much additional production disturbance.

Examples of production stoppages when automation can be introduced painlessly are: between product models, occupying a new factory, beginning a new process, introducing new products, or decentralizing manufacturing operations. Disasters, such as a fire or flood, may also constitute a natural break in production when automation can be introduced with little additional inconvenience.

Automobile owners commonly consider a new

car when they have had a mishap or failure with the old one. So it is with production equipment. If big repairs or improvements are needed, it may be a better move to make a big change to automation. It is seldom practical to replace a machine with an operationally similar one. Upgrading is usually a better course to follow. This means that whenever a machine is to be replaced, for any reason, it should be replaced by equipment that is compatible with an eventual automation scheme for the plant. By this policy, in a few years most of the machines in a plant will be of the types most readily integrated to make possible automatic production. This is true if proper long range planning was done.

### Antedated Methods

The fact that a manufacturing process is ripe for automation is not always obscure. It may be perfectly obvious, as when the methods in use are antedated and better methods are well known. Many manufacturers cling to old methods without good reason, merely because they just never got round to making a change. This indicates inept management.

One of the fringe benefits of an automation feasibility study is the stimulus to make improvements in production methods that, strictly speaking, have nothing to do with automation and should have been done in line with good industrial engineering and production practice.

Some industrial operations that should have been improved long ago were passed over. Instead of merely bringing them up to a routine standard level, it may be advantageous to go directly to automation. For example, manual materials handling can go directly to a programmed *free* conveyor system, omitting the monorail stage of development. Another example is the replacement of a manually operated $A_2$ surface grinder directly with an $A_4$ feedback controlled machine without passing to the $A_3$ automatic cycle machine.

This resembles the development of some countries which advanced directly from ox carts to aircraft without using railroads. The point is that automation permits a leap from backwardness to advanced industrialization.

Examples of antedated methods that shout for automaticity are the hand fitting of parts; manual loading; routine inspection; manual regulation of liquid level in a tank; speed regulation; load regulation; and the use of men to open doors and to carry materials within a plant. Less obvious is the use of small individual containers (as bags of material) when bulk is easier to use (car loads), and delivery in batches when continuous (conveyor or pipe line) delivery is possible.

### Paper Work

It is convenient to speak of *office automation* and of *industrial automation,* the first dealing with paper work, and the second having to do with the actual fabrication and assembly of pieces. However, there is also a large amount of office work on the factory floor. Incidental to their main work, many skilled workmen must do routine counting and information recording tasks, wasting valuable machine operating time. Mechanization of routine recordkeeping in the factory can result in a dual advantage by saving expensive man-hours, and assuring maximum utilization of the industrial machinery. The same methods used to simplify data handling in the office are applicable to data handling in the factory. Measurement and control are especially amenable to data handling automation.

Examples of information tasks on the factory floor that can be automatized are: counting, measuring, inspection, sorting, statistical quality control, machine loading and duty records, material records and routine calculations. These can be automatized to some extent by use of counters, automatic measurements, inspection machines, auto-quality control, centralized information display, and special purpose computers.

## DETERMINING THE AUTOMATION SYSTEM

### SOURCES FOR AUTOMATION IDEAS

Check-off List:

Internal Sources
1. executives
2. engineers

3. salesmen
4. workmen

External Sources
5. consultants
6. machinery builders
7. competitors
8. equipment vendors
9. similar industries

Educational Sources
10. trade journals
11. books
12. conferences and meetings
13. training courses.

Any new automatic machine or process must be a departure from the existing way of doing a job. It cannot be the mere replacement of hands by mechanisms and brain cells by circuits. This means that new ideas and new thinking are mandatory for successful automation.

As pointed out earlier, the quality of ideas is certainly important, but the number of concepts on how to accomplish a design is just as important at the early stages of thinking up automation possibilities. After a good number of ideas and approaches are on hand, it is time to become critical and cull out the obviously deficient and impractical brainstorms. The remainder can then be refined to the most plausible ways to accomplish automation. The ideas that remain after the idea "shake-down" are the basis for further development and improvement, to meet the specific production problems in the most practicable way possible.

Where are these automation ideas to come from? The answer is, from many sources, none of which should be overlooked. The check-off list above shows the most obvious sources for concepts and ideas that apply to automation. The listings overlap widely, for the executives may indeed be engineers. So are the consultants and corporation automation groups, who are engineers engaged specifically to assist the executives by performing automation feasibility studies.

Let us consider automation from the standpoint of an industrial executive who wants to find out how automation affects him and how it can help his production.

The first step toward an active investigation of automation for many executives and engineers who want to keep abreast of developments is a file of magazine articles and catalogs that cover the areas of their interest. They may buy books on the subject from time to time, first the popular automation and cybernetic books, then the more technical versions. It is oftentimes advisable for a firm to assign the duty of actively pursuing and reporting on the state of the automation arts (not limited to their field) to a staff member, in addition to his regular work. However, once an actual automation program is under way, it cannot be handled as a side line.

### EXECUTIVES

Some of the earliest ideas of what automation methods bear further investigation should originate with the executives who have the management responsibility. Although they may not have a detailed familiarity with manufacturing processes or with engineering, they do have a broad view of industrial operations, including the financial and sales aspects.

Contrary to public opinion, executives do get ideas sometimes. Occasionally, something results from their contacts on the golf course, from their attendance at conferences, and from their membership in trade associations, that bears on the potential automation of their plant.

No matter who contributes the key concepts to the proposed automation process, the executive must make the final decisions. Hence, he must keep informed as to the advantages and shortcomings of all proposed actions.

### ENGINEERS

The average engineer now in industry can hardly be blamed for not having his "idea lobe" well furrowed. In college, few men were shown the cross-field relationships of all branches of science and engineering so that they could synthesize new systems and devices from such basic facts. Most graduates, especially pre-1960's, were taught how to design the machines of the preceding generation. Yet, they are expected to be able to anticipate the processes of tomorrow.

Some can do so. They are especially valuable. Every encouragement should be given to the engineers who keep abreast of automatic developments, both in their field and in other branches. Their broad spectrum knowledge breeds ideas. The firm who has creative idea-men of this type would do well to appoint one as automation systems project engineer. However, if the men with ideas and originality are already profitably occupied, the alternative may be to engage an automation idea man to "spark-plug" the automation development. This may be especially necessary in the medium and smaller-size industrial concern.

## SALESMEN

Most salesmen are not especially interested in production systems or technology, but they are still a good source for automation concepts. Successful salesmen know many people and have many contacts. This goes for the sales representatives of your own firm and for those of your vendors and competitors.

Good salesmen know what the public wants and what can be readily sold. Further, the "live ones" are well aware of competitive products and their prices. Their advice as to markets, competitors' moves, and product deficiencies is invaluable.

## WORKMEN

Long before large scale automation is introduced, it may be a good policy to openly invite ideas from the hourly employees, to be suitably rewarded as is familiar "suggestion-box" practice. This has several potential advantages. For one, it dispels many of the rumors concerning automation that develop when no factual information is released. Next, allowing the employees to participate in the introduction of automation of a plant or process is bound to increase its acceptance and reduce the likelihood of opposition. Finally, some of the ideas will be found to be practical and valuable.

In most cases workmen will not suggest big scale or radical changes. Their greatest potential contributions are for spot improvements of existing processes (manual, semi-automatic, or even automation systems) by suggesting how the addition of automatic methods at specific points will improve the system. From this viewpoint, their aid is just as valuable after the new automation equipment has been installed and is undergoing the trials of the shake-down period. Some pointed comments from workmen on how to eliminate "bugs" can be of great value during this critical period.

## CONSULTANTS

Opinions from within one's own organization are valuable, for who know the problems better than do the production men themselves? However, complete reliance on this inbred source for new concepts can result in variations of the same old ways. There must be a free flow of ideas uninhibited by internal politics or timid supervisors.

One source for information from the outside is the consultant. He is supposed to be able to bring in new ideas to complement those of his client, just as is done in the more familiar case of an architect. If qualified, he should be capable of studying a firm's processes, products, or prospective plans, and recommending suitable automation techniques to accomplish the production objectives. He may gather and organize information for final executive decision, or he can carry developments to completion, as required.

This does not mean that consultants deal only in original ideas. These would represent only a very subjective viewpoint. No one has ever accomplished anything worthwhile (at least in the industrial field) without a great deal of dependence upon predecessors, contemporaries, and associates. Ideally, consultants must be cognizant of automation theory, philosophy, and practical know-how, as well as of specialized engineering and technology. They must know especially well their clients' unique problems and objectives.

## MACHINERY BUILDERS

The machine builder is indispensable when it comes to learning how best to apply his line of machines. This applies mainly to standard models of machines, including the various modifications that make them more applicable for a particular production system. Further, most new machines already have many automation features as part of their design. Some specific product machines can be bought right from a catalog, to produce complete items such as pills, bottles, nails, screws, or boxes. If it is just a matter of buying a ready-made machine that does not need to be developed, common sense may dictate to buy it and get on with production, even though the machine may not fit into future automatic production plans.

A machinery manufacturers' information is only valuable for applying *his* line of machines. It is not adequate for devising an automation *system* also involving equipment of other manufacturers.

### Equipment Vendors

The term *vendor* refers to firms who manufacture or sell components such as cutting tools, electrical motors, controllers, and materials handling equipment. The terms *builders* and *vendors* overlap, so the comments made usually apply to both. Equipment manufacturers know how their devices are used in other automation systems. Such *applications engineering* suggestions are valuable to the systems engineer.

A system is much more than the collection of pieces. To develop a suitable system it is necessary to be free from a predisposition to specify types or brands of machines. Only a project engineer who is not associated with the equipment and machine builders can provide the necessary objectivity and recommend the best units regardless of their source. The man (or men) who designs the system must have loyalties only to the user of the system. This is usually an employee of the user, the automation project engineer, or an independent consultant who does not sell machinery or equipment, as explained in the Appendix, Chart 15-1.

### Industrial Examples

Every industry, such as paper, cement, electronic, or automotive, has manufacturing and processing methods which are well known throughout that industry. When one prominent member of an industry automates, it paves the way for the other members of the industry to attain automation. Automobile engine manufacturers learn from each other, but it is seldom advisable to incorporate a "Chinese copy" of an existing automatic process. As is the case in the automotive industry, each new process builds on, but advances upon the other systems then in existence.

How does one learn the automation developments of a competitor? This is not difficult. Espionage is not necessary. Few American manufacturers attempt secrecy. They know that machinery builders, contractors, and consultants already know their newest methods. Employees change employers very freely, without resentment. Hence, most manufacturers make public their latest developments through the technical press and through papers presented at technical society meetings.

Actually, they gain as much as they may lose by exchanging information. This situation is so well recognized by some industries that they accept design engineers from rival firms as official visitors, somewhat as nations have made use of military observers. This is an approach to be encouraged. The first user of a novel automation system can have only one or two years lead time over his aggressive competitors. Desirable or not, this is the situation as it exists.

Each user benefits from knowing the successes and errors of his predecessors. This is learning by experience, without risk or expense.

### Books and Periodicals

Many periodicals have appeared with *automation* as part of their name, and an increasing number of books on the subject continue to appear. To read all books and periodicals discussing automation takes time, time which a busy industrialist, executive, or production engineer cannot easily find. Still, the price of books and magazines is far less than the cost of being uninformed.

The Appendix lists automation books of particular value and the leading journals and periodicals dealing with automation.

Chart 6-5. Automation Injunctions

| | |
|---|---|
| 1. EXPECT BIG IMPROVEMENTS | The choice of what-to-automate is as important as how-to-automate. The automation system is expected to pay for itself in a few years. Automation is a major effort and expense that should concentrate on major benefits. Focus on the items which permit substantial improvement. Leave those where only minor gains are possible. Separate the vital from the trivial. |
| 2. REDESIGN PRODUCT | "The product designed with production in mind," is a must for automation. The design for conventional manufacture is not suitable for automation. Design reference surfaces into the product. Automatic assembly usually simplifies the product design. Avoid fastenings as much as possible, but allow hand disassembly for service. |
| 3. USE PREPARED MATERIALS | The automatic process starts in the material suppliers factory. Use materials that already have some of the configuration needed for the product. Demand that materials come in the most continuous and most convenient form possible. Avoid precut stock. Use material on reels, drums, coils, extruded sections, prepainted; in the most continuous and preworked form possible. |
| 4. DO IT ALL | If economically justified, start the automatic process as close to the basic material as practical. Include machining, measuring, assembly, testing, and packaging operations, in the automation system. The job isn't finished until the product is ready for the user. |
| 5. HOLD ON TO WORKPIECE | Hold on to the workpiece through all the automation process. Location, positioning and identification of the workpiece require expensive machine action. Do not drop the workpiece into a hopper, but hold it for the entire job. The easiest way to hold it is by its parent stock. |
| 6. TRANSFER DIRECTLY | Mechanize transfer of parts directly from one operation to the succeeding one. Avoid intermachine storage, and interstage banking of parts, which increase process lag time. |
| 7. EQUALIZE CYCLES | Equalize individual machining cycles to accomplish straight line flow of parts through the automation process. If necessary, slow down fast machines to attain maximum automation simplicity and increased tool life. Speed up slow stations by using parallel operations, or perform long duration machining operation in stages, not to slow down the process. |
| 8. COMBINE OPERATIONS | Accomplish as many operations as possible at each station. Where practical, use multiple action tooling. The more machining accomplished per clamping and positioning operation of the workpiece, the better; for this assures highest dimensional accuracies of the operations, relative to each other. |
| 9. CORRECT AUTOMATICALLY | Automatically correct the machine when critical measurements drift beyond acceptable limits. Correct according to trends, rather than to individual measurements. If automatic feedback control isn't practical, display the information clearly so that the operator can make the necessary corrections easily. |
| 10. REDUCE CUTTING OPERATIONS | Just as proper product design simplifies automation, automation simplifies products, by reducing the number of parts necessary in an assembly. The operations for a conventional manufacturing process are not necessarily those for automation. Favor nonchip processes such as molding, forming, stamping, sintering, casting or extrusion in preference to metal cutting. |

Adapted from the work of
Charles F. Hautau, consulting engineer
Oxford, Ohio.

## SOURCES FOR AUTOMATION DESIGN

Let us assume management has decided that automation is feasible and desirable for their product, and that they want to obtain automated production. What sources are there for automation system design? It will be shown here that there are three sources for automation design information, and that *all* are necessary. The automation user who depends on only one or two of the three sources is compromising his chances of success. The three automation design sources are:

1. own organization              *do-it-yourself*
2. equipment vendors and builders
                                  *free engineering*
3. automation specialists        *systems architects*

In the discussion that follows, an analogy is drawn between the procurement of an automation system, and the design and erection of an industrial building. The automation user is likened to the owner of the contemplated building. The automation equipment suppliers and vendors are likened to the contractors and traders of the building industries. The automation systems engineer is likened to the architect. This is more than mere simile. The analogy exists in depth.

Until the automation era emerged from the era of mechanized powered tools, production was accomplished almost entirely by use of individual machines. Thus, individual machines could be evaluated on their merits and characteristics. Now, however, production based on automation is a *complex* of equipment working as a unified system. This ordinarily requires more than catalog picking or the modification of common machine tools. All of the machines and materials handling devices used must be considered in relation to the other units of the system.

What is needed for automation, not a feature of ordinary production, is the systems approach. Automation is but one facet of our modern technology which displays such complexity that it must be considered as a system rather than a collection of separate entities.

The question here is, "Who is to assume the role of coordinator of the entire automation system?" Until recently, the machine builder had complete jurisdiction over the machinery he built. He still is the one best suited to design his own machines and to evaluate their characteristics and their applications. However, the machine builder is not necessarily qualified for the job of coordinating *all* of the machines and devices used to formulate an automation system. This job must be assumed by someone directly accountable only to the user of the equipment.

The over-all systems coordinator, otherwise known as the *systems engineer* or the *project engineer,* must be in the employ of the user, either on a permanent or assignment basis. In any event, he may not have any pecuniary ties to the vendors and manufacturers of machinery and equipment used for the automation system.

The awareness among users of manufacturing equipment that the machine builders cannot be cognizant of the over-all system is not yet widespread. By long established practice, machine purchasers do not pay a separate fee for machine design. It is ordinarily, even today, included with the price of the machine.

The transition from thinking of individual machines to thinking of integrated manufacturing systems is not easy. Product manufacturers who attempt to procure automation systems by the old methods by which individual machines were purchased seldom get their money's worth. They are apt to get a patent medicine production system instead of a prescription one.

The point is that the automation user must participate actively in the development of his automation system or he will not be satisfied with it. He should accept the aid and suggestions of the manufacturers and vendors of automation machines and equipment, but he must make use of unbiased automation experts in his employ to coordinate the automation development.

### Do-It-Yourself

To what extent the user does his own automation design depends on the capabilities of his organization and whether or not he can delegate this to a competent outside firm. Some users have undertaken the complete design of the automation systems they require and have had good success. Their own engineering department accomplished all of the necessary design and specifications.

This is not too common however, for only large industrial organizations can have the skilled men as part of their organization. Most small- and medium-size firms don't want to establish an automation design department. In all cases, however, the user's staff must at least *contribute* to the original conceptual design of the automation they are to use. It is also the user's task to explain their production problems and goals to the automation systems engineers and equipment vendors for their recommendations.

The advantages of developing the automation system entirely by the user's own staff are that they know their plant facilities and problems best, and that intraplant coordination without interference is facilitated. If the user does the whole system design job, he has firm control over the results and has the undivided responsibility. This may or may not cost less than calling on outsiders to act as systems project engineers.

If a manufacturer chooses to rely on his own staff entirely, he may take his best men away from their regular duties; if he chooses to hire men, he faces the problem of selection and what to do with them when the project is completed. Excessive dependence on the "home team" precludes the new ideas that come in from the outside. This does not apply to very large organizations that have full-time automation departments to advise the manufacturing divisions.

FREE ENGINEERING SERVICES

Vendors and manufacturers of industrial equipment have conditioned the users of their products to expect free engineering. This policy is backfiring, for many users have come to demand that all engineering services be at no explicit charge, even for systems-wide engineering. This is comparable to expecting the complete architectural service for a complete building from the steel contractor at no extra charge.

Suppliers whose equipment is to be but part of a complex system cannot provide a system design at no charge if it is to be worth anything. The vendor's advice is very valuable but should be viewed in the proper perspective. His proper role is *applications* engineering, not *systems* engineering.

The heavy cost of free engineering led some machinery builders to offer to design the over-all automation systems as well as to supply the equipment. This appeals to many executives, for the all-in-one package deal is deceptively attractive. It implies a guaranteed, integrated system, free from many tedious details on the user's part. However, it has caused repeated disappointment to both the equipment builders and users.

The similar problem was met and solved years ago in the construction industry. When structures were simple, design was not a problem. Carpenter *architects* were the rule. The barn designer was also the barn builder. As buildings became larger and more complex, innovations such as central heat, elevators, steel framing, gas, electric power, plumbing, and concrete had to be considered. It was found necessary to divorce planning from building.

Architects now design and plan the structure (system) representing the user only, unbiased by any interest in materials and construction companies. Contractors bid on the basis of specified goods and services.

This does not preclude applications advice to the architect from the manufacturers of materials and equipment (such as boilers and elevators), nor does it prevent the owner (user) from realizing his own objectives without outside help if he is capable.

Some building owners who have dealt with contractors directly without the assistance of an architect have discovered that costs equivalent to an architect's fee have been paid in the form of functional inadequacy of the structure and equipment. A person who tries to be his own architect, lawyer, doctor, or consulting engineer, may be sorry afterwards. Just as the architect may not deal in building materials, so the persons with over-all systems responsibility may not ethically be sponsored by the manufacturers of equipment.

Chart 6-6. Automation Admonitions

| | |
|---|---|
| 1. MECHANIZE ROUTINES | Routine means machine; so all obvious routines are potential areas for automation. Furthermore, active measures can be taken to routinize existing operations that are not repetitive. Such routinizing may be by mathematical or logical analysis. |
| 2. USE FUNCTIONAL APPROACH | Plan the automation in three stages — functional, operational, physical. This permits formation of the basic system by management, leaving operational and physical details to be developed by specialists. |
| 3. GET THE FACTS | The decision whether or not to automate, and to what extent, must be based on a knowledge of the facts. This requires active efforts but is unavoidable. Insufficient, excessive, or improper automaticity are all costly mistakes. |
| 4. AVOID PREJUDICE | Adherence to "favorite" production techniques may preclude improvements. Antagonisms to unusual methods may rule out valuable advantages. An automation system is a compromise, making optimum use of all available techniques. |
| 5. AUTOMATE PROGRESSIVELY | Automation part-at-a-time when feasible results in less disturbance or risk than the all-at-once procedure. This applies particularly to products already being manufactured. |
| 6. PROCESS RATHER THAN FABRICATE | Automating a continuous process is easier than producing pieces or fabricating an assembly from parts. Materials are easiest to work on while they are in their longest, most continuous form. Strive to perform operations close together in time and space, to emulate continuous processing. |
| 7. ESTABLISH HIGH DUTY CYCLES | A machine and its elements should be worked continuously to get maximum benefits. Balance operation times. |
| 8. AIM FOR ADAPTABILITY | Consider a system which can manufacture a range of product sizes and variations, by means of adaptable tools, forms, clamps, and control settings. |
| 9. STRIVE FOR STABILITY | All systems — man and machine — are subject to external and internal disturbances. Careful design can reduce the effects in part, but self-correction based on self-measurement (feedback) stabilizes the output by compensating for disturbances from many causes. |
| 10. MAINTAIN SURVEILLANCE | Maloperation results in much spoilage if not detected at once. Surveillance does not necessarily imply self-correction, though self-correction demands some self-surveillance. Automatic alarms and "shut-offs" aid the human overseer of a process. Some human surveillance is always desirable. |
| 11. OBSERVE HUMAN ENGINEERING | Some functions are best done by man and some best done by machine. Ideally, man and machine complement one another, each working at their optimum functions. The machine controls and instruments should be designed to simplify the operator's actions and judgments, to reduce chance for human error. |
| 12. DON'T WASTE INFORMATION | "Cybernetics efficiency" dictates that information be valued and economized, as is its running mate, energy. Avoid rehandling information signals or losing workpiece positional data. |

## INJUNCTIONS and ADMONITIONS

Chart 6-5, Automation Injunctions, and Chart 6-6, Automation Admonitions, pertain particularly to the fabrication industry, which manufactures piece parts and assembles products from piece parts. The electronics industries are covered too, for they can be considered specialized fabricators.

The two charts outline some of the considerations that should be kept in mind when contemplating or designing automated production machines and systems. Summing up this section of the book, the charts serve as a guide, and are not to be followed slavishly, for many conflicting factors must be reconciled.

### MONEY

The most important automation design factor of all is one that is not even listed. This is money.

Invariably, the only justification for the use of any automatic method is that ultimately it results in less cost for the product, or in better quality, which can also be interpreted in terms of dollars. Hence, along with every one of the "injunctions" and "admonitions" is implied, "Does it pay off in money?"

## SIMPLICITY

Another consideration to keep in mind is *simplicity*. A simple system should be used instead of a complex one whenever possible; for example, use a relay instead of an amplifier; a molded part instead of an assembly; a packaged pre-engineered unit instead of a newly designed one; on-off control instead of modulated control. We are frequently compelled to make use of complex systems, but even in such systems, greater or less simplicity is possible. Simplicity is often the decisive reason for doing some operations manually.

Of the two charts, the injunctions pertain mainly to automatic machines of the special purpose and specific product type, assembly machines for example. The admonitions are more general in their coverage and apply to the overall system concept of automation rather than to automation machines alone. Some of these points are amplified in the following discussions.

## ROUTINIZE

As only routines can be mechanized, it is advisable to actively routinize information and energy operations to make them amenable to being performed by automatic methods. Routinizing may be in the form of procedures that call out the step-by-step logical and sequential operations, or it may be in the form of a mathematical *model*, an equation or family of simultaneous equations that describe the interrelated factors that must be reconciled.

## FUNCTIONAL APPROACH

It is advisable, when planning a machine or production process, to first consider solely the functions of *what* the machine is to do, holding in abeyance the operational mode for accomplishing the function and the physical devices by which the function is accomplished. This approach prevents preconceived attitudes from effecting system design. The functional approach can be used by nonexperts, to formulate the general system. Then, operational and physical details can be developed by specialists.

## SURVEILLANCE

The old adage, "Good masters make for good servants," applies to machines as well as to men. This is especially needed by modern high speed industrial machines, for high rates of automatic operation result in great losses in a short time if a malfunction is undetected. Someone must function as the machine tender or overseer.

Sometimes the maintenance men can be used to patrol the automatic machines. Because it is not possible for the machinery tender to monitor every part of a machine, it is advisable to display critical information of machine operation (such as a defective part or dull drill alarm) at a central location. Self-stopping and feedback control can be considered as being advanced forms of automatic surveillance.

## ADAPTABILITY

It is comparatively easy to accomplish a single specific operation automatically in a fixed manner. However, the value of such a device is necessarily limited. As in the case of human beings, *adaptability* makes machines more useful and less subject to obsolescence (unemployment). Adaptability is not easy to attain but is usually worth the additional effort and cost. For example, a machine that can produce a full range of sizes and forms of pipe fittings is more costly than a machine which produces only elbows, but fills a broader demand. One such machine constitutes practically an entire factory. Desirable forms of machine flexibility are: wide *ranges* of speeds, positions, diameters, size, depth; *easy set-up* of programming, stops, cams, turrets, tool selectors; a wide *variety* of tooling, modes of operations, classes of products, sizes of products.

## MAN versus MACHINE

For the most part, this text cites advantages obtainable from the use of automatic methods for many purposes. It could therefore be inferred that this constitutes complete endorsement of automaticity as a general rule, and that automation is practically always desirable. This is not so.

Objectivity must be retained. First decide what a machine or a system is to do, then decide whether full automation, semi-automation, or a human operator is best. The advantages of mechanized methods must be weighed against their shortcomings. The flexibility and judgment of a human operator are generally superior to a machine. Properly incorporated into a system, man can be an efficient *control element,* often a real bargain compared to equivalent mechanisms. The cost of controls to replace man may be far greater than the cost of training an operator. Unless the cost can be amortized over a great volume of production, man may be the better choice.

It is true that computers can solve intricate problems far better than man. However, the problems must first be stated in machine language, the program prepared, and the operations monitored. The results may require analysis or reprocessing.

Is purchase of costly computers always justified? Perhaps occasional rental of computer services or graphical solutions may be adequate. The optimum choice often is a combination of human skills and machine abilities.

If a man's responsibilities are simplified, such as operating a numerically controlled machine tool, the system is known as *semi-automation.* Here the vital control is automatic; but presetting the tool, starting the program tape, and loading the part are manual. This gives the most rewarding benefits at least cost and is ideally suited to short-run precision production.

For man to work most effectively, he must be considered part of the complete system in early design stages. Human engineering dictates that his tasks be made as simple as possible. He must not be burdened with unnecessary details. Information must be easy to understand and to act upon. The operator must have immediate knowledge of the effect of his actions.

Chart 12-2, *Man versus Machine,* compares many characteristics relative to their accomplishment by man or by machine. A quick look shows that man is superior to machine for some functions, and machine surpasses man for others. The chart should be considered only as a rough guide. Each of the functions is subject to many influences bearing on whether a man or machine should be used for a particular job.

The only production operations (of goods or of services) that man alone can do are nonroutine tasks, besides making decisions. The best work man can do with his intellect is to raise the information potential of work tasks by routinizing them. He can then give the repetitive work to machine.

Further, only man can perceive to accomplish pattern recognition. Machines are not suited to select from their environment the basis by which they are to operate, what they are to *think* about. Only man can work in situations that are ambiguous and not strictly clear. Man can tolerate considerable cybernetic "noise" (unwanted conditions).

Another big advantage of using men rather than machines, not obvious from the chart, is that man requires little capitalization, whereas machinery requires that considerable money be invested. Thus, where labor is cheap, as in Asia, Africa, and South America, installing an elaborate automatic warehousing system for example, is not as practical as assigning men to perform the roles of materials handling and record-keeping.

As shown on the chart, man's physical faculties do not compare very well with those of machines, but his senses are amazingly acute and selective. Routine mental operations are best done by machine; nonroutine decisions need men. Man is not predictable, unless he is doing routine work, and has been well trained. This applies especially to motor skills but is also applicable to straight mental operations.

Hence, we have the ironic condition that man is not predictable when he does what he alone can do, acting extemporaneously rather than from a rigorous forehanded procedure. Therefore, if extreme dependability is needed and no human lapses can be tolerated (as when machining a turbine reduction gear or piloting a

Chart 6-7. Design Check-Off for Advanced Control Systems

| | |
|---|---|
| 1. System objectives | Set up the "goal-posts"; what is to be accomplished. |
| 2. Performance requirements | What is the minimum acceptable performance? |
| 3. Functional design | Block diagrams and flow charts of what system is to do. |
| 4. Operational design | Simplified details of how the system is to work. |
| 5. Mathematical analysis | Find the "soft spots" in the system before hardware is committed. |
| 6. Computer simulation | Try out the system by analog simulation, working into actual parts. |
| 7. Physical design | Specification of actual hardware and designing details of actual circuitry. |
| 8. First tryout | The "bread-board" system, operationally tested. |
| 9. Redesign | The results from the mathematical, simulation, and "bread-board" studies incorporated into a refined system design. |
| 10. Utility systems | Power, timing, switching, self-testing, maintenance, interlocks — systems subordinate to the principal operational control system. |
| 11. Construction | The first operational system in useable form; plug-in, modular, and standardization aspects. |
| 12. Operational tests | Extensive proving and adjusting of the system. |
| 13. Corrections | Improving the system where performance is inadequate. |

transcontinental jet aircraft), then as little as is possible should be left to man. He should best be used in such cases to merely oversee the automatic system.

Probably the best criterion for evaluating man versus machine is dollars.

*Demand a big pay-off.* Small potential savings by the use of automatic devices or machines means that the contemplated change is not justified. Only if the estimated yearly saving is great (a quarter of the cost of the improvement) should the proposal be further considered.

Chart 6-7, *Check-off for Complex Systems*, briefly lists some of the steps that must be followed by control engineers in designing an advanced automatic control system. These are discussed in greater detail in following chapters. Typical machines where such a procedure would be necessary are the design of servo-mechanism positioning, numerical control programmed machine, computer controlled continuous processes (chemicals), and high performance feedback control. This involved procedure is not needed for the design of more or less routine control

circuits for $A_3$ automation, which covers most automatic machines, such as transfer machines, in-line automatics, and specific product machines.

## CASE HISTORY: DEVELOPMENT AND DESIGN OF A TRANSISTOR ASSEMBLY MACHINE

No single case history of an actual automation project can demonstrate more than a few of the many points cited in the foregoing text. The case history which follows was selected because it is median. It is not overly complex, yet not too simple. It involves assembly operation which is typical of most special machines for automation. Further, it is an example of ordinary $A_3$ automatic cycle automation, which does not depend on feedback or computer control.

The case history which follows is much abridged. The early decisions and considerations that were necessary in its development are treated more fully than are the purely design details. This is done because the functional and operational concepts of the early design stages are transferable to other cases, whereas the physical design considerations are not.

The example here cited includes the development, design, and construction of a transistor assembly machine, accomplished entirely by the engineers and workmen of the Allentown works of the Western Electric Company without outside help. The original transistor design was modified to take advantage of more suitable materials that became available, and to facilitate automatic assembly. This is shown in Figure 6-8.

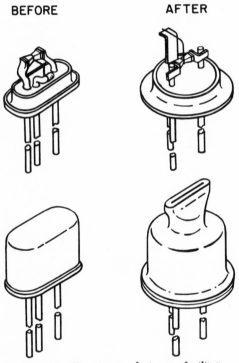

BEFORE          AFTER

**Figure 6-8.** Transistor redesign to facilitate mechanical assembly.

### PRELIMINARY CONSIDERATIONS

At the time this project was undertaken, transistor assembly was regarded by other manufacturers as unmechanizable, but it had to be done. The shortage of transistors was limiting the development of new electronic equipment.

When they first started the job, the Western Electric engineers realized that the full development of a complex automatic transistor assembly machine might require several years. They took the view that an early start would be the best economy in the long run, even though there was a chance that much of the earlier work might have to be abandoned. From the onset, they set up an engineering group whose *exclusive* function was to accomplish a continuing feasibility study of the mechanization of transistor assembly processes.

One of their first jobs was to select the sections of the entire manufacturing process that appeared to be most suitable for improvement by intensified mechanization and which would justify their efforts. The two criteria governing which operations to consider for mechanization were:

1. Significant cost reduction was possible.
2. True development engineering was needed, not merely purchase of machines.

In studying the existing manual transistor manufacturing methods, the development group learned that most of the cost was in assembly. The materials, though critical, did not offer much chance for savings, so this justified concentrating on the development of an automatic assembly machine.

Further study showed that a number of the assembly operations could be done by using commercially available machines. These pertained to late stage assembly operations which required welding of the enclosure seal, exhausting the air, and refilling with oxygen. In accordance with their self-imposed criteria, the design team did not attempt to develop equipment to accomplish the operations which could be done with commercially available machines.

Focusing their attention on those operations which could not be accomplished by purchasable equipment, they limited their efforts to the mechanization of operations applying to the assembly and treatment of the NPN transistor bar, up to the point where the assembly is ready for enclosure. Thus, establishing the limits of the job to be done was the *functional* phase of the project. Next, they considered methods for mechanizing the manual assembly operations. This was the *operational* phase of design.

The direct substitution of mechanical actions

for manual actions could probably have been done, but it was found advisable to redesign the transistor assembly procedure first, to a form more amenable to machine accomplishment. Then suitable mechanisms were devised, the *physical* or equipment phase of design. The ultimate means by which the elemental mechanisms could be combined into machines was kept in mind in selecting suitable mechanisms.

The automatic machine embracing all of the individual operating stations is paced by the speed of the slowest station. One operation, electrolytic etching, required 2.5 minutes. This was not compatible with the other operations, the slowest of which was a soldering operation requiring but 10 seconds. This necessitated the development of a new, intensified high speed etching method which could do the job in 28 seconds. Then the job was done in two stations of 14 seconds each, which was acceptable for the rates of production required.

## FINAL DESIGN OF THE MACHINE

How many of the individual assembly operations should be incorporated into a single machine was a key decision. The choices were: 1. to make use of separate individual machines for each operation, 2. to combine the whole group of operations into one composite machine, 3. to mix the two approaches.

The development team noted that although there are several types of equipment for transporting parts, a simple rotary indexing table offered the maximum accuracy of position combined with the necessary indexing speed. Two such tables were decided upon since the assembly operations have two parallel paths: processing of the *headers*, and assembly of the *bar-ribbon assembly*. This led to the purchase of a sixteen-position index table and an eight-position index table. Each came with individual motors and index controls. The two index tables were mounted on a single base with one work station common to both units so that parts from both machines would be combined at this common station.

Purchase of ready-made index tables reduced

the design task to perfecting the work station mechanisms and the special tooling. There were a number of different types of tooling that might function acceptably. The unique features of the individual process operations influenced each tooling decision. Machine motions were expected to be slow but accurate. The work stations had to be compact because they were to be located on mounting brackets arranged along the periphery of the rotary table.

Another consideration was the amount of adjustability desirable. Two contradictory factors confronted the Western Electric engineers. Adjustability is desirable, even necessary, on an experimental machine. For example, the final location of many of the parts of the assembly machine was established only by working on the actual product. However, it is usually best if the number of adjustable features is kept to a minimum when a machine is in production, to lessen the risk of out-of-adjustment conditions which might result from loose screws or human errors. Some adjustment features are needed even for the production version machine to compensate for wear and for product design variations. The solution was to use set screws until the machine was proved acceptable, then to fix the shafts and slides permanently once the best locations of the tools and mechanisms were established.

## THE "PROVE-IN"

The Western Electric engineers term the evaluation, testing, and correction of the equipment the *prove-in*. The transistor assembly machine prove-in started with limited tryouts of the tooling and the mechanisms. Ultimately, the assembled machine, bearing all of the individual stations previously tried out individually, was subjected to a rigorous prove-in.

A number of minor changes were made to the individual stations and to the complete assembly machines during the construction stages and the prove-in tests. Three major changes were found to be necessary. The mechanism for applying soldering flux had to be changed from a rotary device to a dauber, to assure consistent results. The solder coating on the ribbons was abolished in favor of using a ribbon solder applied to the continuously moving heated-and-fluxed transistor ribbon. The electric control system had to be modified to permit manual operation, which was sometimes desirable for adjusting and checking work. Electrical interlock protection was extended, too.

After the usual problems, such as those mentioned above, the assembly machine, Figure 6-9, worked satisfactorily. With the machine itself finished, the development teams undertook to educate the shop personnel in the operation and maintenance of the machine.

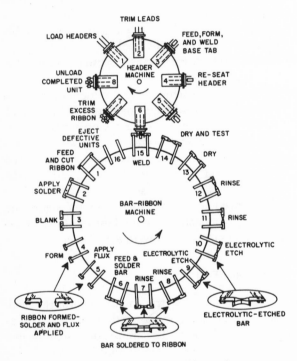

Figure 6-9. Transistor assembly machine.

## POST DEVELOPMENT COMMENTS

Having successfully completed the complex assembly machine, the Western Electric Company engineers had some comments pertaining to their interpretation of the job and its significance. They note that transistor technology is still a very new art and that improvements in the product may make obsolete the manufactur-

ing process. They anticipate that the machine they developed may be superseded by one set-up to accomplish an entirely different process for the production of transistors but feel, however, that the experience of this successful development has created among their engineering, machine construction, and operating personnel a spirit of confidence that endures all design changes.

The Western Electric automation design team concluded that the choice of machine builder is critically important, for it affects the ease with which prove-in work and routine design changes can be accomplished. They are firm believers in the do-it-yourself approach to automation. Conceding that an initial cost advantage might be achieved by giving the whole job to a special machine builder, they claim many advantages in doing the job themselves, namely, 1. they themselves profit from the experience gained, 2. their operations can be more flexible, 3. Less paper work is involved, 4. their own personnel have an active interest in contributing valuable suggestions.

## LESSONS LEARNED FROM WESTERN ELECTRIC

It is interesting to note that the Western Electric people did not refer to their transistor assembly machine as *automation* in their published reports. They consider it *mechanization,* for their object was the mechanical performance of heretofore manually accomplished tasks, the assembly of transistor parts.

This is, however, an example of automation, for automation is a convenient term applicable to the level of mechanization that constitutes self-action without the need for human intervention. Because the transistor assembly machine does its direct assembly jobs without human aid, it exemplifies $A_3$ automation.

To do the job, Western Electric set up a special group with no other responsibilities. They avoided the false economy of assigning the task to men already busy with production, administrative, or research work.

The necessity for an early start was appreciated, so a sensible development schedule could be followed without the need for "crash" programs. Western Electric started out in easy stages, gaining invaluable experience in the process. They acknowledge that this successful machine provides valuable experience toward greater undertakings in the future.

They started with feasibility studies to determine where and how their efforts should best be concentrated. The study included the examination of manual assembly methods and covered possible redesign of the product to simplify mechanized assembly operations. The most troublesome and expensive operations were isolated from the facile and inexpensive operations, making the real problems and goals apparent. Criteria were established for determining where significant savings were possible and what actual development work (not just machinery purchases) was necessary. Every effort was made to use commercial equipment and components when possible.

After the product was redesigned to make mechanized assembly operations easier, the Western Electric engineers decided on the tooling and methods necessary to do the assembly jobs. This required radical revision of certain operations to speed them up.

Once the tooling was decided on, the mechanisms for manipulating the tooling were worked out. Then the devices (the indexing tables) which would bear the individual mechanisms and tooling were considered.

The use of separate individual machines in series with intermediate storage devices was evaluated against continuous transfer methods. The rotary transfer method was deemed best for this application, so work station mechanisms and tooling were adapted to the index bases. The controls and sequencing circuits were developed at the same time.

The advantages and disadvantages of flexibility of adjustments was considered. The decision was for adjustability during tryout stages but to fix most of the adjustments when in actual production.

The policy of prove-in was followed throughout the development. Each type of tooling was first tried out, then each mechanism that manipulated the tooling was tested. Finally, when all of the separate stations were installed onto the rotary index machines, the entire machine was subjected to extensive prove-in. The prove-in operations revealed a number of major and minor shortcomings that were corrected. Not until the final assembled machine was proved out was the machine released for production.

The development team undertook to train the necessary technicians for maintenance and repair and testing of the machine. Even after being in production successfully, they studied its operation and compiled performance data to guide future automation development work.

# Anatomy of Automation

# 7

Anatomy is here used in the sense of dividing something to examine or analyze its parts. The title of this book and of this chapter, therefore, implies separating the different functions of automation to ascertain their relationship, structure, and operation.

That anatomy implies an organic body is also appropriate. The intention is to show that automation is a quasi-living thing, that there is functional similarity between corpus automation and corpus man. The purpose in bringing out such similarities is to relate the new concepts of automatic work and control to familiar ground, for learning is most effective when new concepts are related to existing knowledge.

To the man in the street, automation is continuous automatic production. A broader meaning of automation goes beyond manufacturing

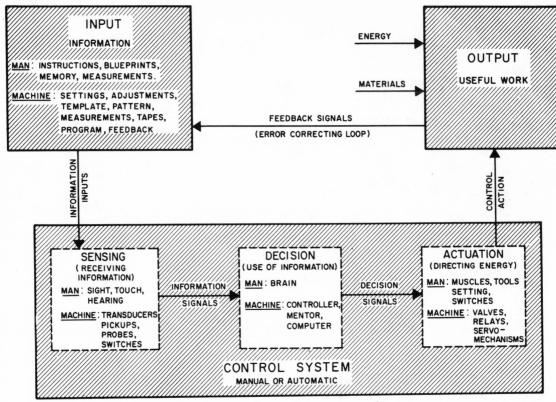

Figure 7-1. Production by man or machine.

and includes all means of doing useful work automatically. Replacing any of man's brain or muscle actions with a mechanical equivalent constitutes automation to some extent. Therefore, the broad picture of automation includes data handling, household devices, transportation, medicine and agriculture, as well as manufacturing. See Chart 1-2, and page 30.

The output of any useful work is based on energy and information. The result may be based mainly on the use of energy, as when chopping down a tree, or mainly on the use of information, as when writing a letter. Ultimately, all useful work by man or by machine requires both energy and information.

The first chapter explained that manual effort is the fundamental reference of useful work and that higher levels of automaticity develop as man's energy functions (muscle) and information functions (brain and senses) are mechanized to become progressively more self acting.

For producing real goods, information directs energy to act on materials. For producing services (record keeping, computing), information directs energy to improve information.

Useful work always requires both energy and information. Energy without information (control) is chaos. Information cannot exist without the use of some energy by which it can be manipulated.

## BASIC MAN OR MACHINE SYSTEM

Figure 7-1, *Production by Man or Machine*, is a functional block diagram representing any system for producing useful work, whether by man or by machine. The same basic functions are required of man alone (manual), man and machine together (semi-automatic), and machine working unaided (automatic). This is further illustrated by Figure 10-1.

In the manual mode, an operator measures the size of a workpiece in a grinder and makes all

OPERATIONAL BLOCK DIAGRAM

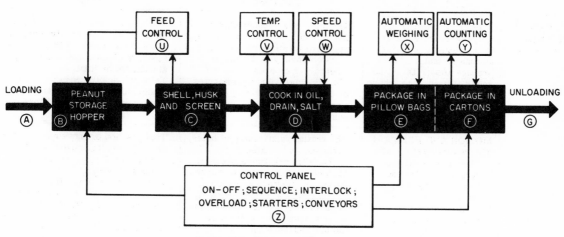

Figure 7-2. Peanut packing process.

necessary adjustments to the machine to finish the part to the desired size.

In the semi-automatic mode, the operator is aided by automatic measurements apparatus which indicates parts size at all times during grinding, thus preventing both overgrinding and undergrinding. Indicator lamps warn him when the final size is being approached so that he can withdraw the wheel. This mode of control is sometimes termed *semi-feedback*.

In the self-correcting version, automatic measurements information from a gage head (sensing) signals an electronic control unit (decision) which energizes (actuates) the wheel advance and withdrawal mechanism.

To be fully automatic as well as self-adjusting, the grinding machine must be self-loading, too. These three modes of controlling the same type of machine show that control by man and control by automatic means is functionally identical.

The output of all production systems is *useful work*. The input is *information*. All production systems require a control system which senses the information, decides what to do, and then acts on the decision. As illustrated by the block diagram, any of these essential requirements can be done by man or by machine.

Output is the effect of energy, such as in shaping a workpiece. Input is information, such as

the required shape of the workpiece. The third essential requirement is control, the use of information to direct energy. Control includes the function of sensing (receiving information), decision (use of information), and actuation (directing energy). To further illustrate these basic functions, consider the production system consisting of a carpenter installing a lock in a door.

| | |
|---|---|
| Output required: | Drill and chisel door and jamb. Assemble lock. Attach strike plate. Adjust for free action. |
| Input: | Information from plans, instructions and memory; style of lock, knob height, and assembly. A marking template or drilling jig are also forms of information. |
| Control: | The carpenter is the entire control system and provides the sensing, decision and actuation functions. |
| Sensing: | He receives the information by sight and touch. He also tests for free action (uses feedback information). |
| Decision: | His brain uses the input information, including visual feedback from his work, to decide how to act. |
| Actuation: | His muscles direct the hammer and chisel. An electric drill may provide part of the energy under his control. |

Chart 7-3. Output: The Effect of Useful Work

|  | EXPLANATION | DISCUSSION | EXAMPLES |
|---|---|---|---|
| ACTION ON MATERIALS (physical work) | FORMING A PRODUCT Output generally refers to the result of physical actions on materials, to produce goods. Often the result (length, size, shape, form) is by cutting action, but "chipless" methods are important too. | The form of a product may result from machining (cutting actions), pressure forming, or molding. Less commonly by chemical, electrolytic or erosion action. The material being transformed by the output result may be the work-in-process, raw stock or semifinished goods. | The output (result) may be a hole, slot, flat surface, cavity, contour, shape, size, form, finish, marking, seam, hardness, magnetization, attachment or joint. This includes the results of machining, stamping, extruding, casting, welding and cold forming. |
|  | MOTION AND POSITION This refers to the positioning of the work-in-process and of the tool, cutter or process mechanisms; also to the controlled movement of objects. Assembly and materials handling also fit this category, where the output is based on motion and positions. | The spatial relationship of holes, surfaces, and related parts is essential in creating a product. Movement of the work-in-process during and between operations, whether manual or mechanized, is part of any production system. An important special form of motion-and-position output are servomechanisms, where the resulting action is feedback regulated. | Tool position or movement, as for drilling, tapping, milling, and planing; work position, as for shaping, grinding, stamping, rolling or printing, loading, lifting, inverting, transfering, or any form of conveying. Also, tracer following duplicators and automatic coordinate setting of machine tables. |
| ACTION ON INFORMATION (mental work) | The output of a system can consist of _information_ rather than physical effects on material goods. Information can be the result of data processing, counting, solution of equations, automatic analysis, or automatic measurements. The information can be the end result, as warehouse stock records and aircraft design calculations, or part of the auxilary control system, as indicating oven controllers and automatic measurements readout. Power station control rooms, refinery graphic panels, and computer readout consoles are all information output centers. | INSTRUMENTS: Readout of quantity is by instruments. These are devices which visually present the extent or level of a variable or parameter that is being measured; also, the solution to problems and computations. Instrumentation refers to both input devices (sensors) and output devices (instruments). | Includes chart recorders, meters, instrument dials, counters, automatic graphing, oscillograph screen presentation, scaling tubes, automatic typewriters, punched tape recorders. |
|  |  | INDICATORS: indicators are devices which reveal whether or not a condition exists; that is, the state. Indicators usually act visually but sometimes audibly, often as a warning or caution signal. Indicators convey information in an easy to understand manner. | Indicators show state, such as full-not full; in place-not in place; go-no go; pass-reject; normal-warning; stop-caution-go; loaded-not loaded. Pilot lights, "flags," annunciators, blinkers, bells, "tell-tales," buzzers, and horns are used as indicators. |

To replace man, these essential functions must be mechanized. Output (use of energy) has long been highly mechanized. Man's muscles and tools have been replaced with motors, machine tools and transportation devices. Input (information) is mechanized by patterns, models, taped programs, and automatic measurements, including information from the output (feedback). The control system can be mechanized as a whole or in part. Sensing can be by transducers and probes. Decision can be by controllers or computers. Actuation can be by switches, valves, and servomechanisms.

Figure 7-1 relates the system _output_ and _input_ and the three essential control system functions, _sensing_, _decision_, and _actuation_. It is convenient to consider output first, for "results" is the purpose of every production system. Information and feedback are discussed in the next chapter, after which control system, sensing, decision, and actuation are discussed.

## OUTPUT

The output of any production system consists of the action of energy on materials. For example, the output may consist of the physical work accomplished by drop-forge forming a connecting rod. This is typical of output applying to the formation of a product, or the work output may consist of motion and positioning, such as transferring an engine manifold to a subsequent work station. In both cases, actual "working" of the product, or moving it to the machine elements, represents outputs dependent on energy.

Output may also consist of information, acting on other information or on the use of energy. The first case, information effecting information, is typical of data processing. The second case, information acting on the use of energy, is typical of machine control. A point worth repeating here is that output of a man or machine system is not only muscle work on material goods as in manufacturing, but may also be in the form of mental work, such as automatic measurements and recordkeeping.

The output of a manufacturing system is commonly made up of several individual processes. Some of these processes act physically on the product. Other of the local processes are really control subsystems and do not act on the product directly, but instrument and control the processing equipment.

Figure 7-2, an operational block diagram, shows that some of the *outputs* of units within the process consist of direct physical action on the product, whereas some outputs consist of information for further control purposes. The process as a whole (considering energy-handling and information-handling elements collectively) acts physically on the product. It converts a raw, shelled peanut to a finished product, cooked, weighed, and packaged. The output of each process station acts to change the form of the

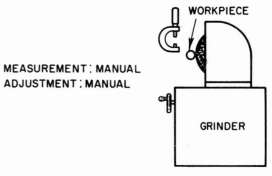

MEASUREMENT: MANUAL
ADJUSTMENT: MANUAL

**MANUAL CONTROL**

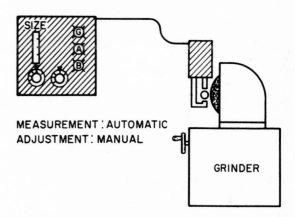

MEASUREMENT: AUTOMATIC
ADJUSTMENT: MANUAL

**SEMI-FEEDBACK CONTROL**

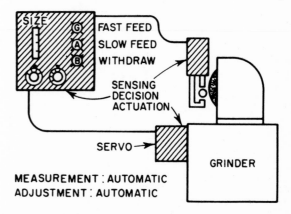

MEASUREMENT: AUTOMATIC
ADJUSTMENT: AUTOMATIC

**SELF CORRECTING CONTROL**

Figure 7-4. Measurements for control.

peanuts. The outputs of the controllers, which are independent subsystems, direct information such as temperature, speed, weight or count rather than energy to conform the product.

This process could be made up of separate machines, interconnected by automatic conveyors, or it could be an all-in-one specific product machine. In either case, it is an example of $A_3$ automation (fully automatic) with localized $A_4$ automation (self-measuring and correcting), such as temperature control.

Information output is often by means of indicators and instruments. The information may be made available to an operator who must perform the control actuation. Otherwise, the information output, while also available as a *readout*, is part of a control system which will respond to this information automatically.

*Instrumentation* refers to the sensing and display of pertinent factors (information). It includes the necessary sensors as well as display instruments. Instrumentation is essentially an automatic measuring operation with convenient data presentation by dials, indicators, and recorders.

Chart 7-3 illustrates the output of a process, consisting of action on materials or on information, the result of the physical work being to form the product or to position (move) the product or machine elements. The result of mental work, as from automatic measurements or data processing, is made available by instruments and indicators.

*Output* (effect of useful work) should not be confused with the control function *actuation* (directing energy), discussed in Chapter 9.

# Information and Feedback

8

## INPUT

As previously discussed, information is one of the two essential factors of useful work, the other being energy. *Input* refers to information from any source, man, machine, process, or product. Input should not be mistaken for the raw material or goods of a manufacturing process. Information from the output (result of work accomplished), called *feedback,* is a particularly important type of input.

## INFORMATION CONCEPTS

Information is transmitted to and from machines and men by communications. The messages may be in speech, print, or in *machine language,* such as coded signals.

Chart 8-1.  Information Concepts

| TERM | DEFINITION | DISCUSSION | EXAMPLES |
|---|---|---|---|
| INFORMATION | The knowledge of facts, measurements and requirements necessary for accomplishing useful work. | Production of goods requires information as well as energy and materials. Information is not physical (material) or energy (power, work) but is essential to all useful activity. Information reveals the job to be done, how it is to be done, the location and position of the work and tool, mode of operation; choice of materials, conditions and process requirements, etc. | Information to man: books, specifications, plans, verbal instructions. Information to machine: adjustments, stops, cams, patterns, signals from sensors, signals from computers, actions by man. Information from process: feedback, error information, preprocess factors, instrument indications, graphical data recordings. |
| INFORMATION THEORY | The cybernetic concept that information has a statistical basis and can be measured and otherwise evaluated, according to methods heretofore applied to thermodynamics and mechanics. | Information theory shows that control is a form of message, and that information tends to degenerate at each stage of its transmittal. Entropy (originally a thermodynamic concept) is the index of disorganization in an energy system. Information theory uses entropy to represent the state of disorganization of messages. The information content of a message is considered equivalent to the negative of its entropy, its state of disorganization. | Typical information theory activities: converting messages from human language to machine language; measuring "bits" of information; determining maximum amount of information possible over a given channel; evaluating effects of "noise" on communications, devising more efficient "codes" for transmitting information, and "translating" from one carrier to another; mechanizing library files; cross-indexing patent records; machine translation of real languages. |
| COMMUNICATIONS | The process of transmitting and receiving information between men and/or machine. | Communications can be from man to man, man to machine, machine to machine, machine to man. Cybernetics points out that control is merely the imperative (command) mood of communications. So communications is control and control is communications. This is why information handling is so important to automation. | Introducing data into data processing machines, or machine control systems; transmittal of information from transducers (such as automatic measuring) to mentor for feedback machine control; transmitting visual information to the operator via dials and graphs; transmittal of forward-reverse message to drill head feed motor; "readout" (dials or automatic printers) of solutions to problems by computers. |
| LANGUAGE | The code or "formula" by which signals develop messages. | Electrical signals and shaft rotations are languages suitable for automatic control. An important phase of automatic control consists of translating graphic and verbal language messages into a suitable machine language. | Speech is verbal language; blueprints are in graphic language; objects are in "real life" language; machine language may be pulses, as in numerical control, voltage levels for speed regulation; shaft rotation for positioning, and hydraulic pressure for force control. |
| MESSAGE | The arrangement (organization) of "patterns" (such as words) imposed upon a carrier, by which the carrier conveys specific information. | A message contains information, what is wanted, and noise, which is not wanted. There is a natural tendency for the noise in any message (meaning anything that impares or tends to obscure the information content) to increase, and for the information to degrade, for its entropy to increase. This is especially likely to occur when "translating" a message from one "language" (such as one composed of electrical signals) to another language (such as one composed of mechanical control lever positions). | Words on paper, telegraph pulses, spoken words, audio frequency signals on a telephone line, open or closing of a limit switch on a machine, thermocouple voltage relating temperature, pneumatic pressure relating valve setting. Message-man to machine: stop-go-reverse, also taped programs. Message-machine to man: any instruments readings; size, temperature, position. Message-machine to machine: completion of one operation signals start of succeeding one. |

(see also Chart 8-2  INFORMATION SIGNALS, for further key information concepts)

Information theory explains that information deteriorates during transmission. That is, the information loses meaning and correctness. A natural tendency is for noise to obscure the desired information, resulting in raising the entropy (unavailability) of the message content. These terms are explained in Chart 8-1.

Information for control purposes is *communications*, consisting of specific messages to and from the machine and operator. Such control messages consist of language elements (bits of information) organized in specific ways to contain the data. The organization of the bits of information that comprise the message also tends to degenerate, to increase in entropy. This is further explained in Chapter 13.

### HIGH-FIDELITY MUSIC

The high-fidelity recorded music fancier recognizes the fact that the reproduction of a message (music in this case) is in continual danger of becoming noisy and distorted. He knows that strict measures are necessary to preserve the original quality of the message, the purity of the musical sound. Otherwise, after several stages in the reproduction process, the distortion of the original message makes it unacceptable. High fidelity is another way of saying that great pains are taken to keep entropic disorganizing processes of the musical message at a minimum. Machine messages, too, must be of high fidelity, to prevent errors.

### SEMANTICS

One of the most prevalent problems encountered in communications among men is semantics, the specific meaning of the terms used. Semantics is no less a problem in the case of communications from man to machine then from machine to machine. To combat the chance for error, to preserve the high fidelity of the message, the language used in communicating with machines must be in such a form as to minimize the semantic problems. Each term must have a specific unambiguous meaning. This is why mathematical control systems are resorted to and why so much use is now being made of numerical control systems for automatic ma-

chines. This is because mathematical "language" (including numbers) has strict meanings and can be free of ambiguities.

### INFORMATION SIGNALS

Any number of schemes can be used to construct a message by signals, various *carriers* being best suited for certain forms of signals. When messages are relayed from one carrier (vehicle by which a message is transmitted) to another, as from a vocal speech to machine operations, there must be a change of *language* at each stage. Examples of language changes are from spoken to written, to taped, to electrical signals, to actuator position on a machine.

Not only does machine language differ from human language, but machine languages differ very much from one another. Each part of a machine or of its control system may use a language different from another part. A thermocouple transducer (temperature sensor) output signal may be in a different language (form) than a signal to a fuel valve in the same system. Signals may be proportional (analog) or numerical (digital). Chart 8-2 explains data transmission by signals.

## INSTRUCTIONS TO MACHINES

Blueprints, diagrams, specifications and spoken orders are some of the ways information (instructions) can be given to a workman. A workman also has information from training and experience stored in his memory and skills.

A machine cannot accept information in human language, but only in the form of settings or adjustments of *controls* (knobs and handles), or in the form of models, templates, or patterns to follow. The instructions a machine is supposed to follow can also be recorded in special codes known as *taping*.

The set of instructions a machine is to follow are known as a program. The boundaries and conditions of action are set by limits and criteria. These terms are explained in Chart 8-3 and other charts in this chapter.

Chart 8-2. Information Signals

| TERM | DEFINITION | DISCUSSION | EXAMPLES |
|---|---|---|---|
| DATA | Specific "pieces" of information, to be processed mathematically or logically, or to be used as the basis for the control of a machine or process. | Sets of data are encountered in accomplishing information processing or control. Each simple datum has at least two parts. The first is its numerical value, or its level, or its logical (on-off; yes-no) condition. Second, that to which the value, level, or condition applies. This portion of the datum is understood even if not explicitly stated. It is the "dimension" of the datum, such as centimeters, pounds, or °C. | Business records: cost, stock levels, customer accounts. Engineering data: strains, temperatures, velocities, acceleration, voltage, deflection, flow, viscosity, acidity. Manufacturing data: position of work piece, material, choice of tool, dimension desired, size by actual measurement. Simple data: individual variables, such as measurements, weight, speed, count, temperature, hardness. Complex data: functions of simple data; such as averages, totals, dispersion limits, rates, areas, trajectories. |
| CARRIER | The "vehicle" (unmodified signal) which is modulated or varied to bear messages, to transmit information, or for control. | The carrier, when modulated, constitutes the signal. The instantaneous value of the signal may reveal one "bit" of information, but ordinarily the accumulation of bits over a period of time is required to create a message. Pneumatic carriers are used by the process (chemical) industries. Thermal integrators and signal converters use heat as the data carrier. | The ink on paper (of written words), electrical currents on telephone lines (of speech), sound waves (of speech), electric pulses (of telegraph messages), light waves (of sight), electromagnetic waves (of infrared or radio information transmittal), movie film (of visual messages), punched cards (of letters and figures), magnetic ink (of bankcheck accounts). |
| SIGNALS | Data in a form usable by a control system, usually as electrical voltages or pulses, or as shaft rotations. | The big advantage of signals in electrical form is that they can be switched and controlled easily, without precision mechanisms. | On-off signals from a limit switch, voltage signals from a differential transformer revealing size; voltage signals from a tachometer generator revealing speed; electrical pulses revealing movement of a machine part. |
| ANALOG SIGNALS | A signal used for control or computation purposes, continuous in time, and proportional to the dimension or variable it represents. | Most dimensions are of a continuous nature, so they are most readily converted to analog signals. Some controls are digital however, so an analog-to-digital conversion is needed to adapt analog measurements to digital controls. | A-c or d-c signals of machine or tool position, temperature, angle, strain, resistance, rpm; continuous control of voltage, level, or speed. Shaft rotations proportional to the level of any dimension or function. Pulses with width or amplitude proportional to dimension or variable. |
| DIGITAL SIGNALS | A signal of separate discrete pulses used for control or computation purposes, the number of pulses (rather than pulse width or amplitude) referring to the dimension or variable which it represents, according to a logic or numerical code. | Digital signals can be obtained from digital transducers, or from analog-to-digital converters. Analog-to-digital readout is used where it is desired to present a visual numerical number rather than a pointer location on a dial, as numerical readout is less subject to reading error. | On-off signals, number counts, pulses representing revolutions, pulses whose number represent relative position, stepping control, "inching" control. Telegraph and teletype pulses, player-piano rolls, music box drums, holes in warehouse record cards and computer program tapes. |

## DIMENSIONS

A control system must have available information concerning the pertinent *dimensions* of the process. Such dimensions include both the process factors and the desired measurements of the product being produced. This is the case whether the control system is manual or automatic. Even with automatic machines, some input control information originates from manual control settings.

This is the point to be made here. In manually controlled machines, information of variables and operations parameters (field conditions to

Chart 8-3. Machine Instructions

| TERM | DEFINITION | DISCUSSION | EXAMPLES |
|---|---|---|---|
| PROGRAM | The plan of procedure of the operation of a machine or process; also termed a routine, especially when the machine is a computer; a set of instructions in machine language arranged in proper sequence to cause desired operations. | A machine's program may be by means of its internal control or external control. Only the external control is adjustable. The most flexible and readily changed program is via taping. The program includes internal control (fixed program) and external control (adjustable program). A program may also select between several preadjusted subprograms. | The cams and tools of a turret lathe, the sequence of operations of an automatic radio tube manufacturing machine, the sequence and mode of operation of an automatic capacitor testing machine; the message on tape of numerically controlled machines, a master part or template, a "deck" of punched cards for automatic positioning of a machine table. |
| MEMORY | The functional part of a control system where data are stored for future use; also, termed storage and memory storage. | Data in any form that can be readily retrieved constitutes a memory. A simple form of memory in an automatic process consists of keeping track of the parts measured and remeasuring them when needed, as done for automatic averaging. Also used are potentiometer positions, tapes, and magnetic drums. | The memory of the operations and their sequence constitutes the program. A latching relay or a flip-flop circuit is a memory for digital information, such as on-off, go-not go. Memory may also be on electron screens, relays, and delay lines. |
| TAPING | The process of recording the program, or the record of the program the machine or process is to follow; commonly recorded on magnetic or punched tape. | The term taping also includes flexible programs not on tape, but on drums, punched cards, blueprints, and films. Taping may not only determine the sequence of operations but the mode of such operations. From the cybernetic viewpoint, a taping is a second order program. It is a program of programs, dictating the manner in which several programs are combined. | Numerical control, typical taping sequence (1) engineer prepares process sheet, (2) typist punches process tape, (3) computer produces control tape, (4) control tape actuates machine control units, (5) Servo drives position the machine and work, (6) machine produces part automatically as per the taped program. Taping may also consist of recording (in code) the idealized actions of a skilled machinist for automatic record playback duplication. |
| CONTROLS | Devices that are manually set or adjusted to specific positions or values to accommodate process factors. | In manual control systems, controls are used for variables and parameters both. In automatic control systems, variables are controlled automatically, and process parameters are set by manual controls. | Handset potentiometers, synchros, differential transformers, step switches, linkage positions, manual indexing, depth stops, timer settings, speed selector dials, weld current adjustments, size requirement settings. |
| SETTING | The specific position or value of a manual control. Also termed setpoint. | Setting to the frequency desired on the dial of a radio is an analog action, for it is continuous. Setting to the channel desired on the dial of a TV set is a digital switching action, for it is in steps, not continuous. | Voltage, time, gear ratio, sequence of operations, lathe crossfeed, rpm setting, tool position; angle on an index plate detent or an indexing device, limit switch position, discriminator reference level, automatic inspection standard. |

be accommodated, such as size, speed, temperature) alike are manually set. In the case of automatic machines, the information of parameters is usually manually set, whereas the information of variables which change during the process are in the form of signals from transducers or other sensors.

Machines can only work in response to adequate orders or instructions of what-to-do and how-to-do-it. Without such directions, they are worthless. Thus, one problem of the machine and control system designers is how to give such orders to machines.

Both hand tools and machines respond to orders, to imperative commands. The distinction is that a hand tool must receive its orders con-

Chart 8-4.  Dimensional Information

| TERM | DEFINITION | DISCUSSION | EXAMPLES |
|---|---|---|---|
| DIMENSION | A pertinent factor used to specify some of the properties of a machine, process, or especially of an object. May also refer to the numerical value of the pertinent (not negligible) factor. | Any process or object can be described by means of an unlimited number of factors. The pertinent factors constitute the dimensions of the process or object. Of the pertinent factors some constitute variable dimensions, some parametrical dimensions, and some constant dimensions. | Length, width, height, frequency, weight, position, angle, color, hardness, viscosity, strain, rate. Most dimensions used to characterize a process or object can be broken down to basic dimensions of length, mass, time and temperature, by dimensional analysis. |
| CONSTANT DIMENSION | Dimensions of a process that have an effect on the process but can be held to a fixed value or assumed not to change. Also, the numerical value of a constant factor. | A constant is a measurable quantity too. However, it is assumed that for a particular process the constant need not be accommodated for any reason. The division between variables, parameters, and constants is not firm. Supposedly fixed constants may require periodic adjustment. | **Assembling capacitors:** length of leads case thickness soldering technique   **Machining motor shafts:** type of metal hardness finish  **Electric power generation** lubrication, cooling |
| PARAMETRICAL DIMENSION | Dimensions of a process that must be set to specific values for a job but remain fixed during the duration of the job. Also, the numerical value of a parametrical factor. | A parameter is a measurable quality no less important than a variable. However, parameters are only subject to occasional adjustment, not in-process, but pre-process. A parameter can be considered to be an "adjustable constant" or a "semi-fixed" variable. In automatic machines, variables are usually automatically controlled and parameters set manually. | **Assembling capacitors:** thickness of paper size foil overlap   **Machining motor shafts:** key way spline thread size  **Electric power generation** excitation, rpm, frequency, voltages |
| VARIABLE DIMENSION | Dimensions of a process subject to continual change and control to bring about the desired results from the process. Also, the numerical value of a variable factor. | A variable is a measurable quality that can be represented at every instant by a pointer on a dial, for at every instant it has a definite value. A variable can be considered to be a parameter that is continuously adjustable and is subject to such continuous adjustment. | **Assembling capacitors:** turns and length tension humidity   **Machining motor shafts:** diameters shoulder locations length  **Electric power generation** load, power factor, fuel required |
| CONTIGUOUS DIMENSION | A dimension that can be measured at any number of points, each point near or touching other points of that dimension. | The value of a contiguous dimension must be considered statistically, as having the mean (average) of a sample of measurements, and having a specific range of dispersion about the mean value. | Thickness (of strip-like materials), temperature, color, hardness, finish, diameter of a rod, voltage, pressure, acidity, temperature of an oven. Generally refers to continuous (processed) materials. |
| DISCRETE DIMENSION | A dimension that can be measured directly, on a definite article, with reference to identifiable boundaries. | Only one true value exists of a discrete dimension: its direct measurement. Contiguous dimensions are usually easier to average and to control than are discrete dimensions. | Length of an object, weight, location of a hole, relative positions of parts of an object, elapsed time of an operation, count of parts. Generally refers to piece parts (fabricated products). |

tinually, through the continuous manipulation of the tool by the user, whereas machines can work to some extent without direct human intervention. The greater a machine's degree of automaticity, the more it is able to work unaided.

Though a machine may work to some extent unattended, machines require no fewer orders in the aggregate to do their work than does a man on the same job. The orders for machines need not be given continuously, for all machines have some sort of memory whereby they can accept some orders in bulk form, so to speak.

The fact that some orders can be presented to a machine periodically to cover an appreciable phase of its operation is what makes it possible to replace man to any extent at all.

Commonly, machine input information of what-to-do concerns the desired dimensions of the workpiece, and the information of how-to-do-it concerns the mode of operation of the machine. In general, the information of how-to-do-it is imparted to a machine via its original operational design. This is seldom varied. A lathe is not the same as a punch press, and each works according to its mode of operation. The information of what-to-do varies with each job. As a minimum requirement, a machine must therefore receive instructions of what-to-do to cover each dimension of the work in process.

## DIMENSIONAL INFORMATION

The dimensional information of what-to-do can consist of drawings, a master part, templates, tables of dimensions, recorded control operations, equations, punched cards, or coded tapes. The machine must somehow accept its instructions of what-to-do from this information. It should be noted that this information constitutes a sort of memory storage. True machine memory storage has the added feature that the data can be readily inserted, identified, modified, and recalled, as necessary. Terms applying to Dimensional Information are explained in Chart 8-4.

In all cases, machine instructions originate from men who are in active control of the machine, or, in the case of automatic machines, from men who impart instructions to the machines from behind the scenes. Automatic machines are possible only to the extent that their instructions can be predetermined so that the machine can be made to respond to these directions automatically.

Because the original information of what a machine tool is to do is commonly in the form of an engineering drawing, instructions to the machine, "giving a machine its orders," demands a procedure for converting the dimensional information shown on the drawing to a form of information that the machine can use. By some means, the blueprint language must be translated to machine language. Here are some of the ways that machine tools are given their instructions.

### MANUAL CONTROL

Machines with manual control require that the operator translate dimensional information to machine language. The language a manual machine can understand consists of the operator's manual control manipulation, such as moving the cutter or workpiece, to produce the desired machine work.

### RECORD PLAYBACK

Record playback is a form of external program where the actions of a skilled operator are recorded as he machines a part. This record (which could be in the form of musical tones on magnetic tape) is then played back to make duplicate parts on the same machine tool. This is accomplished by manipulating the control handles by servo mechanisms (powered devices that respond quantitatively to signal level), in accordance with the action desired, detected from the taped recording by a suitable "reader" device.

### MASTER FOLLOWER

The information that constitutes the machine's instructions of what-to-do is often in the form of a master workpiece or template. This is the case in tracer type lathe, contouring, profiling, and milling machines, as in Figure 10-3. The piece (or pattern) being duplicated constitutes the information storage device from which the machine receives its instructions.

Another tracer method for instructing a machine does not require an actual master part. By means of photoelectric cells and servo mechanism positioners, phototracer machines follow the outline of a part drawn on paper. This method of accepting instructions is adequate for comparatively coarse two-dimensional work, such as the automatic control of a burning torch to fabricate sections and parts out of steel plate.

### NUMERICAL CONTROL

Numerical control is a form of external program in which the workpiece data is first ar-

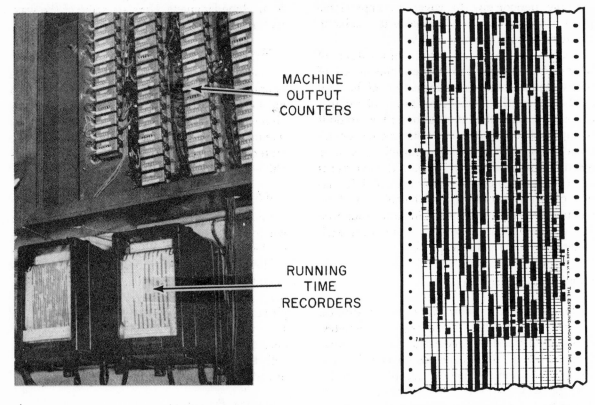

Figure 8-5. Automatic production surveillance.

ranged in numerical form and then translated into punched-tape or perforated card codes. This data actuates the machine control to form the desired parts automatically, as in Figure 10-5. Otherwise, numerically coded information set into the machine by manual dial setting is used for positioning a machine tool bed or cutter, termed *automatic coordinate setting*, as in Figure 10-4.

Chapter 1, Automation Yardstick, discussed programs and taping as instructions to $A_3$, $A_4$ and $A_5$ level machines. Chapter 10, Modes and Types of Control, further compares the different forms of instructions-to-a-machine, including tracer control, numerical control, positional control, record playback, and fixed (internal) control.

## FEEDBACK

This topic, touched on earlier, merits some repetition, for it is the core of all higher order ($A_4$ and above) automation. Information concerning the correctness of the work accomplished (as by inspection) is implied in any process that produces useful work. The information from the output to the input is termed feedback information, whether provided by manual or automatic evaluation of output characteristics. A machine control system that can sense output "quality" by measurements can check on its own performance.

This practice, comparing actual machine performance to a standard of desired performance, has revolutionized control practice. When a process is adjusted automatically to minimize the error between process output and the standard of desired results, it constitutes *feedback control*. This is of great importance to automation because feedback opposes the natural tendency of all systems to continually deteriorate in performance. Feedback is also termed *closed loop* because the process output information signal is "looped" toward the process input, where it is compared to a standard.

Open-loop control (more properly *open-end*) is simple cause-and-effect performance. That is, it is assumed that the desired results from any designed machine action will always be within acceptable limits and that there is no need to continually police the machine action to see if it actually meets requirements. Fortunately, this is usually the case, and open-loop (nonfeedback) control methods are entirely adequate for the majority of machine operations. An automatic record-changer phonograph is a familiar example of a complex device which functions by open-loop control.

Although open-loop processes do not depend on overt feedback for control of the output, some form of corrective action is implied, or the resulting work may be unsatisfactory. The controlling agency may be the operator, machine minder, inspector, supervisor—whoever the man is who keeps an eye on the results to insure normal performance. His surveillance need not be constant if the system is known from experience to be stable in operation, and if the machine (or process) capability of performance is well within the required tolerance range.

In any system, even complex ones of high orders of automaticity, many functions do not need feedback regulation. However, automatic self-correction by feedback is indispensable for the *critical* variables of processes. Feedback control and open-loop control are explained in Chart 9-3.

Information regarding the output of a process is very important in controlling the process. Otherwise the system may perform defective work because product variations would go undetected. Also important for controlling a process is information about input materials, prior opera-

tions, process variations, and desired results. *Cognition* is the awareness by the control system, whether it is a man or automatic device, of *all* of the factors that apply to the correct operation of the system or process.

It is not always recognized that helping the human operator of a complex system to be aware of what is occurring at all times, instead of forcing him to seek out the information, makes his efforts much more effective. This has nothing directly to do with automation but merely increases the scope and efficiency of the human overseer or director.

Figure 8-5 is an example of how simple *automatic surveillance* devices aid in the management of production by facilitating the cognition of the "man-in-charge" of what is going on.

$A_3$ machines tend to work even though wear or tool breakage results in defective parts being produced. This can be overcome by introducing automatic surveillance, which stops the machine and signals for attention whenever a malfunction occurs. For example, a probe may signal that a hole is missing from a tapping position, or a detector may signal a dull or broken drill. Or, post-process gaging may signal when excessive defective parts are produced.

Automatic surveillance constitutes self-monitoring by introduction of automatic inspection, testing, and checking, along with the machining operations. This can be considered as *semifeedback*. Although $A_3$ processes are not self-correcting, use of automatic surveillance methods is a major advance toward the $A_4$ order of automaticity, based on self-measuring and adjusting.

Semi-feedback implies automatic measurements discussed in the next chapter. By measuring (sensing) the dimensions and characteristics of the workpiece automatically, the error (deviation from standard) is made known to the operator. Dials, pointers, and pilot lights are used to notify him of the adjustment needed to correct the error. In simplest form, the operator takes the place of a fully automatic power actuator by keeping a pointer at a desired mark. This is similar to steering a ship to a compass heading.

Semi-feedback has many of the advantages of true self-correction, even though an operator is depended upon to take the corrective action.

## SELF-CORRECTING MACHINES

Self-adjustment of a machine to reduce the error between its performance and a standard serves to minimize variations. Shifts in performance due to wear, expansion, and materials can be compensated automatically by means of feedback control. Self-correcting control systems are most commonly encountered in processes for making continuous products, such as in an oil refinery, for $A_4$ techniques are more difficult to apply to piece-part production, such as the manufacture of typewriters.

Application of sensors and actuators to products which flow, such as liquids, wire, or fabrics, is relatively easy. This is why process controllers are so widely used to regulate temperature, pressure, tension, flow, acidity, and so on. In discrete part manufacturing, the presence of chips, shavings, coolant, and the machine mechanisms make automatic measuring and sensing more difficult. Also, automatic tool positioning is considerably more complicated than is throttling a valve or closing a gate in a continuous process. However, these problems have been largely overcome, and the application of feedback control to piece-part manufacture is becoming more common, particularly on grinders.

Grinders have the advantage that normal wear of grinding wheels requires adjustment in one direction only. Thus, automatic size measurement (usually by air gages) signals the automatic infeed mechanism to advance the wheel. Because the grinding wheel must advance only, the problem of backlash is largely eliminated.

Time is required for any feedback action to take effect. As long as the time lag necessary to bring about self-correction is negligible with respect to the rate of response of the process being controlled, it can be disregarded. However, in most cases, the time necessary for feedback control action cannot be disregarded or the

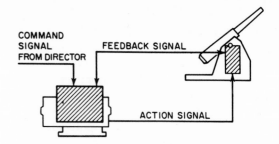

MILITARY (POSITIONAL) CONTROL

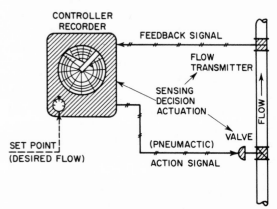

PROCESS (FLOW) CONTROL

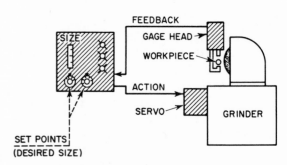

FABRICATION (SIZE) CONTROL

Figure 8-6. Functional similarity of control systems.

correction may exceed the error, resulting in instability known as *hunting*. It may therefore be necessary that the error correction signal anticipate the effect of adjustment to compensate for delayed system response. This requires a mathematical evaluation of control system performance.

## POSITIONAL FEEDBACK

The ideal form of self-correcting control is relative to the product or workpiece itself. Performance would be judged from the machine's actual output results such as size or weight of the product. Positional feedback, which senses tool position rather than tool accomplishment, is not as precise as feedback directly from the workpiece. As positional feedback is from a machine's table or cutter position, errors in actual tool work are *outside* of the control loop. However, positional feedback is very valuable in reducing the need for manual control.

A machine tool equipped for automatic positioning and positioned feedback, such as a precision boring machine, is able quickly to position the workpiece for a series of holes or cuts, without requiring the operator to make precise settings or adjustments.

A machine or process can utilize multiple feedback subsystems working concurrently though independently. The example just mentioned uses separate $X$, $Y$, and $Z$ axis positioners. Similarly, separate controllers ($A_4$ devices) are commonly used to regulate temperature, flow, pressure, and other factors independently in process industries, such as a brewery.

The point to note is that *secondary* feedbacks are valuable, but unless they affect the product directly, the order of automaticity of the process is not changed. It is quite possible to have $A_2$ or $A_3$ manufacturing processes which utilize $A_4$ subsystems for controlling loads, voltage, motor speed, or liquid level, for example.

To summarize, true $A_4$ machines must be self-correcting, in response to feedback information from the work itself, or at the very least, from the position of the workpiece relative to the tool (positional feedback).

## FUNCTIONAL SIMILARITIES

Figure 8-6 compares three automatic control systems, military, continuous processing, and piece-part manufacture. The figure illustrates the striking similarity of automatic control and its dependence on feedback for error correction, whether for positioning a gun, regulating flow in a pipe line, or compensating for variations in machine tool performance.

Any piece-part, or any product for that matter, has dimensions which most commonly apply to its physical configuration, its shape. *Information* commonly refers to physical linear dimensions, but *dimensions* need not refer to lengths, surfaces, and volumes. Dimensions may apply to any characteristic, such as temperature, viscosity, pressure, elasticity, or time. Any process can be resolved into a number of dimensions, the shape and the size of the product comprising only a few of the dimensions defining the process as a whole.

All pertinent factors of a process; constants, parameters, and variables, can be considered to be dimensions. If a process must accomplish a specific output, the pertinent dimensions must be controlled.

Process control requires selection of the pertinent dimensions and their measurement. For automatic systems, the measurements must be made automatically by *sensors*—devices that convert physical condition to information in a form understood by control systems. In most cases, this means conversion of the dimensions being measured into an equivalent electrical or pneumatic signal.

Control is vital, especially for automatic manufacturing, but what should be controlled? What information is important, and what can be safely ignored? What are the criteria of satisfactory results? These are not easy to answer. For practical reasons, only the minimum number of factors should be controlled. Just which of these are to be controlled is always a big problem.

As long as there is man in the background ready to make routine adjustments on an automatic machine, many factors can be considered negligible. As machines assume more human attributes and must work unattended for longer periods, the machines themselves must sense information of changing conditions that affect their performance. Then the automatic control system can take corrective action. This requires that process factors be separated into *negligible factors* and *pertinent factors*. By automatic sens-

Chart 8-7.  Process Factor Information

| TERM | DEFINITION | DISCUSSION | EXAMPLES |
|---|---|---|---|
| CRITERIA | The rules by which decisions are made, either by man or machine. The conditions (such as circuits open or circuits closed) that must co-exist with or precede an action. | The criteria for segregating parts into zones may be their dimensions. The values at which the parts were segregated would be indexes. The upper and lower level values allowable would be the limits. Determining the criteria for automatic process control is sometimes difficult for color, odors, surface defects, freshness, or fraudulent signatures. | The number of pulse counts may be the criterion for nuclear system emergency. Excessive temperature is a criterion for automatic fire extinguishing. Closing a snap switch, criterion for correct position broken light beam, criterion for operator hazard; color, criterion for sorting lemons; noise, criterion for judging bearings. |
| INDEX | A point on a continuous function at which a specific action is desired; or the pulse count of a digital function at which a specific action is desired. | The signal level or pulse count at which a desired action is needed is termed an index. Indexing is the operation of placing a device at a specific position or value. | Positional detents, angular detents, process temperature thermostat setting, air pressure control setting, speed setting, measuring scale reference marks. |
| LIMIT | An index point corresponding to the extreme condition allowable for the system or process. | Indexes and limits can be set manually or mechanically by means of stops and detents, or electrically by means of discriminators, polarized relays, cam-switch arrangements, or limit switch placement. | High-low tolerance limits, speed limits, temperature limits, pressure limits, depth-of-hole stops, end-of-stroke stops, fully-open stop, maximum current limiter. |
| FACTOR | A condition which has some effect on a machine or process to be controlled, or which may have or is suspected of having some effect on the machine or process. | There are an unlimited number of factors possible in describing the physical world. To control a process, a few factors must be varied; some adjusted to a fixed value; others assumed constant; and the vast number of factors may be neglected. | Materials used, environment, positions, timing, tools used, rates, forces, movement, sequence, texture, strength, color, finish, temperature, tool wear, jigs, fixtures, hardness, coolant, deflection, friction. |
| NEGLIGIBLE FACTORS | Factors that have little or no effect on the process and may be disregarded. | Most factors can fortunately be neglected, leaving the few pertinent factors, the constants, parameters and variables, to be set and controlled as necessary. | In the case of drilling: atomic structure of the metal, magnetic field, color of material, light intensity, and noise level, are negligible factors. |
| PERTINENT FACTORS | Factors that do have some effects on the process and must be considered in some way. The pertinent factors constitute the "dimensions" of a process. | CONSTANT FACTORS: factors that do have an effect on a process but are assumed to stay within acceptable limits. PARAMETRICAL FACTORS: factors that must be set for a specific job but remain fixed during the job. VARIABLE FACTORS: factors that are independently subject to change, or must be continually changed to bring about the desired operations. | Constants that must be provided for in the machine design: expansion, backlash, deflections. Parameters that must be selectable: feed rate, cutter shape and site, work holder and guides (jigs and fixtures). Variables to be controlled: form and dimensions of workpiece, position and motion of tool or work, action of treatment. |

Chart 8-7. Process Factors Information (Continued)

| TERM | DEFINITION | DISCUSSION | EXAMPLES |
|---|---|---|---|
| PRE-PROCESS FACTORS (dimensions) | Pertains to factors of the workpiece and process before the workpiece is subjected to the process. | Pre-process, in-process and post-process factors are all relative and must be discussed together. Taking a drilling operation as an example of a process, pre-process occurs before drilling starts, in-process during the actual drilling operation, and post-process after the drilling operation. If the process were a series of transfer machine operations, such as milling, facing, drilling, taping, reaming, and stud driving, a post-drilling operation could still be an in-process "transfer machine" operation. Also, the end product of one process is the semi-finished material of the following process. | Incoming inspection, pre-testing, automatic measurement of rough stock before machining. Also, measuring the ID of a small cylinder so that the OD of the mating piston can be ground to fit. |
| IN-PROCESS FACTORS (dimensions) | Pertains to factors of the workpiece and process during the period the workpiece is being subjected to the process. | | Revealing the exact position of the tool during the process; automatic measurements during the process, as automatic sizing during centerless grinding. |
| POST-PROCESS FACTORS (dimensions) | Pertains to factors of the workpiece and process after the workpiece has been processed (machining or treatment). | | Revealing the condition of the product after the process; automatic measurements after the process, as automatic sizing after internal grinding. |

ing of the pertinent factors, the machine can then be made to correct any tendency to vary in output.

Of the pertinent factors, some are *constants*, which can be ignored once established and compensated for in the basic design of the machine. Others of the pertinent factors are *parameters*, ordinary coarse settings of a process, which, when once set, can be left alone for an extended period. Some of the pertinent factors are *variable*, such as those that determine the exact form of the product.

The designer of a machine or process satisfies the constant factors by establishing fixed and unvarying machine characteristics. He accommodates the parameters of the process by providing adjustments, such as speed selector, stops, and limits. He recognizes the variables of the process by manual or automatic controls.

In gear manufacturing, the positions of the cutting tool are variables, the number of teeth are parametrical, and the pattern of each tooth is constant. In manufacturing printed circuits, the wiring patterns are a variable factor; the width of each conductor is parametrical and the thickness of each conductor is held constant.

The relationship and meaning of factors and dimensions are discussed in Charts 8-4 and 8-7.

Process input information is closely allied with the control system functions of *sensing* (receiving information) and *decision* (use of information) and cannot be entirely separated for discussion. These related functions are explained in the chapter following.

# The Control System

# 9

## THE CONTROL SYSTEM

A means of control, whereby information is used to direct the use of energy, is essential for useful work. For most tasks, man acts as the control system and performs the control functions. He receives information (sensing) by sight or hearing, uses the information (decision) by brain action, and directs the use of energy (ac-

tuation) with his muscles. This was explained briefly in Chapter 7. Chart 7-1, *Production by Man or Machine*, illustrates the relation between the useful work of a process (output), the information required (input), and the control system. The output and input have been discussed in Chapter 7 and 8. The three control system functions, *sensing, decision, actuation*, will now be explained.

Automatic control is a highly technical subject from the operational and physical aspects, which have to do with details and equipment. Automatic control is quite simple, however, from the functional aspect, which only considers what is done, not how or by what means. Although control is a basic requirement for any production system, it can best be considered as an independent subsystem comprised of three functions; sensing, decision, and actuation.

The sensors are the analog transducers and digital or numerical pickoffs that reveal *conditions,* such as process factors and piece-part dimensions.

The controller (which performs the decision function of the system), compares input and feedback signals, then sequences the machine operations in accordance with these signals and program information. If the controller makes use of contactors, static relay devices, electromechanical relays, or other two-state devices, it is said to be a *logical controller* or simply a *controller.* If a controller depends on the operation of a fixed purpose control computer to reconcile the input and feedback signals, the controller is termed a *mentor.*

*Actuators* are the devices that carry out the controller's orders. Actuators may be power servomechanisms. Ordinarily, however, they are simply motors and valves. *Servomechanism,* it is recalled, is the term applied to motor-like devices depending on feedback that accomplish a physical response (movement or rotation) that is a faithful rendition of the input signal. Called *servos* for short, they act as force amplifiers or magnifiers.

## CONTROL SYSTEM EXAMPLES

Consider a machinist turning a motor shaft on a lathe. He is the control system all in one. He performs the *sensing* function by sight and touch, reading the blueprints, and measuring the workpiece with scale and calipers. His brain performs the *decision* function by determining where and how much to cut. His muscles perform the *actuation* function by manipulating the feed, traverse handwheels, and the speed selector.

The control system for a household automatic hot water tank is all in one, too. The controller senses water temperature, "snaps" (decides) at the high limit, and shuts off (actuates) the fuel supply.

## SENSING AND MEASUREMENTS

Sensing consists of receiving information in machine language. Sensors are the perceptive organs of machines, used to "see, hear, smell, touch, and taste." Simple sensors, called *limit switches, probes* or *feelers,* can only report a two-state (on-off) condition.

Transducers are sensors which can recognize a range of measurements and qualities. Almost any electrical or mechanical device which varies as a function of some physical condition (such as temperature, strain, velocity, acceleration, position, or time) can be used as a transducer.

Sensors such as a snap switch, photocell, probe, or proximity switch signal the simple state of a process condition, such as "part is in place," "tank is filled," "drillhead is fully withdrawn." Two-state sensors are digital devices. Transducers are sensors which signal varying *levels* of a condition, such as force, air flow, acidity, or radioactivity. As the signals from the sensors are functions of the values being measured, this is an analog method. An indicator such as a neon pilot light reveals the *state* of a process, for example "on," "broken drill," "not charging," "ready to load." An instrument such as a tachometer (revolutions per minute meter), flow recorder, or viscosity meter, reveals the *level* of a condition.

Obtaining data from a cam or master part, from a tape program or a manually set control is a form of sensing, too. Sensing, instrumenting, and related terms are discussed, with examples, in Chart 9-1.

Manual sensing methods, which may make use of instruments such as micrometers, thermometers, or tachometers are commonplace. An increasingly important practice is to sense the pertinent process factors automatically, even though the control operations are still performed by a man.

Chart 9-1. Sensing Functions and Devices

| TERM | DEFINITION | DISCUSSION | EXAMPLES |
|---|---|---|---|
| SENSING | The control function of receiving information. Determining the state (quality) or level (quantity) of a factor that is pertinent to the operation of a machine or process. | Sensing is accomplished by feelers or probes, which are switch-like devices; or by transducers, analog or digital. The purpose is to abstract information as to the state or level of particular factors in a system. Display of this information constitutes instrumentation. Basing machine performance on the sensed information constitutes control. | Sensing temperature or pH constant in a chemical process; depth of a slot in a piece part; locating a hole or shaft; rpm of a drill, strain on a hoist; edge position of a moving web; flow in a pipe line. |
| INSTRUMENTING | Sensing, together with means for displaying the information sensed. Automatic measurements consists of instrumenting inspection and measurement operations. | Instrumentation can be the display of information (from sensors) by indicators (lamp, flag, alarm) or by instruments (meter, dial, recorder). Amplifiers, computers, or other data processing may be used between the sensing and the display. Display by meter dial or recorder is analog. Display by lamps, counters or printers is digital. | On-off, safe-unsafe, go-no go, clamped-not clamped, forward-reverse—may be instrumented by pilot lights; temperature, pH, pressure—by recorders; voltage, frequency, speed, weight—by meter dial; number of pieces, money or distance—by counters (odometers). |
| SENSORS | Devices used to obtain desired information from a system. They usually act by converting a physical condition (position or force) into a signal (electrical, pneumatic, or mechanical). | Sensors include feelers (probes) and transducers. Although sensor is the term used by engineers, the terms monitor, receptor, and pick-up have also been used. Monitor implies control as well as sensing. | Limit switches and hole probes are feelers; analog transducers sense pressure, temperature, force, light, and sound; digital transducers sense codes, vibrations, impulses, and counts. Electronic sensors can respond by proximity to capacitance, X ray, and to nuclear radiation. |
| FEELERS OR PROBES | Devices used to sense a "two-state condition," such as on-off, go-no go, open-not open. Also termed detectors, limit switches, and fingers. | Feelers can only sense the existence or nonexistence of a condition. The "feeling" action is generally by physical contact (such as by limit switch) but includes proximity switches, photo switches, or heat sensing switches. | Snap switch, push button; proximity switches, float switches; overload, overheat, and fire detectors; and detectors of motion, pressure, strain, moisture or flow, that reveal state but do not measure. |
| TRANSDUCERS | Sensors that measure process factors by converting size, level, or quality to a proportional signal, usually electrical. | When the level of a physical condition (such as size) is converted into a proportional signal (usually electrical) the transducer is analog. This is the most general type of transducer. When the physical condition is converted into a count or pulse signal, the transducer is digital. | Strain gage, thermocouple, piezo-electric pickup, differential transformer, capacitance pickup, photo electric cell, accelerometer, microphone, tachometer generator (analog), tachometer counter (digital). |

An inspector acts as a human sensor. He determines the measurements and characteristics of the product, using measuring tools and instruments, such as gages, scales, patterns, and testers. He notifies the machine operator if adjustments are needed. Insofar as he receives control information, the inspector is part of the control system.

Automatic inspection uses sensors in place of the inspector for automatic inspection of the product. Automatic inspection can also advise the operator what correction is necessary.

Sensors, together with a means for displaying the information sensed, constitutes automatic measurements.

Instrumented and displayed measurements

permit an operator to readily take corrective action. This constitutes semi-feedback, as the operator supplies mainly the actuation function but not the sensing function.

## MECHANIZED INSPECTION

Mechanized inspection machines use sensors to measure the critical dimensions of parts and to segregate the parts into size groups automatically. As an example, hydraulic pistons can be automatically inspected for diameter, taper and roundness, and separated into bins.

Both human inspection and mechanized inspection have a serious shortcoming. Neither prevents a defective part from being made. It is therefore desirable for automatic measurements to act through automatic control to make the machine fully self-correcting. This would constitute self-measuring and correcting $A_4$ automation.

Chart 9-2, *Measurement and Inspection*, discusses inspection, testing, and quality control.

Without precision automatic measurements, there can be no feedback control, computer control, or machines that learn. In the case of automatic machines, control information must come from the transducers and pickups that convert process factors and dimensions into control signals.

Obtaining the necessary control data by means of sensors is the "soft spot" of automation. Immediate and widespread work continues to be needed for devising and installing automatic measuring systems, the indispensable prerequisite for $A_4$ and $A_5$ automation. Until we have data concerning the factors and the dimensions of the workpiece, the process cannot be self-regulating by either logical or mathematical controllers.

## COGNITION

To say a control system features automatic cognition is to say that it operates with an awareness of those factors of a process control system that must be monitored continually to effect satisfactory performance, *regardless of the source* of the signals representing the factors.

A common characteristic of *feedback, reset, preset,* and *feed forward* is that they all involve the automatic cognition of variables from sensors. *Automatic cognition* is a general term covering *automatic system response* (from sensors) to the variable conditions which may affect the process. These variable conditions may be *preprocess*, involving changes in materials before they are worked on. The variable conditions may be *in-process*, involving conditions that must be regulated such as temperature and pressure. The variable conditions may be *post-process*, taking into account the actual performance of the process.

Associated with the growing necessity for automatic cognition of unpredicted process input variables is the development of mathematical control systems, computer control. Algebraic equations can be used to define the mode of process action. Control is then based on the automatic continuous solution of these control equations. Such control computers respond to many variables, including feedback and feed forward as well.

It is becoming increasingly necessary to consider self-adjustment of a control system in a forward direction, as well as in a back direction. That is, the control system must take into account input variables other than the feedback signal, and other than the main program control signals. This is necessary because not all process variables can be completely preprogrammed, nor can all process variables be introduced by manual means. Control systems must at times automatically sense the values of the *unpredicted* input variables, as caused by environmental changes: expansion, exhaustion of catalysts, and non-uniform materials.

Feedback, termed *automatic reset* by some (especially in Great Britain), is well understood. It always implies automatic negative feedback, unless qualified otherwise.

Feedback is such a powerful control technique that the utility of nonfeedback control aspects may have been obscured. However, feedback alone is not adequate for flexible automatic control of complex processes. Feedback, which depends on the automatic cognition of process

Chart 9-2.  Measurement and Inspection

| TERM | EXPLANATION | DISCUSSION | EXAMPLES |
|---|---|---|---|
| MEASUREMENT | The process or technique of determining the numerical value of dimensions or factors, determining the quality, extent, or degree of the dimensions or factors of a process or workpiece. | Prior to measurement, it is necessary to know what is to be measured. Once the factors which characterize a process have been determined, the measurements of these "dimensions" can be made manually or automatically. Automatic measurements lead from instrumentation to automatic control and ultimately to feedback control and mentor controlled automation. | In an automatic welding process these variable, parametrical, and constant factors must be measured: thickness of metal, pressure, movement of work piece, welding current, wave shape. In automatic machining of metal, measurements are needed of work position and tool position, made both statically, and dynamically as they change. |
| INSPECTION | The operation of comparing actual condition of a work piece to standards, manually or automatically. | Receiving inspection is pre-process.<br>Final inspection is post-process. Automatic inspection is based on automatic measurements. | Go-no go inspection; precision gaging, checking dimensions; checking for attributes (color, defects, leaks) weighing. |
| TESTING | The methods of inspection that determine the acceptability of a product or work piece, by determining physical characteristics, or by subjecting the item to real or simulated environmental conditions. | Indirect measurements, such as hardness, capacitance, inductance, resistance, permeability, dielectric constant, "Q", roughness, and leakage are determined by testing. Only nondestructive tests are suitable for in-process automation tests. Operating tests must be simple and fast. Automatic feedback control from automatic tests is ideal but difficult to attain. | Testing — hardness, tensile strength; capacitance, voltage breakdown; Magnaflux, X ray; torque, idle speed; vacuum, pressure. Nondestructive tests: frequency response (amplifier), calibration (meter), balance (wheel), cut-in voltage (charge regulator), sensitivity (radio).<br>Destructive tests: weld strength, bursting strength, color fastness, life test.<br>Operational tests: electronic tubes, lamp starters, engine by dynamometer. |
| STATISTICAL QUALITY CONTROL | The practice of determining characteristics of a group of items, from a sampling. Evaluates the acceptability of the lot, or the capability of the production process. | Two parameters, $\bar{X}$, the machine mean, and $\sigma$ (sigma), the standard deviation, describe the output of a normally distributed process. Valuable for indicating centerline of machine performance, for tool setting, and for feedback control. Sigma ($\sigma$) reveals machine capability and if the machine is "under control." | Determining the average of a given sample lot and the range of the sampling, or, the standard deviation instead of the range. Use of plotted charts to reveal whether or not process is "under control." Usually, a lot is described by its mean $\bar{X}$; and standard deviation $\sigma$ (sigma) or range R. |
| TOTAL QUALITY CONTROL | "Total Quality Control" is the policy of centralized responsibility for quality. All costs attributable to product failure or process deficiency or customer dissatisfaction, are charged as a "quality" cost. | The use of automation (self-acting manufacturing processes) is consistent with the policy of Total Quality Control because of the increased consistency of the product when produced automatically. This is especially so when quality is assured at each operation in process. Reducing human decisions reduces human errors. | Total Quality Control is responsible for: design of product to assure customer satisfaction; manufacturing operations to assure that product meets design specifications; service in the field to assure continued operation of the product. Typical TQC costs: improper door handle design; in-process inspection rejects; garbage disposer flanges shipped with threads omitted; wrong alloy; contaminated dielectric. |

*output,* is only one means. A control function similar to feedback may be necessary to replace a man who is continually presetting the process in compliance with changing input conditions. *Preset,* manual or automatic, depends on the cognition of *input* conditions which are subject to variation.

Control programs are *preset.* Preset, however, usually refers to manually setting up for future or immediate actions. When the controller setpoints are automatically modified by non-feedback information, it is termed automatic preset. *Automatic preset* seems to be an improvement over *feed forward,* a term used occasionally when referring to information signals flowing from *preprocess* transducer sensors to a control system.

As was pointed out, most processes are open-loop (open-end). They respond to nonadjustable system restraints. They also respond to variable input signals, which are commonly in the form of a manually preset program. In the case of closed-loop, the control system also responds to process performance (output) and provides a form of self-compensation. As the term feedback implies, it is control in a back direction, toward the beginning of the process from the output of the process.

A human operator can satisfactorily do his job of controlling a part of a manufacturing process only if he has information about what is going on. He must have cognizance of the process situation. However, most automatic control systems today do not yet have full cognition of what is going on, so their performance is necessarily inferior in adaptability to that of a man.

An increasing number of automatic control systems base process control action on the automatic cognition of process performance. This is mainly feedback, but some process control action is based on awareness of conditions that prevail *before* processing, for *feed-forward* control, also known as *preset.*

The operation of any process, controlled by either electronics or servos, depends on a number of variables and constants. Those that can be predicted, such as sequence and mode of operation, can be set up beforehand in the form of a pro-

gram. Indeed, the basic technique for making machines automatic consists of setting up a program for them to follow.

However, the exact values of many of the factors that are known to affect a process are not predictable because many of the process factors, such as temperature, pressure, and environmental factors, are interdependent. In the case of non-automatic control, an operator would perform the function of cognition. He makes extemporaneous settings of the machine in accordance with his knowledge (cognition) of the immediate conditions prevailing. In the case of automatic control, cognition and machine manipulation must be done without the intervention of a man.

Summing up, the concept of feedback is too restrictive. A broader concept is needed to include system response to unpredicted input variations as well as to programmed input conditions and to feedback signals, too. This is what automatic cognition is intended to mean. The above-mentioned terms are further compared and explained in Chart 9-3.

## POWER SOURCES

As long as power was obtained from a water wheel, a steam engine, or from a large electric motor that powered a number of devices, the problem of transmitting power to each mechanism and component of a machine required considerable ingenuity. The mechanical problems of transmitting mechanical energy where it was needed to all portions of the machine greatly complicated machine structure. Furthermore, mechanical components such as clutches, gear boxes, variable speed drives, and linkages are not readily arranged to work together.

Suppose a modern automation transfer machine had to receive all necessary power from a single overhead shaft by means of belting, as was done before the introduction of separate electric motors. Problems encountered in transmitting and interrupting mechanical power to each stage of the transfer machine would make the operation of such a machine impractical. The trend now is to use a *separate* electric motor, wherever power is needed.

Chart 9-3.  Cognition

| TERM | EXPLANATION | DISCUSSION | EXAMPLES |
|------|-------------|------------|----------|
| OPEN LOOP CONTROL | Nonfeedback; assumes that a system is always satisfactory and suffers no lapse of performance, so that constant "checking up" on the system is not needed. Also known as open-end control. | The assumption that system performance will be correct and that the probability of malfunctions is negligible is entirely justified in the greatest number of cases. Even in highly automatic feedback controlled machines, many elements of the process, both control and operational, work as expected on an open-loop basis. | Automatic screw machine, bottle making machine, nailing machine, automatic stamping, sealing machine, clock works, spot welding, electroplating. Automatic assembly, forging, casting, molding, degreasing, spray painting, drilling, reaming, gas flame cutting, cut-off saw. |
| FEEDBACK CONTROL | Negative feedback: causing a system (machine or process) to respond to the difference (error) between a standard value and the output of the system. The policy of automatically "checking up" to ascertain that system performance is satisfactory. Synonyms: closed loop, closed cycle, self-correcting, automatic reset. | The usual term in manufacturing industries is closed loop, also termed negative feedback. Accidental positive feedback, which causes system oscillations or hunting must be avoided. Only the key variables of any process need be regulated or controlled by feedback. Feedback control makes possible great system stability, as many disturbances can be compensated for automatically. | Feedback: All self-adjusting devices: thermostat control of furnace or refrigerator, automatic thickness, edge guides, servopositioners, self-adjusting grinders, water level pump control, steam engine governor, automatic weighing. Semi-feedback: Automatic measuring with simplified readout, so that an operator can readily make corrections. |
| PRESET | The practice of adjusting the process before the work cycle starts, on the basis of the condition of the piece to be machined; the control system function whereby control is based on the automatic sensing of pre-process conditions. | Also termed forward loop, prefeed, and feed forward. The purpose of preset is to accommodate the machine or process to a wide range of incoming work pieces or raw material. Preset may range from preselection, or simple size adjustments, to extensive change in the mode of operation of the machine or process. | Increasing the amount of heat supplied to a process before an increased amount of heat absorbing material is run through; automatically sensing rough dimensions of a casting so that a machine can automatically make one or more rough cuts; sensing sizes of piece parts so that automatic selective assembly can be accomplished. |
| COGNITION | "The process of knowing," the faculty of a control system of knowing the condition and values of the factors that affect the process, including pre-process and in-process data. An awareness of what is to be done; what is being done; and what was done, and correctness. | Cognition, a more general term than feedback, refers to the ability of a control system to comprehend and respond to process factors regardless of whether these factors consist of past performance or of programmed or nonprogrammed input factors. Cognition covers pre-process, in-process, and post-process factors. A machine with feedback only has limited cognition, data of the process output; a more automatic process may have cognition of many factors and require a mentor (limited purpose computer). | Mentor control of automatic refining process; the mentor has cognition of pre-process product requirements: from manual control settings of desired product composition, from cognition of in-process conditions, and from transducer sensors, of flow, pressure, temperature, and concentrations; and of pre-process conditions from automatic analysis of raw material. The mentor equates these factors to the output, and controls the dependent variables of the process; reagents, catalysts, fuel input, agitation, to get the maximum output of the desired product. (See Chapter 14, AUTOMATION TRENDS) |

Electric motor drives have another great advantage in addition to that of being an on-the-spot power source. Electric motors can be readily connected to the power lines. Furthermore, the necessary application engineering that is necessary in designing a motor drive can be done in a routine manner. That is not so when mechanical power transmission is used, for the development of linkages to transmit mechanical power involves specific problems that must be handled on a custom basis at each part of a machine.

## AMPLIFICATION

Much of automatic control depends on amplification, providing a greatly increased version of a low level signal. The amplification function is widely used, but amplifiers go by many names.

It is well to recognize the role of amplification in automatic control systems and to know just what kinds of units in addition to overt amplifiers actually do amplify. This will show what very simple methods can be used to actuate and control high powers and where actual electronic amplifiers are necessary.

The amplifier most generally known is the electronic amplifier, which makes a direct application to radio techniques. The outstanding characteristic of vacuum tubes and transistors is that they can be used to amplify. Typically, a vacuum tube is arranged in a circuit that provides the proper operating conditions of heater power and the proper voltage levels at the cathode, anode, and grids. In operation, a low voltage signal applied to the control grid is reproduced on a higher scale at the anode, the voltage thus being amplified. A number of tubes can be used to provide any level of voltage amplification desired. The electronic amplifier is still the mainstay of automatic control, though transistors and magnetic amplifiers are often used instead of vacuum tubes.

Voltage amplification is valuable, but what is needed for machine control is power amplification. Although the voltage amplification of an electronic amplifier is unlimited, from the practical viewpoint, the power limitation is very real. Up to about a 25-watt amplifier output rating can be managed readily. The attainment of 100 watts by vacuum tubes is expensive but practical. One thousand watts, little over one horsepower, is just about the limit from vacuum tubes. For higher amplifications of power, motor-generators and gas-filled electronic tubes are used. These are commonly preceded in the control system by voltage amplifiers.

This arrangement makes most effective use of the capabilities of each. The vacuum tube amplifiers (or their alternatives, transistors or magnetic amplifiers) are used for easy voltage amplification, for signal mixing, and for computational control circuitry. The motor-generator or gas tube or transistor power amplifiers are then used to develop the necessary power for machine actuation.

The motor-generator systems include the classic Ward-Leonard system, as well as the more recent Rototrol of Westinghouse and the Amplidyne of General Electric. In all cases, amplification is obtained when the driven generator develops power output that is proportional to the control signal. As a rule, motor-generator systems are used when massive systems (rolling mills, speed regulation of pumps, positioning heavy machine tables) are to be controlled.

Power amplifiers of the gas-filled tube type include the thyratrons and the ignitrons. They are fast enough to split a-c cycles and do not use moving parts. Power transistors now also offer power amplifications for motor control applications, and their range of applicability is increasing.

All of the above-mentioned amplifiers have the ability to provide power or voltage output that is proportional to the input signal. This is necessary for most servo control, feedback control, and for mentor control. However, proportional magnification is not needed all of the time. Far simpler amplifiers can be used to amplify power.

An ordinary switch is an amplifier of sorts. Let us say an electric stove is operated by a switch. Turning on the switch only requires about 50 watts of power. Yet, that actuates a power of 1800 watts. The power amplification here is 36. Contactors, which are electrically operated relay type switches, are commonly used to actuate (start and stop) motors. Power amplification of 50 for motors of 1 horsepower or less, and a power amplification of thousands to actuate multihorsepower motors are possible.

Because their amplification is on-off rather than proportional to the input signal, contactors are technically termed *nonlinear* amplifiers. Such contactors (relays) used for control rather than for power permit very high amplifications. Sensitive relays that can be used as part of industrial control systems permit power amplifications of many thousands. An example is the "electric eye"

Chart 9-4.  Actuation

| TERM | DEFINITION | DISCUSSION | EXAMPLES |
|---|---|---|---|
| ACTUATION | Directing energy. Putting into action available electrical or other power to bring about changes in position, form or operation of a machine or process, or of a workpiece. | Actuation is the cause, output is the effect of the action. Actuation includes initiation (as a valve) and action (as clamping). Initiation and action may be operationally inseparable. | "Turning on" hydraulic valve for extrusion press, electric motor for shearing machine, steam for plastics cure, water for cooling welding electrodes. Motors, hydraulic pistons, air cylinders, may actuate the position of the work or tool; drive motors actuate tool thrust and torque on drill heads; heat actuates brazing or stress relieving; electric current actuates plating or spot welding; nuclear radiation may actuate sterilization of foods. All require energy. |
| ENERGY | The capacity for doing work. Energy due to position, pressure, temperature, voltage, etc. is potential energy. Energy due to motion, current, flow, is kinetic energy. | The energy for gravity feed systems depends on the weight and elevation of the material. This is potential energy. Energy is one of the two basic elements of all useful work, the other being information. Power is the energy used per unit time. Energy may be used fast (high power) or slow (low power) to accomplish the same work. | Any work can be reduced to ft-lb or the equivalent calories or BTU. It may require 200,000 BTU to heat a boiler; or 1,236 ft-lb to fill a hopper; or 81 calories to melt a gram of ice. An engine block moving on a shuttle conveyor may have a kinetic energy of 1,840 ft-lb; a moving bullet may have a kinetic energy of 99,100 ft-lb. |
| WORK | Useful work requires that energy be used in accordance with information. Physical work is the action done to the goods or workpiece. | The word work is also used to mean the same as operation, job, treatment, or the product-in-process. Supporting a load is not work, but lifting or conveying a load is work. Thermodynamic work is equal to the energy used, less losses. | Thermodynamic work is measured in foot-pounds, BTU, calories, gram-centimeters, joules, horsepower-hours, and kilowatt hours. Work equals: torque × D × revolutions, of a grinding wheel, or of a drill; stroke × force × number of strokes of a planer. In physical terms Work equals force times distance: W=F × D; also work equals the product of power and time: W = P × t. |
| THERMODYNAMICS | The science which treats the conversion of energy from one form to another, and the work that results or is necessary to the transformation of energy. | Heat is the lowest form of energy because all of the energy involved in a process ultimately appears as heat. First law of thermodynamics: Heat, energy, and work are interchangeable. Second law: energy normally flows from a higher level to a lower one (entropy must increase). Cybernetics shows that information obeys laws similar to those of thermodynamics. | Energy can be in the form of heat, motion, electricity, or electro-chemical action, as utilized by steam engine, windmill, motor, battery or suncell power. Refrigerator compressors, heat pumps, alternators, engines and fuel cells are common energy transforming devices. Transformation of energy always results in some losses. |

photocell that turns on the lights when the sun goes down, acting directly on a sensitive relay without intervening electronic amplifiers. Such types of amplification and control are used industrially also.

Other nonlinear power amplifiers on the industrial scene are hydraulic and pneumatic valves.

The 15 watts of power that it takes to activate a solenoid on a high pressure hydraulic extrusion press may control power a million times greater. This applies also in the case of a valve in a pneumatic power line.

Nonlinear amplifiers can at times even be made to have the advantages of linear amplifiers.

Let us say a fast-acting pilot valve on a hydraulic power system is switched on and off at a fast rate. The massive mechanism powered by the hydraulics does not respond instantaneously. An example is "inching" a boring machine table. It responds to pulses somewhat as though they were a continuous force equivalent to the time average of the individual pulsed forces.

## ACTUATION

The final function of the control system is that of actuation. Actuation means "to put into action." It is always assumed that the desired action (turning a drill or feeding it into the workpiece) is powered from some source of energy, most commonly by electric motors. The actuation function includes *initiation* and *action*. Sometimes initiation and action, although functionally separate, are operationally inseparable. Chart 9-4 discusses *actuation, energy,* and *work.*

The most familiar example of actuation is switching a lamp on and off. Turning on the switch is the actuation, energizing the lamp with electric power. Another household example is that of turning on the gas valve on a cooking stove or opening the water tap. In these cases, the act of actuation is manual but could be automatically controlled.

The first automatic control methods merely replaced the manual operations of closing switches or turning valves. A mechanism, for example, was used to open an air valve or to close the contacts to a motor-starting controller.

In many cases, one machine actuates the succeeding one by means of interlocks and mechanisms to attain a form of automation. This simple form of actuation is commonly accomplished by merely opening air or hydraulic lines or closing electrical power contactors as necessary. Wherever a man would ordinarily have been used to actuate a contactor, valve, clutch, or speed changer, the machines do it without him. This is automation of the pioneer variety and it has proved by the severe test of time as being simple and practical within its limitations.

*Actuation* (directing energy) is a control system function. *Result* (use of energy) is the process output function, but these functions may overlap. Examples of processes in which *actuation* (directing energy) and *result* (use of energy) cannot be readily distinguished are: electroplating, welding, cleaning, and information handling.

Actuation is often a chain of actions. Consider a man operating a cut-off saw:

1. The operator actuates a start button
2. The pushbutton actuates a motor starter
3. The starter actuates the motor
4. The motor actuates the blade
5. The blade uses energy to cut the workpiece.

However, the energy is consumed almost entirely by the cutting action; everything before is actuation, a control function. The division between *actuation* (initiation and action) and *result* (work output) depends on convenience of interpretation. Where low-powered devices (switches) actuate high-powered devices (motors), the division is obvious.

Resistance welding is an example of where actuation and output are inseparable. This very important industrial operation makes use of electric currents flowing through two workpieces to weld them at their interface. It requires that the current be precisely controlled because excessive resistance welding currents cause burning and currents that are too low or mistimed result in deficient weld strength. The on-and-off current actuation is not separable from the resulting work accomplished.

In most cases, the nonservo actuated system is a simple on-off arrangement, but this does not mean that nonservo systems cannot work at intermediate levels between full *on*-and-*off*. Such "modulated" actuation as the partial opening of a hydraulic valve is possible. An example where this is desirable in a nonservo powered system is to have slow feed at a drilling unit station but to have fast drill head return. This can be accomplished by partially opening the hydraulic valve for slow feed, using the valve wide-open for fast return with the hydraulic lines reversed, of course.

An actuator of increasing importance is the power servomechanism, essentially a power or force amplifier. In one form, it amplifies a mechanical movement. A small force at a control lever causes a corresponding yet much greater force at the output end of the power servomechanism. Here is the familiar case of a low-energy actuation of high-energy power. However, the actuation in a servosystem is not necessarily mechanical. An electrical signal going into the servo amplifier may be the actuation, the output being the self-adjusted position or action.

Summarizing, it can be seen that to control large powers by low level controllers and actuators, we must have amplification. Electronic and motor-generator amplification are very good but usually are not needed. Simple on-off switches and valves are amplifiers too, on an all-or-nothing basis. Even such amplifiers can be used to give linear control of large machine elements by pulsing them so the average of their *on* time is comparable to the proportional linear signal that would be needed for the task. Because of their high power handling ability and high amplification possible, simple on-off actuators are in widespread use.

*Actuators* are the final functional elements of the control system. Beyond the actuators are the power drives of the machine that do the actual work. Most of the energy consumed by a machine tool is in the metal forming, the act of cutting or shaping the workpiece to the desired shape. However, some energy is needed to position the work on the machine and to feed the work and tool together. Each power function calls for its own actuation.

The actuation can be linear (modulated and proportional), generally by servos. More commonly, actuation is nonlinear, by contactors, switches, or simple valves.

## CONTROL ENGINEERING

Control engineering concerns itself with the creation of a *system* to accomplish the desired control objectives. It is therefore not essentially different from systems engineering. Here is how a control engineer goes about designing a complex control system.

First, he studies the problem from the systems viewpoint, which means that he considers *all* factors that may pertain to the control system. This includes the source of the information, the machine to be controlled, the function of the machine, and the nature of the product, including rates and ranges. He then makes up a preliminary functional flow block diagram of the system.

Following this, he learns of the physical characteristics of those elements of the system that cannot be changed. He tentatively assumes specific characteristics of the elements (components) for making up the control system. Then he performs a quick mathematical analysis of the response and stability of the *paper* control system. The outcome of this mathematical evaluation gives him the information necessary to synthesize an actual design and to specify the characteristics of components. In performing his mathematical analysis and synthesis of the control system, he may make use of an analog computer of the differential analyzer type for solving equations and to simulate system response. Otherwise, he may devise a special purpose analog computer-similator as will be shown in Figure 14-9.

Once some of the key components or equivalents are determined, design enters the *mock-up* stage. For this purpose, physical components and the computer are used in concert to make up a synthetic control system which has the dynamic response of the proposed system. This mock-up evolves to the *bread-board* stage, where all of the necessary components are used in a trial system for experimental and test purposes.

If results from the bread-board tests confirm the mathematical analysis, then the prototype stage begins; but if the bread-board tryout shows some major changes in the system or components are needed, a partial redesign of the control system is in order.

The prototype is a functional control system with some physical resemblance to the final version. It is largely handmade and could not necessarily be produced commercially in that form.

The prototype model of the automatic machine or control system is sure to reveal serious prob-

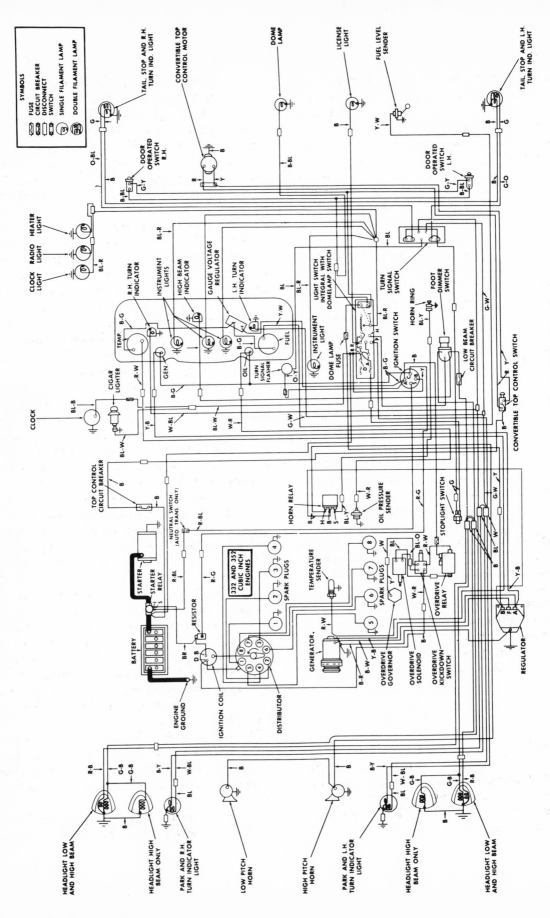

**Figure 9-5a.** Increased System Complexity. Thunderbird wiring diagram.

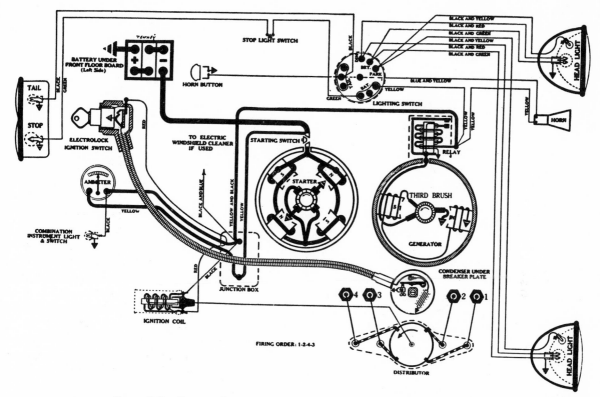

Figure 9-5b. Increased System Complexity. Model "A" Ford wiring diagram.

lems such as instability and minor problems such as mechanical interference.

When the prototype seems to work satisfactorily, the pilot model can be made. This is the first of the final working versions of the automatically controlled machine. The pilot model, too, will likely show a spate of troubles that must be corrected by the control engineer and machine designer, collectively.

Finally, there is the production or final model, which is also apt to reveal some shortcoming in the functioning of the control system, and sooner or later, it will need to be improved.

The previously discussed example of the development of a control system is obviously idealistic. Seldom are all the steps taken. In most cases, some short cuts are possible in the development process of an automatic control system or machine.

Many a *crash* program has found that omitting the bread-board stage or the prototype or the

pilot model, and going right into production is not the short cut it seemed to be. Before satisfactory results are attained, the design must evolve and develop, if not by the relatively cheap use of bread-boards and prototypes, then by the use of successive expensive *production* models. The facts are that a bread-board model always exists, whether it is made of plywood and sheet metal or is a would-be final model that does not work right.

The industrial installation which is to be one-of-a-kind is obviously at a disadvantage. The design team cannot afford to build half a dozen models to perfect the system. Therefore, they must live with the new automatic system even after it is in production and rebuild and redesign as necessary. The factory floor becomes the development laboratory. This does not please the executives who want a ready-made automatic system that need merely be unwrapped and connected to the power outlet. The fact remains

153

that a radically new system requires extensive development, and there is no satisfactory way to omit development steps. For complex systems, novel in concept, require extensive development and elimination of *bugs* will be necessary. This indicates that designers should try to learn from the successes and failures of others with similar control problems.

Later models are often simpler and more reliable than pioneer developments. Examples of this are seen in computers, missiles, automobile testers, and letter sorters.

### SIMPLICITY

What is a simple control system? What is a complex control system? From the control engineering viewpoint, simple systems are those used on $A_3$ and below; complex systems are those used on machines $A_4$ and above. They are simple if they rely mainly on sequential operation and do not use feedback. If the control loop is closed with feedback from the workpiece, the system is not simple. This division is *vertical*, as it is obvious that a large $A_3$ transfer machine has many more circuits and control functions connections than does a single $A_4$ feedback control centerless grinder. The $A_3$ machine is an example of being complicated in a horizontal way rather than in a vertical way.

Much of ordinary machine control circuitry, the open loop sequencing, consists of relay contactors and some *static elements* and timing devices. Such designs can be and are commonly designed solely on the basis of experience and judgment, but even here analytical methods are being used. The use of symbolic logic, such as variations of Boolean algebra, assures use of the least number of components for a specific control function and avoids *sneak circuits,* where unexpected interactions occur.

Noncomplex control systems can be designed somewhat separately from the actual design of the mechanical members of the machine. In fact, commonly, the electrical circuit designers were not called to participate until the machine proper was actually designed. This is no longer the case. The machine and its control system are best designed concurrently by team action. Mechanical design cannot be independent of electrical or hydraulic design.

Complexity is a condition to avoid, for added complexity brings with it unreliability, often at an exponential rate. How to keep complexity at a minimum and how to increase reliability are immediate problems. Figure 9-5 shows how the complexity tends to increase, especially when more automatic features are added.

One approach to reduction of complexity is to develop proven subsystems that can be integrated into complex systems. Each subsystem, termed a *module* or *unit,* is developed to the point where it can be treated as though it were a simple component.

Improving reliability of components and subsystems by greater care in their manufacture is about at its limit. Newer approaches are to design some redundancy into critical circuits, to make more use of local feedback loops to stabilize subsystem units, and to rely on self-testing circuits in complex control systems.

# Modes and Types of Control

## 10

### FIXED OR VARIABLE CONTROL

All machines are subject to control. They respond to both internal controls and to external controls. As is implied by the terms used, the internal (fixed) controls are those pertaining to the *organic* nature of the machine, whereas the external (variable) controls are those from outside of the machine proper.

The internal control of a machine, the mutual constraints caused by its individual parts, is what dictates the actions and interactions of its component parts. For all practical purposes, it is inseparable from the physical design of the machine. It is usually *fixed* and cannot be changed without altering the machine.

External control is the means whereby a machine is made to conform to variable conditions

155

and to immediate requirements. Most commonly, the external control of a machine is a human operator. Mechanization of external control (internal control always being fully mechanized) renders a machine automatic, self-acting to some extent.

Two familiar machines, a pocket watch and a bench lathe, illustrate the roles of internal control and external control. The internal control of a watch, what it does and how it works, is all *built-in*. It is inseparable from the gears, balance wheel, hair spring, and other mechanisms and component parts. The external control consists of the person who sets the hands as necessary, and who may affect the fast-slow adjustments.

The internal control of a lathe consists of the actions and behavior of its mechanism and parts, such as the lead screw, back gears, and drive mechanisms. The operator who controls the lathe provides the external control.

Separating control into internal and external components is done mainly for theoretical considerations, as internal control is inseparable from the machine proper. Hence, when we refer to a *machine*, we also include the intrinsic control caused by the physical actions and mutual constraint of its parts.

There is no sharp dividing line between internal control and external. For example, the size of a hole made by a drilling machine is controlled by the diameter of the drill. If the drill is considered to be a part of the machine proper, then hole size is a function of the internal control of the machine. The hole size should be considered to be a function of external control, as the drill size can be readily changed by an operator.

If a control factor can be readily adjusted or varied, it is external; if it requires structural changes, it is internal.

Machines that rely almost entirely on internal controls, such as a cigarette-manufacturing machine and other single purpose devices, do not require a human operator, but they have little ability to accommodate to changing requirements. A machine using a human operator, such as a milling machine, can accompilsh a wide variety of work because the operator can adapt to varying needs, changing his mode of opera-

tion as required. However, machine work dependent upon the external control of a human operator is limited by both his ability and his failings.

Completely self-acting machines are not new. Such self-acting machines dependent on internal control were in fact prevalent before manually operated machines were widespread. We have had 100 per cent automaticity for generations, driven by clockworks, windmills, and waterwheels, but the machines, dancing dolls, waterpumps, flour mills, were internally programmed, inflexible, single purpose devices.

A big step forward was the trend toward external control, even though such external control required use of an operator. Although most early external control was by an operator, some machines such as the Jacquard loom worked in accordance with a punched metal card program, a most "modern" sort of external control.

The use of power machines represented mechanization of the *energy* required for useful production. The use of an automatic control system is for the purpose of mechanizing the *information* concerning the production job that is to be done.

*Automatic* external control renders a process flexible, somewhat as though a human operator were present. External *programming*, depending on cams, detents, and patterns, is rather rigid. External programs, on magnetic or punched paper tape, are very flexible to changes.

In automation and control work, the term *taping* refers to flexible external programming of any sort, even though it is not on tape but on punched cards or in the form of a "master part." Programming may be in the circuitry of a logical-digital control system whereby the program concerns the mode of sequencing from one operation to a succeeding one.

Summarizing, machines that work according to their internal or *built-in* control can be self-acting but are not flexible in their program of operation. Machines can attain flexibility by relying in part on external control. Until recently, external control demanded an operator, but now automatic devices with external control permit machines and processes to be both self-acting and

Chart 10-1. Modes of Control

| TERM | EXPLANATION | DISCUSSION | EXAMPLES |
|---|---|---|---|
| CONTROL | The act or method of causing a process to perform as desired; also the decision making function of man and machine (or process). The use of information to direct the use of energy. Control may be wholly by man (manual), wholly by machine (automatic) or partly by man and partly by machine (semi-automatic). | Control may govern a simple action (as depth of a hole) or extend to an entire complex system (as an automatic bakery). Control may be based on logic or on mathematical relationships, and may be digital or analog in nature. A control system (man or mechanism) includes these functions: sensing (receiving information); decision (processing of information); and actuation (use of information to direct use of energy). | On-off, speed, position, location, sequence, time, segregation, are subject to control. Also force, pressure, temperature, deflection, coupling, torque, braking, regulating, compensating, mix, weight, acidity - any variables of a process. Switches, rheostats, gearshifts, tuners, knobs, levers, handwheels, and similar "controls" are devices that sense manually supplied information. |
| MANUAL CONTROL | Machine (or process) control performed by man is manual control. This includes regulating (flow, pressure, and temperature) by an operator, in response to process instrument readings. Manual control is external control. | All control that can be performed as a routine can be mechanized. "Routine means machine". The basis of all control is man, because self acting devices depend on man for their capabilities and program of actions. | Sewing machine operator, factory crane operator, truck driver, dentist using drill, tool room machinists, loom operator, printer, freight yard dispatcher, file clerk, power shovel operator, elevator operator. |
| AUTOMATIC CONTROL | Machines and processes that are self acting and can work for an extended time without human intervention. Machines only partly self-acting are known as semi-automatics. The information to the machine, what-to-do and when-to-do it, is known as the program of actions. | Processes (and machines) that are seemingly non routine can be controlled automatically if the process is first reduced to a formula or equation that relates the factors of the process. Writing the functioning of the process in mathematical form routinizes the process, and makes it amenable to automatic control. | Automatic thickness control, voltage and speed regulation, servo-mechanism tracers, automatic navigation, bowling pin setter, in-line transfer machines, bottle washing and filling, and coffee vending machines. Automatic control may be digital or analog, based on logic or mathematics. Automatic control does not require feedback (error sensing). |
| INTERNAL CONTROL | The constraints and interaction of the frame and mechanisms of a machine, that guide its functioning, constitute internal control. | Internal control is "fixed" and cannot be changed without altering the machine design physically. | The gears, balance wheel, hair spring, and other component parts of a watch; the lead screw, back gears, and drive mechanisms of a lathe. The crankshaft, cam shaft, timing belt of an engine. A simple music box; all represent internal control. |
| EXTERNAL CONTROL | The means whereby the action of a machine (or process) is caused to adjust to variable conditions and requirements, without change to the machine structure proper. | External control includes adjustable depth stops, change of drill sizes, replaceable cams or patterns, choice of back gears, start, stop, reverse and speed control and numerical programs. Mechanization of external control renders a machine automatic. Internal control is always fully mechanized. An automatic home laundry, for example, has internally controlled fill, agitate, rinse, and dry operations. But external start, water temperature, and cycle time controls. | Setting the hands on a watch, operating a lathe, driving an auto - these are manual external controls. Control panels, computers, sensors, actuators and program tapes are elements of automatic external control. A player piano is an example of external automatic control. |

flexible. In this way, machines can readily follow a program, the pattern of operations that they are to follow without human intervention. Yet, such externally controlled machines readily allow changes to be made in their program.

Chart 10-1, Modes of Control, compares internal control versus external control, and manual control versus automatic control.

## MECHANIZED LOGIC FOR AUTOMATION

In discussions of control systems, the term *logic* is frequently applied to various functions of automation control. This is so because the mode of control is patterned after formal logic, which obeys strict rules (criteria) for action.

Just as logic obeys a rigid course of reasoning, logic control obeys a rigid course of action; but there is more than mere similarity between logic control and logical reasoning. The automatic control system is consciously designed to duplicate mechanically a specific line of logical reasoning. Hence, logical control is actually a mechanization of logic, a mechanization of thought processes.

In solving a puzzle or an impasse in daily life, it is apparent that logic of the common sense variety is often used, even if formal logic is seldom appealed to. Machines, however, have no "common sense" at all. They are entirely "literal minded," so they must follow a formal logical line without deviation.

An identifying characteristic of formal logic is its yes-no, all-or-nothing nature, with no intermediate stages. Any action to be manipulated logically (be it a mental or machine action) must be broken down into a series of simple two-state decisions or actions.

The two-point orientation is ideal for the mechanization of intelligence because this simplifies the judgment needed to make a decision.

It should not be inferred that logical machine decision based on two-state criteria is necessarily more or less satisfactory than is a control decision based on a complex multipoint orientation. For one thing, the machine designer established the logical sequence of automatic machine op-

erations by intensive use of his own high levels of judgment. Any design, therefore, incorporates the result of the designer's brain power. Furthermore, the *points* used as the basis for two-point orientation can be as close together as desired.

The familiar go-no-go inspectors gage is an example of whereby a limited amount of intelligence is mechanized on the basis of two-state criteria. Let us say that we want to pass only those valve stems produced by a centerless grinder that are from 1.000 in. diameter to 1.004 in. diameter. The gage jaws that have been set 1.000 in. apart comprise the mechanization of the lower limit of acceptance. The gage jaws that have been set 1.004 in. apart, comprise the mechanization of the upper limit of acceptance. If a stem diameter is greater than the preset lower limit, and the stem diameter is less than the preset upper limit, it is judged acceptable by the strictly mechanical process of gaging, requiring no immediate human judgment.

It is obvious that the judgment of acceptance or rejection is made automatically, according to the use of the preset criteria, the spacings of the two gages. As the operator's decisions are routinized in the matter of acceptance or rejection, he can be readily replaced by a mechanism.

Segregating the valve stems into groups, according to zones of 0.001 in. diameter, can be done by using a series of graduated snap gages. Thus, any desired accuracy can be attained, even from simple two-point decision by setting the gaging points close enough together.

In practice, a typical work process, such as drilling and tapping a workpiece, may be represented by many actions. Each follows in a logical order and performance of each step is conditional on the satisfactory accomplishment of the steps that preceded it.

The $A_3$ automatic cycle machines depend almost entirely on logic circuitry, contained in *control panels* and *controllers*. These make use of two-state sensors (limit switches, push buttons), to make logical decisions (cut, retract) by means of digital two-state elements (contactors, transistors, static devices).

The conditions upon which digital-logical decisions are based, are the *criteria* for making the

Chart 10-2. Types of Control

| TERM | EXPLANATION | DISCUSSION | EXAMPLES |
|---|---|---|---|
| LOGIC CONTROL | Control based on the operations of logic: and, or, negate. Actions (decisions) depend on occurrence or non-occurrence and sequence of required previous conditions. Information exists in simple two state form, as yes-no; true-not true; in position-not in position. Logic control operated on the "either-or" principle, eliminates intermediate values of information. | Logic control is digital as the information is two state, like binary numbers. The logic operations are performed by storage (memory) and gate (action) devices. The decision to act is the make-or-break of an electrical circuit in response to information from two-state (flip-flop) storage devices and from feelers (on-off signals). Logic based control circuits can be designed by use of Boolean algebra notation. | Most machine control (control panels) consists of logic operations. Latching relays and contactors are the storage devices and gates. Limit switches on the machine frame signal information. Delay timers are used both to hold an action (time) and to delay an operation (sequence). Inter-connection of relay and switch contacts makes up a programmed sequence of machine operations. Typical actuation is the energization of motor starters or valve solenoids. |
| MATHEMATICAL CONTROL | Control operations which take place, usually simultaneously, based on inter-related process factors, by means of computer type devices. Mathematical operations for control are analog in form, and deal with algebraic equations rather than arithmetic. | In order to automatically control a complex process, it is necessary that the process variables can be predicted and expressed mathematically. Automatic solution of this process equation, taking into account the values of the terms of the equation from instrumentation, makes possible continuous control of the process. | This is the foundation of control by mentors (limited purpose computers). Automatic optimizing, machinability, interpolation, proportioning, analysis, and simulation, depend on relationships of mathematical equations. On the other hand, data processing, record keeping, payroll, sorting and sequencing (all digital) are based on logic operations. |
| DIGITAL CONTROL | Control based on manipulation of information in the form of numbers. These numbers represent the characteristics of the problem of interest. Digital control is based on rules of logic. | Analog and digital control each have their particular features and characteristics. Analog and digital control are not "competitors", but should be selected according to the application, as for example choice between AC or DC, hydraulic or pneumatic, tube or transistor, contactor relay or static element. Often, the most effective control system uses both analog and digital techniques. | Digital control, also known as numerical control, is particularly suited for handling numerical data (data processing), as in sales records, inventory control, automobile registrations, fingerprint files, and numerical control of machines from punched paper tapes or cards. Arithmetic and engineering type problems can also be programmed. However use for proportional control or response to equations requires input and output apparatus for analog-digital conversion, as the transducers (sensors) and actuators are generally analog. |
| ANALOG CONTROL | Control based on information and action which is proportional to the dimension and function it represents, not on pulses or counts, or numbers. Analog control uses "models", either mechanical or electronic, of the problem or system being considered. A relationship by mathematical equation is implied. | While general purpose computers (analog or digital) are capable of solving diverse problems, limited purpose computers (mentors) are intended for specific machine or process control or instrumentation. | Analog control readily performs mathematical operations such as addition, multiplication, differentiation, discrimination, triangulation, subtraction, division, integration, limiting, and function generation. Analog control is naturally suited to analog signals from proportional (analog) transducers. |

logical decision. For example, a tapping head may not be allowed to descend unless there is a workpiece with a predrilled hole in the proper position beneath the tapping head. The existence of the hole in the casting and the proper position of the casting satisfy criteria for permitting the tapping operation to take place. The control system must logically take into account the signals which represent these positions before making a decision.

A nonmanufacturing example of decisions based on several simple criteria is the control of a household steam generating boiler. The action of the boiler and its accessories is as follows:

a. If pilot ignition flame is extinguished, close fuel valve
b. If boiler steam pressure drops below 8 psi, open fuel valve
c. If boiler steam pressure rises over 11 psi, close fuel valve
d. If boiler water level is below low level, open water feed valve
e. If boiler water level is below critical level, close fuel valve
f. If steam condensate return tank water level is above high level, operate condensate return pump
g. If outside temperature rises above 65°F, close fuel valve
h. If outside temperature drops below 55°F, open fuel valve

In this example of logic applied to the control system of a domestic process, the fuel valve closings have priority over the valve openings, so a series circuit is used to operate the fuel valve. Furthermore, the control circuitry is *fail safe*, so that any failures result in shutting off the gas fuel supply.

Chart 10-2, Types of Control, discusses logical and mathematic control as well as analog and digital control systems.

## METHODS OF AUTOMATION CONTROL

Automation machines used for metal cutting fabrication can be divided into two groups. The most familiar, because they are the most dramatic, are the machines used to accomplish automatic production. These machines have come to be called *Detroit* automation. They are useful whenever there are many identical items to be made for high volume production. Until recently, almost all industrial automation has been of this type, that is, machines and groups of machines to accomplish automatic continuous manufacturing of fabricated products in large quantities.

The machines for high volume automation are predominantly $A_3$ level, with occasional $A_4$ feedback size control. Such automation stresses automatic loading and unloading, automatic advance of the workpiece to the next station, rapid action, and the elimination of direct labor.

The program these machines follow is mostly internal (fixed). They rely on built-in guides, stops, limit switch locations, sequencing, and specially designed work-holding fixtures. Even the external programmed features, such as changeable drill sizes, depth adjustments, and drill head positioning are relatively inflexible, for readjustment is slow and difficult and requires use of tools. However, length of set-up time and need for special fixtures do not matter if the automation is to machine 1,300,000 engine manifolds before major changes are necessary. This is typical of Detroit Automation, using transfer machines.

Not all manufacturing is mass production. It has been estimated that 75 per cent of the metal cutting fabricators produce less than 25 items of a single type. Obviously, Detroit Automation is not for them.

Production of short runs and single pieces, as in a job shop or tool room, presents different problems. Automatic handling and loading are not so important. The emphasis must be on flexibility and versatility, as the machines must permit rapid changeover to different jobs and cannot rely on special work-holding fixtures. This means that job-shop automation must follow an external (variable) program more than an internal (fixed) program.

Basic job-shop production is done with $A_2$ machines, which rely on the operators' skill and knowledge to interpret the drawings or other instructions and to control the machine to accom-

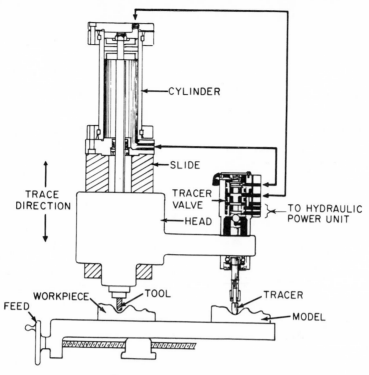

Figure 10-3. Tracer control.

plish the desired results. Reliance is heavily on external control. The operator (machinist) supplies the control functions of sensing, decision, and actuation. The machines have only minor self-acting qualities, such as constant traverse or constant feed, though these are important functions.

The object of job-shop automation is not to attain fully automatic action but to decrease the need for operator skills, thus preventing human error and speeding operations. Following are the methods by which small lot production is being automated, from simple operator assist to multitool externally programmed "do everything" machines.

The following methods are sometimes referred to collectively as servopositioned or positional feedback, as each relies on servomechanisms to act as force amplifiers or to position tool or workpiece in response to the external program command. Servopositioning is classified $A_4$ whenever feedback is used for positional error cor-

rection, which is often the case. As was discussed earlier, positional feedback is inferior to feedback control from the workpiece itself but is satisfactory in many cases, with due allowance for machine or tool deflection, backlash, or wear.

SERVO ASSIST-MANUAL

This is almost entirely operator controlled. Because positioning heavy workpieces and machine elements requires much energy, the operator is sometimes provided with a servosystem to act mainly as his force amplifier. An example is a giant band saw that can cut steel a foot or more in thickness. The operator steers the work into the blade by means of a power steering servomechanism. This is similar to power assist of aircraft controls or a ship's rudder. The operator's skill and decision are still required.

FOLLOWERS AND TRACERS

Machines can be arranged to duplicate a sample part (or plaster or wooden model) by

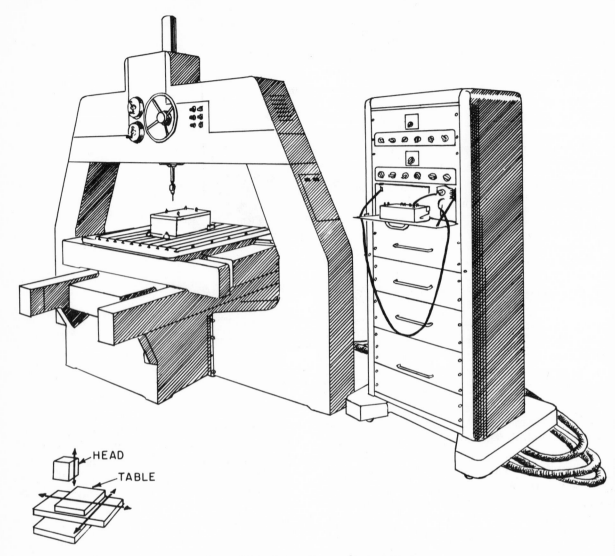

Figure 10-4. Automatic coordinate setting.

tracing its shape with a stylus (or optically) while a cutter shaping the workpiece follows the action of the stylus. Servocontrol is used to relieve the stylus of the force necessary to adjust the cutter, thus reducing wear and deflection errors. A program governs the path by which the model is traced. Three-dimensional duplicating (called *contouring*) is possible, by advancing the stylus and cutter incrementally after a plane is traced.

A typical application is *Kellering* dies for automobile fenders. An operator is needed for secondary control of feeds and speeds and for set up.

Figure 10-3 illustrates a common method of duplicating a handmade model or master part. For two-dimensional tracing, the model may be an ink drawing, which is traced by an electric-eye guided servo. The model or pattern may be at reduced scale. Tracers and followers exhibit flexibility, for job changes do not require changes to the machine itself.

### RECORD-PLAYBACK AND TRACE-PLAYBACK

If a number of pieces are to be machined, the *record-playback* method is sometimes used. A skilled machinist operates the machine to produce the first piece. A tape records his manipulation of the control levers. After he is finished, the tape is "trimmed up" to cut out needless dead time between operations, and movements are set to the maximum permissible level. Following this, the tape is used to control the machine in producing successive identical parts.

As a variation of record playback, instead of having an operator actually make a piece, it is possible to make a tape (record) by tracing a drawing or pattern of the desired part with a stylus. Errors are reduced by having the stylus trace a scaled up drawing (4 to 1 for example) of the workpiece desired.

The taped information may be in analog (proportional) form, such as musical tones on magnetic tape, or the information may be in digital form, such as taped pulses. The tape reading and machine control servos must of course match the form of information signals used.

Playback is similar to tracer duplicating but eliminates the need for a model by recording the information in tape form. Computers are not required and the tapes can be re-used as needed.

Existing machine tools can be adapted to playback by *retrofitting* servopower units to the machine tool head and table slides. That is, existing machine tools are fitted with auxiliary control features, thus increasing their automaticity. Retrofitting is a good way to upgrade *good* existing machinery.

### POINT-TO-POINT POSITIONING

Sometimes known as "automatic coordinate setting," this is particularly valuable for precision boring. The problem here is careful layout of the many holes required in a part. Manual layout takes much longer than the actual metal cutting, and an error may result in loss of the part and all of the previous work contained in it.

The advantage of automation here is in eliminating the dependence on the operator for critical measurements. The workpiece on the

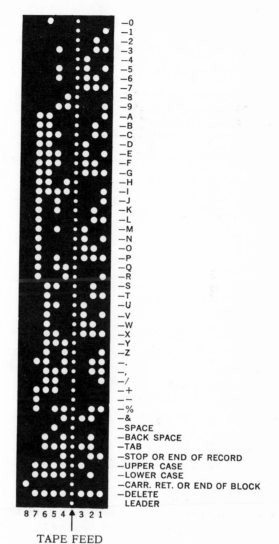

Figure 10-5. Code for tape control.

machine table is positioned to the desired coordinates, point-to-point, in response to the external program. The operator is needed to insert the proper cutter and to initiate the cut, but he has been relieved of the positioning responsibility with its consequent delay and risks of human error.

Any form of external programming can be used as convenient. These are commonly digital, known as *numerical control,* for numbers represent locations. One form is dial setting. The operator sets the *X* and *Y* locations on a panel-

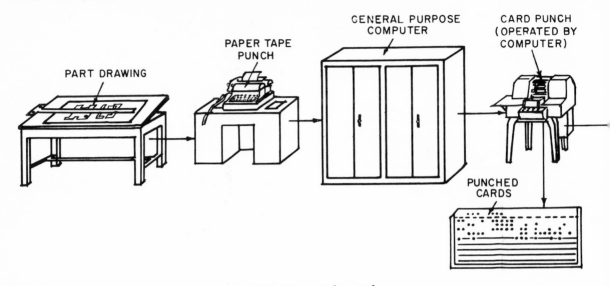

Figure 10-6.  Numerical control.

board. The machine table automatically seeks this position by servocontrol in reference to built-in measurement standards. Figure 10-4 illustrates this method.

Punched cards can be used, too. Each card in the "deck" codes the location of a particular hole on the workpiece. Position coding on tapes is also commonly used with a different tape for each workpiece. Figure 10-5 illustrates the code used for tape control.

Tape controlled point-to-point positioning evolves naturally into *continuous path positioning*. Programming workpiece movement in relation to a cutter constitutes three-dimensional tape controlled numerical profiling or contouring. Figure 10-6 illustrates a machine tool which cuts contours in response to dimensional information.

## NUMERICAL CONTROL

Numerical control means "the control of machine tools by numbers." A more practical definition is: a form of tooling that controls the motions of a machine by numerical values stored on a suitable medium. Numerical control is not for all jobs but offers savings, accuracy, and other benefits on suitable applications.

Numerical control systems, although differing considerably in complexity and detail, have the same general elements. They operate a machine tool in more or less the same way, as outlined in the following steps:

    a. Numerical data are fed into the system by punched tape, punched cards, or magnetic tape

    b. A translating unit reads the tape or cards and puts the data in electrical form usable by the machine tool

    c. A memory system stores the data until needed

    d. Servo units convert the data into actual machine motions

    e. A gaging device measures machine motions to determine if the servo units have given the correct commands

    f. A feedback device, on closed-loop systems, feeds information back from the gaging device for comparison of response with command so that machine operations may be stopped or corrected if necessary.

There are several means for feeding data into numerical-control systems. Punched cards, punched tape, magnetic tape—each has its own particular advantages. Each is being used with success. Punched tape, however, is gaining in favor with the 1-in., 8-channel tape predominating. Standardization of the input media is con-

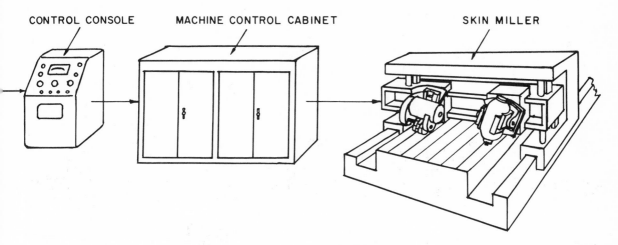

CONTROL CONSOLE          MACHINE CONTROL CABINET                    SKIN MILLER

Figure 10-6. Numerical control.

sidered a major need in the industry to eliminate confusion, cost, and the necessity for programmers to learn and remember different methods.

The electronic industries, the machine tool builders, and aircraft industries have participated in the standardization program. Physical dimensions and character coding have been standardized. Work is underway on standardization of format systems—fixed sequential, word address and tab sequential, as explained in the Numerical Control Glossary, Chart 10-8.

### POSITIONING VERSUS CONTOURING CONTROLS

There are two types of numerical control: (1) *Positioning*, also called point-to-point or discrete, and (2) *contouring*, or continuous-path.

Numerical control permits the machining of profiles and contours without the need for tracing a pattern or model. The dimensional information from the drawing is first tabulated into numerical form. The figures must be converted to machine language, and data points must be interpolated between the reference points. This may necessitate use of a general purpose computer or data processing, but the computer is *not* in direct control of the machine. Indeed, the computer can be in a different city, where the machine control tape is prepared from numerical

data of the design and mailed to the factory. Such machines are $A_4$ not $A_5$.

Some numerically controlled contouring machines utilize mentors for interpolation between data points on a curved surface and for adjusting traverse speed to suit the cutting angle. These are true $A_5$ computer controlled machines.

Positioning control, also called *coordinate setting*, is the simpler of the two varieties of numerical control. Positioning control is used for boring, drilling, and similar operations that require positioning in one plane only. One example is moving the workpiece from one position to the next drilling, tapping, or boring location.

Contouring control, far more complex, is used in milling, turning, and other operations where the entire path must be described and controlled. An example of this is milling intricate aircraft-wing contours where the cutting tool is moved along a predetermined path.

### PROGRAMMING NUMERICAL CONTROL

Programming for positioning can be done quickly and easily. A process which shows dimensions of points to be programmed in $X$ and $Y$ coordinates is prepared from the engineering drawing. The process tape (Figure 10-5) is then

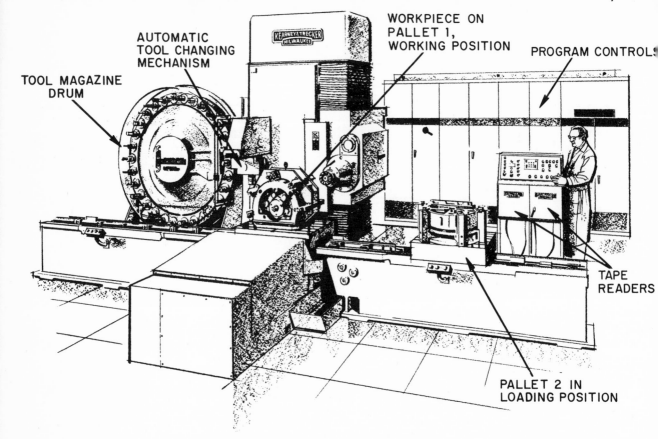

Figure 10-7. Universal machine tool.

prepared by a special typewriter which at the same time types a manuscript. The process sheet is then retyped to produce a second tape while the first tape is in the typewriter's reading unit. This provides a mechanical proof reading as the second tape will not punch if it differs at any point from the first tape. The process tape is now ready for insertion in the reader at the machine tool. The reader device interprets the data and commands the machine control.

Programming for point-to-point position operations such as drilling stud holes for a pressure housing may take only an hour. Programming for continuous-path control, as for a fender die, is more complex than for positioning only. This takes longer, too, possibly three to four days on difficult jobs. The steps required to program for continuous-path control depend on the particular system so the description given here should be regarded only as typical. Although manual programming may be practical for simple contours, the use of a computer makes programming faster and easier.

In preparing the process sheet, the programmer enters the starting and end points of each major section of the contour, the type of curve, cutter size, speeds, feeds, machining sequence, and so on. All of this information is converted to cards on a key-punch machine.

From the card data, the computer calculates the incremental points along the cutting path, time intervals, cutter offset, and other information needed to direct the machine control system. The computed information is obtained in the form of a second set of punched cards. These cards are fed to a card-to-tape converter to produce the punched process tape (or magnetic tape) that controls the machine tool.

Chart 10-8. Numerical Control Glossary

ADDRESS—A number identifying a location.

ANALOG—Using measurements of physical variables, such as distance or rotation or voltage, to represent and correspond with numerical variables that occur in a computation; contrasted with Digital.

BINARY—The binary number system uses the number two as its base of notation. A binary choice is between two alternatives.

BINARY DIGIT—A digit in the binary scale of notation may be 0 (zero) or 1 (one), equivalent to an "on" or "off," or a "yes" or "no" condition.

BINARY NOTATION—The writing of numbers in the scale of two. The positions of the digits designate powers of two; thus, 1010 means one times two cubed, 0 times two squared, one times two to the first power, and 0 times two to the zero power = one eight plus no fours plus one two plus no ones = 10.

BIT—1. An abbreviation of binary digit.
    2. One of the characters of a language employing only two distinct kinds of characters.
The absence or the presence of a hole in a piece of paper tape.

BLOCK—A group of words considered as a unit.

BLOCK ADDRESS FORMAT—Means of identifying words in a memory storage by use of an address specifying the format and meaning of the words in a block.

BUFFER STORAGE—An intermediate place of storage between data input and internal storage.

CHAD—The punches, pieces of material, which have been removed from tape or card.

CHANNEL—Same as track.

CHARACTER—One of a set of elementary marks or events (such as numerals or alphabet) which may be combined to express information. All marks, such as a group of holes in a paper tape, necessary to identify a numeral or letter.

CLOSED-LOOP SYSTEM—A system in which the output, or some result of the output, is fed back for comparison with the input, for the purpose of reducing the difference.

CODE—A system of characters and their association for representing information.

CODED-DECIMAL CODE—The decimal number system, with each decimal digit expressed by a code.

COMMAND—A pulse, signal or set of signals initiating a performance.

CONTINUOUS DATA—Data of which the information content can be ascertained continuously in time.

CONTOUR CONTROL SYSTEM—A system in which the cutting path can result from the coordinated, simultaneous motion of two or more axes.

CONTROL CIRCUITS—The circuits which effect the carrying out of instructions.

COORDINATES—Positions or relationships of points in the X, Y, Z planes.

CYCLE—A set of operations performed in predetermined manner.

DATA—Any facts or information, particularly as taken in, operated on, or put out by an information handling machine.

DECIMAL CODE—A code in which each allowable position has one of 10 possible states, such as the conventional decimal number system.

DECIMAL DIGIT—One of the symbols zero through nine when used in numbering in the scale of ten.

DIGIT—1. One of the symbols zero through nine when used in numbering in the scale of ten. 2. A character in any numbering system.

DIGITAL—An adjective describing a discrete state in steps or the presence or absence of quantity or state of being.

END-OF-BLOCK SIGNAL—A symbol or indicator that defines the end of the block of data, commonly sumbolized by $E_L$.

FEEDBACK LOOP—The part of a closed-loop system which allows the comparison of response with command.

FIELD—A set of one or more characters (not necessarily all lying in the same word) which is treated as a unit of information.

FIXED SEQUENTIAL FORMAT—Means of identifying a word in memory storage by its location in the block. Words must be presented in a specific order and all possible words preceding the last desired word must be present in the block.

FORMAT, INPUT MEDIA—The physical arrangement of possible location of holes or magnetized areas. Also, the general order in which information appears on the input medium.

INCREMENTAL COORDINATES—Coordinates measured from the preceding value in a sequence of values.

INPUT EQUIPMENT—The device which takes outside information into a machine.

INSTRUCTION STORAGE—Storage media containing basic machining instructions in coded form.

LANGUAGE—The association or rule which is used to represent code information.

MANUSCRIPT—Storage media, such as planning charts, containing raw data in a sequential form suitable for translation.

NUMBER SYSTEMS—Positional Notation. A systematic method for expressing numerical data such as binary or digital.

NUMERICAL CONTROL SYSTEM—A system in which actions are controlled by the direct insertion of numerical data at some point and the system automatically interprets this data.

NUMERICAL DATA—Data in which information is expressed by a set of numbers or symbols that can only assume discrete values.

OPEN-LOOP SYSTEM—A control system that has no means for comparing the output with the input for control purposes.

OPERATION NUMBER—A number indicating the position of an operation in performance sequence.

Continued on page 168.

Chart 10-8.  Numerical Control Glossary (Continued)

PARALLEL ENTRY—All characters displayed simultaneously as opposed to serial.

POSITION CONTROL SYSTEM—Point position control system as opposed to continuous line contour control system. A positioning system in which the controlled motion is required only to reach a given end point, with no path control.

POSITION SENSOR or POSITION TRANSDUCER—A device for measuring a position and converting this measurement into a signal convenient for transmission as a source of feedback.

POSITION STORAGE—Storage media containing major positions of tools and instructions for auxiliary functions.

PRINTER—An output mechanism which prints or typewrites characters.

PUNCH CARD—A card of constant size and shape, suitable for punching in a pattern that has meaning, and for being handled mechanically.

PUNCHED TAPE—Paper tape punched in a pattern of holes so as to convey information.

QUANTUM—The numerical value of the smallest unit measure used in a system.

RAW STORAGE—Storage media, such as drawings, containing all information (geometry of part, cutter size, feeds and speeds, etc.) necessary for preparation of the manuscript.

READ—To sense the characters' numerical input information such as performed by input equipment.

ROW—A path perpendicular to the edge of the tape along which information may be stored by means of the presence or absence of magnetized areas or holes, singly or in sets.

SAMPLED DATA—Data in which the information content can be, or is, ascertained only at discrete intervals of time. May be analog or digital.

SEGMENT—That portion of a path joining two successive points stored in position storage medium.

SEQUENCE NUMBER—A series of numerals programmed on a tape and displayed as a read-out. Normally used as a data location reference.

SEQUENTIAL—Arranged in some predetermined logical order.

SERVOMECHANISM—A closed loop system in which the controlled variable is mechanical position. In the usual case, some amplification is utilized between the relatively weak feedback signal and the strong command signal.

SIGN DIGIT—A plus or a minus to designate the positive or negative characteristic of a coordinate.

STORAGE—The device into which information can be introduced, held, and then extracted at a later time.

STORAGE MEDIUM—The means of accomplishing storage.

STRAIGHT CUT CONTROL SYSTEM—A system in which the controlled cutting action occurs only along a path parallel to linear, circular, or other machine ways.

TAB—A nonprinting spacing action on typewriters and tape preparation devices whose code is necessary to the tab sequential format.

TAB SEQUENTIAL FORMAT—Means of identifying a word by the number of tab characters in the block preceding the word. The first character in each word is a tab character. Words must be presented in a specific order but all characters in a word, except the tab character, may be omitted when the command represented by the word is not desired.

TAPE FEED—A mechanism which will feed tape to be read or sensed by the machine.

TEMPORARY STORAGE—Internal storage locations reserved for intermediate and partial results.

TRACK—A path parallel to the edge of the tape along which information may be stored by means of the presence or absence of magnetized areas or holes, singly or in sets; same as level or channel.

VERIFY—To check, usually with an automatic machine, one typing or recording of data against another in order to minimize the number of human errors in the data transcription.

WORD ADDRESS FORMAT—Addressing each word in a block by one or more characters which identify the meaning of the word.

ZERO-SUPPRESSION—The elimination of nonsignificant zeros to the left of the integral part of a quantity before printing is begun.

### WHEN TO USE NUMERICAL CONTROL

Numerical control is best suited for short or medium-size runs and can sometimes pay out on only a single part. When high production calls for the use of cam-controlled and tracer-controlled machines, the cams and templets can be made on numerically controlled machines to save time and money.

Numerical control permits versatility in production, giving the advantages of automation without the limitations of mass-production inflexibility. Prototype parts and making parts that would require the storage and handling of obsolete tooling or patterns also call for numerically controlled machining.

### "DO EVERYTHING" MACHINES

These machines represent an advance over numerical contouring machines. In addition to numerical control of the part or of tool position, these machines can be programmed to select and change tools. Thus, profiling, shaping, drilling, facing, and milling are possible on one machine without transfer of the workpiece, under automatic control of a taped program. This combines the advantages of transfer machining with the flexibility of external control. Multitool tape controlled "all-in-one" machines, similar to the one in Figure 10-7 are finding use in mass production, as well as for short-run jobs.

In summary, automation for small lot production has different goals than automation for volume production. Quick changeover and flexibility (external control) are essential. If an operator is used, he must not be taxed with demands for precision adjustments or excessive details. The potential advantages of job shop automation are:

1. Increased machine productivity by reducing setup time and repositioning time.
2. Reduced defects by eliminating operator error.
3. Reduced tooling costs by eliminating drill jigs, index tables, and patterns, in some cases.

4. Reduced need for operator skills after the machine is first set up for a job.

## MACHINE MECHANICAL CONSIDERATIONS

Servomechanism controlled machines (such as numerical control or tracer control) are far more than just machines with controls attached to them. Because of feedback, the physical characteristics of the machines and the control systems are inseparable. A mechanical shortcoming can compromise the entire machine-control system.

The following mechanical considerations must be minimized if they are not to degrade the overall accuracy of a servo-controlled automatic machine:

1. Backlash in the feed drive mechanisms
2. Wind-up (torsional springiness) of the feed drive system
3. Stickiness (nonlinear friction characteristics) of the machine ways
4. Deflection of the machine elements, of the workpiece, or of the cutting tool
5. Vibration (especially of measuring devices).

# Controllers and Computers

# 11

In the early days of electric power there was spirited *a-c versus d-c* controversy. This is a dead issue now for engineers use the form of power that does the job best and they do not hesitate to mix types. Similarly, in the 1950's there was a mild *digital versus analog* stirring that never actually attained the stature of a controversy.

Each technique has advantages and disadvantages. In the specific area of control, neither analog nor digital methods can be ruled out arbitrarily.

Control systems, computer systems, and computer-control systems are commonly hybrids. Mixed analog-digital systems offer advantages by combining the best features of each.

In general, analog provides continuous control,

171

whereas digital provides incremental control. Digital control systems (including the familiar machine control panels), also termed *logical*, are the most common. However, data from dimensional sensors (transducers) is usually analog, being continuously proportional to the characteristics (temperature, flow) they pick up. Analog data from sensors is therefore often converted to digital form for control purposes.

Digital computer and control systems offer greater *possible* accuracy at the price of complexity. Analog computer and control systems offer simplicity with limited possible accuracy which may be adequate, however.

### ANALOG CONTROL

Any continuous control whereby the control action is directly proportional to the desired machine action is analog control. An example is the self adjustment of the lens aperture in response to light conditions, by an automatic camera; also the loudness of a radio in response to adjustment of the volume control.

### DIGITAL CONTROL

When control is by steps, in increments, it is digital in character as is the telephone dial and all push button controls. Controllers operate digitally because the relays contactors and magnetic (static) logic and decision elements usually have only two specific *states*. They do not work in between these states in a continuous manner as do analog controls. Controls that work by pulse counts, such as numerical controls, are another form of digital control.

### DIGITAL-ANALOG CONTROL

Some analog machine controls, such as lead screws and gearing, respond to digital-impulse signals. Numerical control machines exemplify continuous control of tool and work position in response to pulse counts and stepping switch positions. *Logical-mathematical* controls usually superimpose sequencing on an analog control computer.

### OPERATIONAL-DIGITAL

Operational-digital techniques combine the advantages of the two conventional methods, *oper-ational analog* and *programmed digital*. It offers the accuracy of digital with the simplicity of analog. Ordinarily, digital system programs require complex circuitry. Analog systems usually work continuously and concurrently, not sequentially, so only simple programming suffices. In operational-digital, the functional elements, which are digital (that is, they handle counts not levels) are arranged as in an operational system whereby all units work concurrently rather than sequentially, as in conventional digital systems.

As examples, an analog discriminator compares voltage levels, whereas operational-digital discrimination is performed by adding and subtracting a series of pulse counts. Operational-digital summation of pulse counts replaces analog time integration (as performed by a kilowatt-hour meter). An analog method of obtaining a revolutions per minute signal is in the form of a tachometer generator voltage. By operational-digital method, revolutions per minute would be obtained by counting the number of pulses during a period of time.

### ANALOG TO DIGITAL CONVERSION

The variables of any process are commonly of a continuous nature, and it is often easier to sense them by continuous analog means than by digital means. Most control systems are basically digital, so it is common practice to perform automatic analog measurement and sensing, such as of *temperature, pressure, size, revolutions per minute,* and so on. The analog signals are made available to the relays, static elements, and numerical control digital systems via an analog-to-digital converter.

Typical transducers that can be used to change physical properties to analog signals are thermocouples, straingages, differential transformers, and tachometer generators. These analog transducers are suitable for instrumenting the four variables listed above in the order discussed.

The problem of data reduction also demands analog-to-digital conversion. At times, a mass of analog data from an industrial process must be processed to provide condensed information for administrative and supervisory purposes. A digital computer is usually used for data reduction,

Chart 11-1.  Control and Computation

| PROPORTIONAL METHODS | | LOGICAL METHODS |
|---|---|---|
| TYPICAL FORMS | Mentor, equation solver, analog computer servomechanisms, process controller | Control panel, industrial controller, sequence timer, digital computer, numerical controller |
| MOST SUITABLE APPLICATIONS | Equation solving, Multifactor process control, Design, Simulation | Machine control panels, data sorting and analysis, numerical control, business records |
| FORM OF CONTROL | by proportion and ratio | by digital (binary) or decimal counts |
| BASIS OF FUNCTION | Mathematics | rules of logic |
| MANUAL EQUIVALENT | solving problems graphically | solving problems by arithmetic |
| COMMON FORMS | sliderule, nomographs, curves, models | abacus, desk calculator, charts, tables |
| CONTROL ACTION | proportional, linear, concurrent, continuous | discrete; incremental, sequential, discontinuous |
| SIGNAL ON CARRIER | amplitude, frequency, or phase modulation | pulses, modulation, perforation codes, steps |
| TYPE OF SENSORS | transducers; convert conditions to proportional signals | switches or feelers; convert conditions to two-state signals or to a series of pulses |
| TYPE OF PROGRAM | interconnections, cams, knob settings, sound, film, cards, or tapes | wired in; also external coded messages from cards or tape |
| FORM OF MEASUREMENT | by measurement of amplitude | by pulse counts |
| QUANTITY SIGNALS | signal level, shaft angle, or linear position | signal "state" (on-off), or pulse counts |
| TYPE OF INDICATORS | meters, dials, graphs, oscilloscope, patterns | pilot lamps, annunciators, typewritten data, readout counters |
| FORM OF NOTATION | algebraic equations | symbolic logic notation |
| SEQUENCE OF OPERATIONS | concurrently, in "parallel"; simultaneous operations | sequentially, in "series"; consecutive operations |
| DUTY CYCLE | components function continuously | components commonly at stand-by |
| MEMORY STORAGE | ordinarily small; potentiometer settings, cam profile, bank of parts | can be large: drums, tapes |
| ARITHMETIC | not readily accomplished | easily accomplished |
| ALGEBRA | easily accomplished | only if converted to arithmetic |
| DIFFERENTIAL EQUATIONS | readily accomplished | requires conversion to numerical form and programming |
| PRECISION | moderate; high precision is expensive | high precision at little increase in cost |
| SPEED | can work in real time, fast time, or slow motion | time not adjustable but usually fast enough for control purposes |

so it is first necessary to convert the analog data to digital.

Through human engineering studies, it has been found that machine or process operators may be able to read a series of digits more readily and with less likelihood of error than they can interpret dial pointer positions on a calibrated instrument face. As a result, instrumentation is now available that gives a visible digital readout from analog measurement.

Among the many techniques for performing analog-to-digital transformation is the direct count of signal pulses over an elapsed time, the frequency of which is proportional to the level of the analog signal. Another conversion technique consists of sensing the increase of the signal in incremental steps, each step corresponding to a digital value.

## CONTINUOUS versus DISCONTINUOUS PROCESSES

The difference between a continuous and discontinuous process is the difference between a continuous part (or a continuous stream of parts) and a periodic batch of parts. Continuous processes are those that are more or less continuous in time, with no breaks for an appreciable period. Examples are heat treating and brazing in a pass-through oven; manufacture of fluids, powders, and granules; wire drawing, roll forming, strip rolling mill; and the manufacture of paper. Many automatic processes are continuous, for discontinuity usually means unproductive waiting time between operations.

In a typical automation installation, the part being worked on is either being subjected to work at a machine station or is undergoing transportation between stations. An example of discontinuous processes is job-shop production where pieceparts are made up in batches. Specific operations, such as turning, milling, or welding, may however be continuous in nature during the actual machining operations.

Continuous operations are easier to control than discontinuous operations mainly because control of intermittent or discontinuous operations requires extra equipment to position the transducer to the workpiece. Furthermore, it may be necessary to compute statistical variations of the discontinuous product measurements for quality control.

### CONTINUOUS AND DISCONTINUOUS PRODUCTS

Continuous products, such as metal strip, wire, roll-formed sections, pipe, gasoline, cereals, and so on, are almost always produced by continuous processes. *Continuous product* refers to its physical continuity. *Continuous process* refers to the continuity of processing time.

As usually interpreted, automation is a continuous process, but most fabricating industry automation and individual machines produce discontinuous pieceparts. The automation process is continuous in time, but the pieceparts are discontinuous in dimension.

Automatic instrumentation (measurements) of individual piece-part dimensions is less readily accomplished than when the dimension is a continuous variable. One reason is that a continuous variable (a dimension for example) can be averaged by time integration, which can be done electronically with no moving parts. A discontinuous variable must be averaged by computation of discrete values, usually requiring a servo-actuated electromechanical computer.

## CONTROLLERS

Both the continuous processing industries and the piece-part fabricating industries make use of controllers. The term is used quite differently in each field, however. As long as the fields of fabricating and processing were entirely separate this did not matter, but now the skills and equipment of the chemical engineer and control engineer working on continuous processes are finding their way into the factory. The continuous processes are leading the way for the fabricating industries. Thus, it is necessary to resolve the conflicting usage of the term *controller*.

### INDUSTRIAL CONTROLLERS

On the industrial scene, meaning the fabricating manufacturer, the controller is usually a motor starting and regulating device. It can be manually actuated, turned *on* and *off*, or set to desired action. Such motor controllers are very commonly used, especially where machines are manually controlled. With automatic manufacturing methods, however, a number of motors must be controlled collectively. For this purpose, the control equipment for the several motors is grouped together in a control panel.

The function of a control panel is to start, stop, reverse, change speed, or otherwise operate a machine by acting on motors or solenoid valves. The control panel sequences the machine actions where the operations are initiated by limit switches, push buttons, interlocks, and by timers.

In short, the industrial controller takes care of only one powered device, such as a motor. The industrial control panel takes care of a number of powered devices and is responsible for operating them according to the desired program. Both work on a logical-digital basis.

Timing and sequential programming are considered logical functions also and are roles for the industrial controller. The controller receives input information, operates on the input information in accordance with predetermined *logical* criteria, and actuates the necessary machine actions on the basis of the logical decisions. An *industrial* controller or control panel operates by logical reasoning. It should not be confused with the *process* controller, which usually works on an analog basis.

As automation commonly consists of a *line* of semi-autonomous machines or sections, it is common for an output signal from one controller to be used as an input signal to the next sequential controller, the several controllers being housed centrally in a control panel.

All Detroit-type automation and all automatic cycle $A_3$ machines depend heavily on the controller or control panel for their logical operations. One machine whose operation is dictated by a simple control panel is a punch press that won't operate if the metal blank is not in the correct position or if someone is in the danger zone. An automatic assembly machine is an example of a machine that requires a complex control panel, for each part must be inserted in proper sequence and the position of each part is critical.

Sensors for logical operation do not reveal graduated levels, but only report whether a condition *does* or *does not* exist. They are switches, or switch-like proximity devices, used to determine the status of prepocess, inprocess, and postprocess conditions.

Controller output consists of actuating a motor, valve, servo, or another controller. The controller components proper consist mainly of two-state devices. These are commonly *contactors*, as electrical relays are termed in industry. Gas-filled tubes are used as contactors in some cases. A late trend is to use static logic elements in place of contactors. Timers, and multiposition switches are also used in controllers whenever the logic is predicated on time, or when a multiple choice condition exists rather than the simple two-state basic logical action.

Generally, industrial machine decisions are performed by contactors (power type electrical relays). These work rather well but require an appreciable amount of power to function. They also have moving parts and contacts, are physically large, subject to wear, and are relatively slow acting. These deficiencies led to the development of *static controls*, mentioned previously.

Magnetic amplifier type static controls work at a low power level. They have no moving parts or contacts, are small and fast acting. The basic logic functions are available as static elements. These are: *and; or; not;* also *memory* and *time delay* elements. Any decision-making function can be made up from these five logic units. The Westinghouse Company calls their static control devices by the trade name of *Cypak;* the General Electric Company refers to their version as *Static Switching Control.*

## PROCESS CONTROLLERS

The automatic *process controller* is an offshoot of the ordinary feedback control thermostat. Its purpose is to sense a process variable, display and record this information if desired, and compare the value sensed to the desired set-points.

Chart 11-2.  Controller Family

| TERM | DISCUSSION | EXAMPLES |
|---|---|---|
| SWITCH | The simplest form of control. In basic action, a switch is a two-state device, namely open circuit-closed circuit, operated manually. A switch operated by electrical action (as for remote control) is known as a relay or contactor. Clock operated (timer) switches and pulse count operated (stepping) switches are forms of controllers. | Manually operated are toggle switch, trigger switch, horn button, fan switch, and pullchain socket. Also manual, but more complex in function are the three-point switch, four-point switch, reversing switch, and tap switch. Switches which are not operated manually are usually forms of sensors (feelers). Limit switches are actuated by the location of a part or mechanism. Photoelectric switches, proximity switches, and pressure switches are other examples of switches which have a two-state sensing function. |
| CONTROLLER (INDUSTRIAL) | A control device, usually manually operated, which incorporates some self-acting features. A-c motor starters are the most common form of controller. Available from fractional horsepower to multihundred horsepower sizes, these provide overload protection with motor starting time lag and no-voltage release. Reversing types of motor starter controllers include electrical and mechanical interlocking of the relays, to prevent short circuits. | Other forms of controllers are two-speed motor switches, rheostats, light dimmers, d-c motor starters, and time or count operated switches. A-c motor starter type controllers evolved into control panels by the addition of remote control pushbutton stations, reverse buttons, jog, inch, and emergency stop features, in the starter relay holding circuit. |
| CONTROL PANEL | Automatic and semi-automatic machines depend on control panels. Control panels perform sequencing and timing functions, in accordance with built-in programming, on a logic basis. Control panels often include integrated "packaged" units, such as weld current controls, motor speed regulators and automatic inspection discriminators. Also time and count operated switching units. | Control panels are used universally for machine control, from a self-acting cut off saw to a continuous forge line. Gear hobbing, elevator control, shuttle conveyor, stamping press loading, transfer machine, and automatic packaging also depend on control panels, or the equivalent apparatus. Static elements (magnetic or transistor) replace contactors (electrical relays) for many control panel applications. |
| PROCESS CONTROLLER | An automatic "instrument" in standardized unit form, for feedback control of continuous processes. Usually installed on a panelboard with other controllers. Combines the function of decision with recording and indication. Acts in conjunction with sensors (called "transmitters") and actuators (valves or "operators"). May utilize pneumatic or electrical signals. May modify feedback signal for anticipation, rate, droop, or averaging effects. | Temperature process controller: senses temperatures from transducer in tank, records on chart, compares temperature to desired value, actuates steam valve to heat tank for minimum temperature error. Flow process controller: senses rate of flow from transducer in pipeline, records on dial, compares to setting of desired rate, actuates pump to maintain desired rate of flow. Other process controllers: BTU, pH, position, liquid level, viscosity, weight. Most common process controller is the household thermostat which combines sensing, indication and decision in one unit; actuation being accomplished at the fuel valve. |
| MENTOR | A limited purpose computer used for control, instrumentation, or simulation. A mentor has one or more equation solvers with auxiliary circuitry. Permits mechanization of physical and mental operations which can be related by mathematical equations. Reconciles output with input, inprocess, and feedback information. | A mentor is not an all-purpose computer. For many applications a mentor may be an inexpensive unit of few parts. Common mentors are watt-hour meters, gasoline computer pumps, cash registers, and speedometers. Mentors are used for automatic quality control, machinability, and for training simulators. |

If correction is necessary, the process controller actuates a valve, rheostat, or regulating device to reduce the error between the measured variable and the desired value.

Process controllers have been perfected in the flow industries. Any of a wide variety of inputs from various transducers can be accepted. Process controllers respond to any variable that can be sensed, both by direct measurements such as *temperature* and *pressure,* and derived measurements such as *acidity* and *refractive index.*

Almost any single process variable can be regulated by selecting standardized process controllers and auxiliaries from manufacturers' catalogs. Components of different makes can often be used together without difficulty. Process industry sensors are sometimes termed *transmitters.*

The decision function is performed by a recording controller, which can be set to respond to the sensor signal to operate proportionally, on-off, derivative, or provide for automatic reset of the setpoint. This flexibility permits the process controller to be matched to the process to compensate for system lags and to prevent overshooting. Selecting the desired controller response approaches computer control in an elementary way.

The process industry actuator can be any of a large variety of valves, dampers, rheostats, or throttling devices, sometimes termed *operators,* powered by air, hydraulics, or electricity.

The signal from the sensor to the controller and then to the actuator is commonly air pressure in the 3 to 15 psi range. However, electrical signals are also being used, particularly where the sensors or actuators are remote from the controller location.

If industrial machine variables (such as dimensions) can be in continuous form, then process controllers can be used to control and regulate such fabricating variables. Consequently, in some cases it is possible to utilize perfected process control devices for the control of fabricating machines by first averaging the discontinuous measurements to obtain continuous signals.

Summarizing, the term *controller* by itself implies an industrial controller as for controlling an electric motor for a machine. A *control panel* is used to coordinate the many power devices of an automatic manufacturing machine or process. The term *process controller* refers to the standardized units for controlling and regulating continuous variables, as in chemical plants.

Chart 11-2, *Controller Family,* compares all controllers, from a simple switch to a mentor. Being equation solving devices, mentors are again listed in Chart 11-3, *Computer Family.* Mentors should not be mistaken for large general purpose computers, the digital giant brains and the analog differential analyzers.

## COMPUTERS

A computer is the functional part of a control system that operates by mathematical relationships. Its function complements that of a controller, which operates on logical rather than a proportional basis.

Mathematical decisions are those that require the solution of a mathematical equation. They are based on the concurrent or continual reconciliation of the constants, parameters, and variables of a process function. As already pointed out, control apparatus that performs logical decisions constitutes a *controller;* control apparatus that reconciles control function factors (constants, variables, and parameters) mathematically constitutes a control computer.

Control computers vary from a simple proportional mixing controller to a giant general purpose computer capable of controlling a dispersed multiplant complex. Most needs for computer control requirements can, however, be satisfied with relatively simple computing devices intended for solving a particular type of problem and actuating the desired response. These limited purpose computers, *mentors,* primarily make mathematical decisions (by solving equations) but may make logical decisions as well.

Machine decisions are either *logical* or *mathematical,* or both. Mathematical machine decisions are not *illogical,* and logical decisions can be represented mathematically. In general, however, *logical decisions* are considered to be those that are sequential and alternative, in accordance with strict rules.

Chart 11-3. Computer Family

| TERM | DISCUSSION | EXAMPLES |
|---|---|---|
| MENTOR | A limited purpose computer used for control, instrumentation, or simulation. A mentor has generally one or more equation solvers with auxilary circuitry. Permits mechanization of physical and mental operations which can be related by mathematical equations. Reconciles output with input and feedback information. | A mentor is *not* an all-purpose computer. For many applications a mentor may be an inexpensive unit of few parts. Common mentors are watt-hour meters, gasoline computer pumps, cash registers, and speedometers. Mentors are used for automatic quality control, self-optimizing, dynamic process control, machineability, and for training simulators. |
| EQUATION SOLVER | A means of solving specific algebraic equations by analog computation methods. Usually consists of simple electro-mechanical components, servo actuated. Used as part of mentors, simulators, and for solving a wide variety of nondifferential equations, including simultaneous equations. Often called a servocomputer. | An equation solver for a lathe cutting speed mentor (surface fpm) consists of only two resistors, two potentiometers, and an instrument servo (a null seeking amplifier-motor unit). Equation of areas, rates, triangulation, summation, and roots, are also solved by a simple "electrical slide-rule" equation solver. |
| SIMULATOR | A model, usually electrical, of a physical system or of a situation.<br>For example, an aircraft landing gear can be simulated by a network of resistors, inductances and capacitors, analogous to damping, mass, and compliance. Thus, velocity and displacement could be determined from electrical current and charge measurements. This is called a dynamical analogy simulator.<br>Examples of mechanical-electrical analogies:<br>force $F \doteq$ voltage E; mass $m \doteq$ inductance L; damping $c \doteq$ resistance R; velocity $v \doteq$ current i; compliance $\frac{1}{k} \doteq$ capacitance C; displacement $x \doteq$ charge q. | Training devices depend on simulators which imitate real operating conditions. An instrument flight trainer (synthetic situation simulator) relies on equation solvers to synthesize the effects of drift, altitude, direction, airspeed, engine conditions, fuel level, and other factors. This is accomplished by interconnecting equation solvers, each solving one of the equations of flight. By connecting these equation analogs to the actual instrument panel and pilot controls, take-off, cruise, landing and emergency conditions are simulated. |
| GENERAL PURPOSE COMPUTERS | Because general purpose computers must be flexible to accommodate a wide variety of problems, such computers are necessarily large and complex. They may be of either analog or digital types, but "hybrid" features are common, as well as considerable electro-mechanisms. The solution to a problem is generally in graphical or numerical form but can be made to actuate control apparatus.<br><br>ANALOG COMPUTER<br><br>Commonly known as differential analyzers. Capable of a wide range of applications, particularly the solution of differential equations, for engineering and scientific studies. Operation is based on variables in the form of voltages, currents or shaft rotations (analog values), and are measured rather than counted. Analog computers can be made to operate in real-time, high-speed, and extended time, as required. Repetitive solutions and change of parameters while in operation are also possible.<br><br>DIGITAL COMPUTER<br><br>Can solve a wide variety of problems. Includes memory devices, input-output elements, accumulator, control element, instruction register, and instruction counter. Best suited for data processing, and for working problems that require great numbers of repetitive operations. Digital computers perform multiplication, integration, and trigonometric operations by repetitive summations. Operation is based on counts or numerical data (digital information) rather than on physical quantities such as voltage or shaft rotations (analog information). | Popularly thought of as "giant brains" or "information machines" general purpose computers can be used in four principal ways:<br>1. Problem solving. Solves engineering and scientific problems which are difficult or time consuming.<br>2. Control. Any physical situation, process, or event, which can be described in mathematical terms, can usually be controlled.<br>3. Simulation. A computer can be made to simulate a process or system.<br>4. Information processing. High speed sorting and evaluation of data.<br><br>Typical of design problems solved on general purpose analog computers are missile, auto-pilot, steel mill roller controls, wind tunnel drive, airfoil sections, prestressed concrete structures, and nuclear power stations.<br><br>Programmed information in the form of coded tapes or punched cards is much used with general purpose digital computers. Typical data processing tasks are high speed accounting, inventory control, production planning and machine scheduling control, marketing studies, survey analysis, scientific data reduction, census.<br>Many kinds of problems can be solved by either type of computer, although programming would be quite different. This enables use of an office digital (data processing) computer for solving engineering problems during slack time. |

An example of computer control is the analog controlled lathe, that automatically maintains optimum cutting speed regardless of the position of the cutting tool. This necessitates a mentor that takes into account the desired cutting speed and the radial position of the cutter, then adjusts the turning revolutions per minute to develop the desired cutting speed. This is specially important on a facing cut, or taper, or for metal spinning, where the working radius is continually changing. However, logic control functions are also needed for timing, sequencing, and programming the automatic actions of the lathe.

An example of rather complex computer control is the nuclear steam generator simulator. The many variables and parameters of the nuclear process being simulated are reconciled simultaneously by control computers. The analog solutions are then used as the input signals to the simulation actuators, records, and indicators on a realistic control panel.

## GENERAL PURPOSE COMPUTERS

It was explained that a control system is used to direct the use of energy (output) of a machine or process, in accordance with received information (input). Also, that inherent in all control systems (including man) are the functions of *sensing*, *decision*, and *actuation*. These functions are related in Figure 7-1, *Production by Man or Machine*. It was there emphasized that a control system is required to control machines or processes for the production of goods. A control system can, however, be a *process* in its own right, where the product is *information* rather than goods. Such use of a control system is known as *data processing* or *information handling* or *ADP* (automatic data processing).

Data processing is accomplished by computers, with suitable information input and output equipment. In spite of their name, computers are *not* limited to problem solving or to numerical manipulation. All uses of computers are forms of information handling. Electronics and electromechanical computers (not including desk type mechanical calculators) can be used in four principal ways to aid production, management, and control:

1. *Problem Solving.* The use of electronic and electromechanical computers for the purpose of solving problems is familiar to all. Many scientific and engineering problems are too tedious or too time consuming to be readily solved by conventional methods. Designing large transformers is an example. Hence, the battery of design equations are programmed into a computer which solves them and provides numerical answers or plots the answers as graphs. Though this is an important area in the use of electronic and electromechanical computers, other less well-known applications are of equal importance.

2. *Control.* Any physical situation, process, or event can generally be described in mathematical terms. A computer can be used to solve the mathematical expression to effect control based on a number of variables.

3. *Simulation.* Likewise, a computer can be used to solve equations which describe the function of a system. In this way, a computer can be made to simulate (imitate) a system or process.

4. *Data Processing.* Another large field of application for digital computers consists of high speed sorting and evaluation of data. Commonly, the data is on punched cards, magnetic tape, or magnetic drums. Here, too, a computer can be used for an operation that does not at first appear to be mathematical because most operations can be interpreted on a mathematical basis.

Chart 11-3 describes both general purpose and limited purpose computers.

Because computers make it possible to handle problems involving a great many variables, they are an indispensable aid to modern production management. The need for general purpose computers to assist management in recordkeeping and for the analysis of business problems is of equal importance to control uses of computers. General purpose computers are regularly used for accounting, inventory control, payroll, stockroom issues, machine and equipment scheduling, and product design applications.

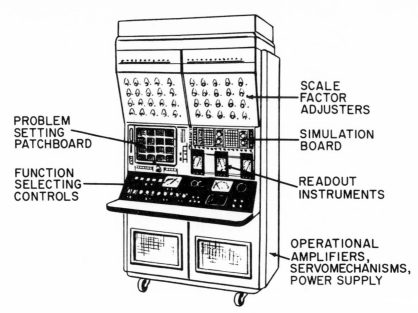

PROBLEM
SETTING
PATCHBOARD

FUNCTION
SELECTING
CONTROLS

SCALE
FACTOR
ADJUSTERS

SIMULATION
BOARD

READOUT
INSTRUMENTS

OPERATIONAL
AMPLIFIERS,
SERVOMECHANISMS,
POWER SUPPLY

Figure 11-4. General purpose analog computer.

There are three categories in which computers are of benefit to business because of their data handling abilities:

1. Simple cost reduction, where present methods of keeping records such as inventory and accounts is too expensive
2. Increasing value of data, by speeding up reports and operational summaries
3. As a direct aid in making management decisions, when the relationship of costs, sales, time delays, and marketing conditions can be established

General purpose computers are available in many types and variations. The purpose for which they are used determines the choice and the input and output equipment. Programming varies greatly between different types and different makes of computers. The general characteristics of computers are given in Charts 11-1 and 11-3.

### REAL TIME VERSUS MACHINE TIME

Automatic control has always had to consider response time. Automatic control action must be concurrent with the machine or process it controls. If anything, it should possibly anticipate and predict future requirements rather than lag. Thus, machine control has depended on *real-time* control systems.

Data processing systems, however, usually run sequentially and take all of the time they need. Though most data processing systems are high speed, the mass of material they must work on renders their working time appreciable. Obviously, they cannot be used for direct control if the machine to be controlled must wait for results of the data processing activity. Direct control of a machine by a data processing system is highly desirable. This has led to the development of data processing systems "with deadlines to meet."

The meaning of *real time* is the actual time we live in. Control is always in real time, for real events do not take place otherwise, but simulated events and computations can apply a scale factor to time, just as a scale factor can be applied to any of the variables entering into a computation or simulation.

Nonreal time is referred to as *machine time*. This does not refer to the industrial production machine. *Machine* here refers to the simulator or computer. This may be confusing but it repre-

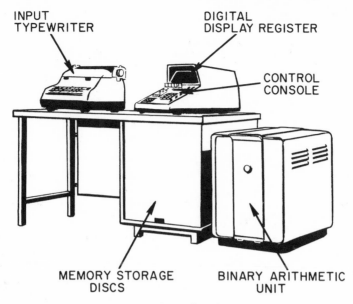

**Figure 11-5.** Desk size digital computer.

sents current usage. Machine time is the time base of a computer or simulator if it is working at *slow motion* or *fast motion*.

As an example, motion pictures can be considered to be a form of simulator. When time is speeded up, as by time lapse photography, so that the one week growth of a plant is shown in one minute, it is in *fast time*. If a high speed event is shown as though it occurred very slowly, it is the familiar slow motion and represents *slow time*. In both cases, they are *machine* time, which is different from *real time*.

The use of machine time, especially fast time, is mainly of value to engineers for analysis and development work. Fast time makes it possible to rapidly try out a number of solutions or simulations to an immediate control problem to determine the optimum values. Solutions are often made at a rate of 60 per second, so that the *answers* can be shown on a cathode ray oscillograph screen, *electronic graph paper*.

## ANALOG versus DIGITAL COMPUTERS

There are two general computing processes, analog and digital. In an analog machine, Figure 11-4, analogy exists between the operation of the computing device and the type of problem it is intended to solve.

Information is supplied to the analog computer in the form of a physical quantity, such as voltage or current or the rotational angle of a shaft. The analog computer transforms these input quantities into output quantities in accordance with the programming, the instructions to be followed. If the computer is programmed to simulate a mathematical problem which in turn describes a physical system, the output of the computer can be used for control purposes. If an analog computer is to be used for control purposes, its output is used to provide the desired control.

Analog devices, which include computers, simulators, and differential analyzers, all share the characteristic that the numbers in the problem they handle are represented by corresponding levels of physical or electrical quantities.

In contrast to analog computer elements, the digital device, Figure 11-5, works by counting. For the digital computer, the input data for the problem must be in the form of pulses representing numbers. The input information is acted upon in accordance with the rules of arithmetic or logic. The output of the digital computer is also in numerical form. To operate as it does, by numbers, a digital computer makes use of special input and output devices to translate the input data into a form usable by the computer and, in turn, to convert the computer output into a form usable for control and information purposes.

## EVALUATING THE USE OF COMPUTERS

The production planner or industrial engineer attempting to evaluate the use of computers as a time-saving aid in analyzing production prob-

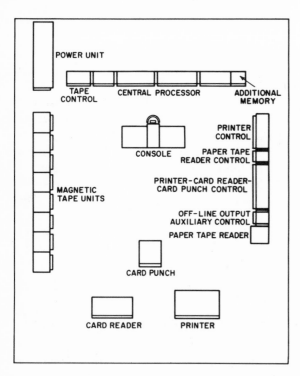

Figure 11-6. Data processing system layout.

lems must keep in mind that each type of computer, analog or digital, is best suited to a particular type of application. His specific problems can be handled better on one type of computer than on another.

Digital and analog computers differ substan-

tially in their accuracy, versatility, and cost. These differences arise primarily from the fundamental differences in the two methods of computation. Digital computers, because they represent input information by integral numbers of electrical pulses, are inherently more accurate than analog machines. If sufficient time permits, a high digital precision can be obtained by increasing the number of pulses used to represent a number. Depending on the complexity of the problem, precision to the order of 0.01 per cent or better can be readily developed.

Although analog computers are not ordinarily as accurate as digital computers, they may be much faster for some classes of problems than some digital types. Furthermore, analog devices are generally cheaper than digital, but the initial cost for analog machines rises rapidly as greater demand for precision is made. As long as errors of 0.1 per cent can be tolerated, an analog machine will cost considerably less than digital machines.

The digital computer is best in the area of large scale computation where a high degree of accuracy must be maintained. This is the reason why production problems involving scheduling, inventory control, sums of money, and data processing are usually handled by digital computers.

Digital machines further require central pulse generating units, so they must be rather large (Figure 11-6). Consequently, it is not economical to use small digital computers. The economics of computer design places the digital machine in the high capacity category.

Electronic analog computing machines range in size from desk size models that incorporate ten to fifteen amplifiers, to large installations that use hundreds of amplifiers. The very large analog installations require considerable associated equipment, such as patch boards and power supplies, and a large staff to maintain them. The small analog machines are less expensive to run and maintain than are comparable digital computers.

Analog computers are especially well suited for limited accuracy design studies of dynamic systems. Programming, that is setting up analog machines to translate input data, is reasonably simple and can be carried out by ordinary production or engineering personnel who need not be computer specialists. The *variables, parameters,* and *coefficients* that are basic to the problem being solved by the computer can be quite readily varied during the problem solution on an analog machine. This feature is of particular value in design and system studies that require many trial solutions to determine the best operating conditions.

Digital machine programming, that is, introducing the methods of logic and arithmetic by which the input information is handled, usually is carried out by an experienced computing staff. It is also somewhat more difficult to introduce changes in a digital problem while it is in the process of a solution, even though a partial solution shows that a change in the program would be desirable.

Because the use of computers has become commonplace rather than a novelty, those who own large digital machines find that they are in use most of the time, in fact, they have a waiting list of problems. The large analog machines are idle a good part of the time, so they are available for scientific and engineering problems as they arise. Once they are programmed, analog computers work very fast.

An analogy to the use of electronic computers lies in the use of a slide rule and a desk-type calculator, true counterparts of the analog and digital computers, respectively. The slide rule usually lies idle in the desk but when used produces the answer (not perfect but good enough) in a hurry. The desk calculating machine is used more frequently, is more precise, but takes a comparatively greater skill, and the actual computing process is much longer than with a slide rule. These same statements apply to the electronic analog and digital computers.

# Automation Philosophy

## PHILOSOPHY OF AUTOMATION

Anyone who looks beyond his own narrow speciality recognizes that automation is not a specific discipline but a philosophy of doing things. The philosophy undertakes to organize all knowledge, developments, techniques, applications, and theories applicable to or resulting from automation.

Examples of philosophical automation activi-

ties are: defining and comparing automation terms, comparing similarities and differences among existing automation activities and techniques, and pointing out advantages and hazards of automatic methods. Philosophy of automation also attempts to reveal present and future applications for automatic techniques. This requires study of the history of mechanization and all fields of technology.

The reader and the authors alike belong to

185

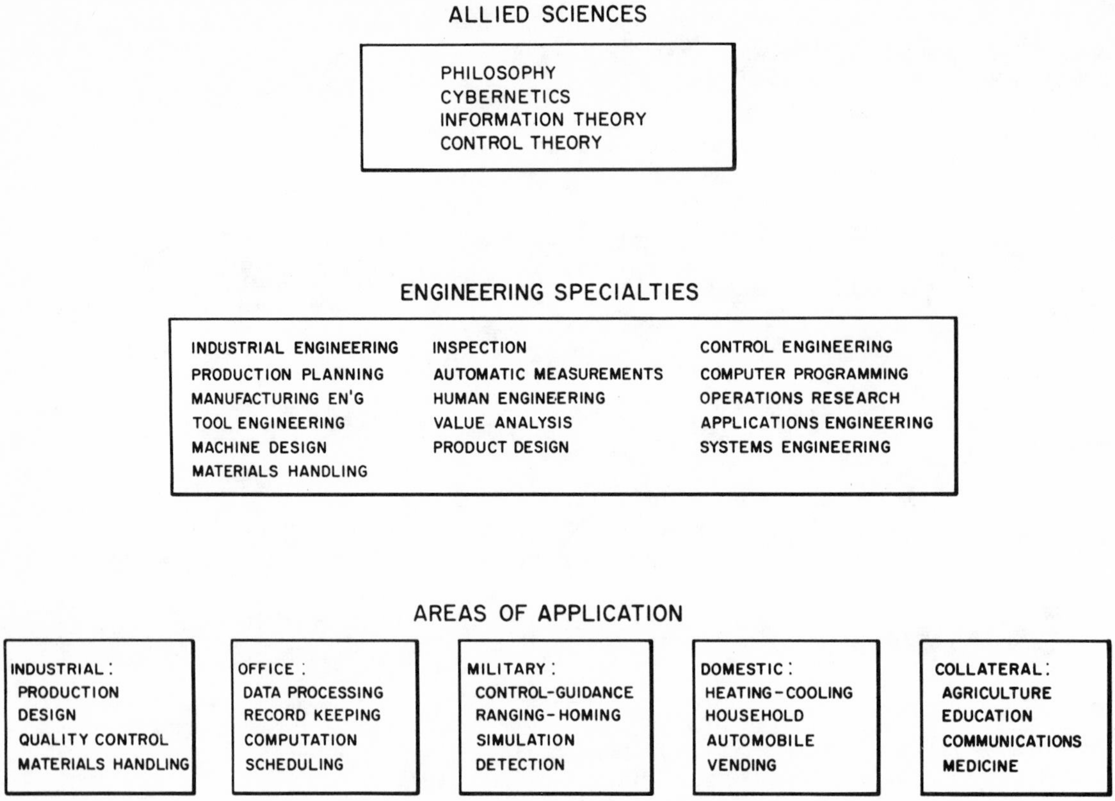

ALLIED SCIENCES

PHILOSOPHY
CYBERNETICS
INFORMATION THEORY
CONTROL THEORY

ENGINEERING SPECIALTIES

| INDUSTRIAL ENGINEERING | INSPECTION | CONTROL ENGINEERING |
|---|---|---|
| PRODUCTION PLANNING | AUTOMATIC MEASUREMENTS | COMPUTER PROGRAMMING |
| MANUFACTURING EN'G | HUMAN ENGINEERING | OPERATIONS RESEARCH |
| TOOL ENGINEERING | VALUE ANALYSIS | APPLICATIONS ENGINEERING |
| MACHINE DESIGN | PRODUCT DESIGN | SYSTEMS ENGINEERING |
| MATERIALS HANDLING | | |

AREAS OF APPLICATION

| INDUSTRIAL : | OFFICE : | MILITARY : | DOMESTIC : | COLLATERAL : |
|---|---|---|---|---|
| PRODUCTION | DATA PROCESSING | CONTROL-GUIDANCE | HEATING-COOLING | AGRICULTURE |
| DESIGN | RECORD KEEPING | RANGING-HOMING | HOUSEHOLD | EDUCATION |
| QUALITY CONTROL | COMPUTATION | SIMULATION | AUTOMOBILE | COMMUNICATIONS |
| MATERIALS HANDLING | SCHEDULING | DETECTION | VENDING | MEDICINE |

Figure 12-1. The automation pyramid.

the widespread "company of automation philosophers." This group includes technicians, labor representatives, professors, management, sociologists, clergy, economists, and the not-to-be-replaced working man.

The average automationist limits his philosophizing to an unwritten mental picture of how the various concepts interrelate, how the terms are used, what constitutes its basic elements, and in what direction automation is heading. A few try to express their interpretations on paper and exchange their views with contemporary workers in automation, commonly via magazine articles and professional papers. In this way, their work is made available to the public.

The fact that so much has already been said concerning automation, both pro and con, implies that the state of the art of automation is not yet common knowledge. Some advocates of automatic factories claim that completely automatic production is at hand, and that because of giant brains, few men will be needed on the industrial scene. The conservatives are those who say that automation is merely intensified mechanization, and that computers are not needed in automatic production. Even workers in the field of automation have at times been confused as to what has already been done, what represents the frontiers of automatic machine development today, and what may be accomplished by automation in the future.

## AUTOMATION'S PRESENT STATUS

Man is limited by his brain and muscle. He alone cannot work with the strength, speed, and accuracy he desires; thus, he has always sought tools, methods, and machines to enable him to accomplish extraordinary tasks. The desire to use machines to do our work is not new. The will but not the way has been with us for centuries, yet only recently has the way existed, to complement the will. Still, as Chart 12-2 shows us, machines are inferior to man in many ways.

Automaticity is now possible because of a "1-2-3" development that began circa 1900 and was ripe at the time of World War II. This development was as follows:

1. Availability of convenient power, the electric power lines
2. Perfection of the electric motor so that it could be applied at any point where power was needed
3. The availability of cheap and reliable methods of control

This trinity made automaticity a present day possibility. Before the automation era, the main efforts at easing man's tasks were confined to mechanizing the use of energy, "machines to replace muscle." Now efforts are directed toward the task of mechanizing information and control, to ease man's mental tasks. The bulk of all energy consuming work is approaching complete mechanization; there is not much room for dramatic improvement here.

The last link in the mechanization of energy was the intensified use of materials handling equipment.

The mechanization of mental work has hardly begun. The extent to which information and control can be mechanized seems limitless.

## INDUSTRIAL AND SOCIAL REVOLUTIONS

Study of the history of mechanization shows that the first industrial revolution occurred in the 1700's with the advent of water- and steam-driven machines. The present development of techniques to mechanize information justifies looking on automation as the *second* industrial revolution. Automation's philosophy shows the similarities between the first industrial revolution and the second industrial revolution, and thus orients today's mechanized brains to yesterday's mechanized muscles.

Machines that supplemented muscular energy led up to the mass production era. Such machines were effective and did their job of supplying energy well.

Division of labor into repetitive routines for mass production tended to force machine operators to act as mechanisms. The present trend is for machines to assume more and more human attributes, even those requiring mental operations.

It has been pointed out that machines are ideal for routine work, and that they are increasingly taking over the routine work in both the office and the plant. By replacing men who have been forced to do routine work, automation can eventually make life for the human race much more enjoyable. However, this will not take place in a short time. Those of us who participate in the replacement of men by machines to any extent must recognize the economic and social problems that accompany the introduction of automation.

In the long run, most labor saving discoveries have increased the actual need for manpower. This was so because the reduced cost of the labor saving technique increased demand for the product to such an extent that the total number of people employed in that general activity (such as telephone operators replaced by dial phones) increased. Figure 12-3 shows another reason why automation does not necessarily reduce employment.

Automation should ultimately prove to be a boon to humanity. It can supply many of man's wants from cheap energy, and free man to pursue his idea of happiness (which is a problem not to be solved by engineers). In the immediate short-run picture, automation is obsoleting an element of the working population, so an awareness of this fact and an open-minded attempt at reducing the shock and disruption when automation is introduced must be our policy.

Observations indicate that our increasing dependence on automaticity in industry, office, and the home may cause us to forget the non-mechanized way of life. Even now, any disruption in electric power, transportation or communications tends to become a disaster. However, these aspects of the effect of automation on society are beyond the scope of this book.

Chart 12-2. Man versus Machine

| | TERM | EXPLANATION | MAN | MACHINE |
|---|---|---|---|---|
| PHYSICAL FACULTIES | STRENGTH | The ability to exert and sustain a force or torque | Limited and rapidly diminishes | Limited only by design. Easy to attain. |
| | SPEED | The rate at which an action can be accomplished. | Comparatively slow response time. Limited ability to act rapidly. | |
| | POWER | The amount of energy available for expenditure per unit time. | Good for short periods as a self-powered system. | |
| | ACCURACY | The correctness of action and freedom from mistakes. | Subject to many errors; becomes bored and inattentive by routine tasks. | |
| | SKILL | The ease and precision (fineness) of action dexterity. | Requires training of persons who have suitable aptitudes. | |
| SUBJECTIVE CHARACTERISTICS | FATIGUE | The tendency to perform less effectively after a period of activity. | Readily fatigued | Not subject to fatigue |
| | SATURATION | The tendency to respond only to a limited amount or number of signals or instructions. | Readily saturated. Limited cognition ability. | Limited only by design. Does not become confused. |
| | CONSISTENCY | The ability to repeat performance uniformly. | Poor. Influenced by temperament and distractions. | Excellent. Limited only by design. |
| | DISPERSION | The tendency for performance to vary about an average. | High. Depends on skill and dexterity. | Low. Can be feedback regulated. |
| | OBEDIENCE | The faithful compliance to orders. | Poor. Personality conflicts. | Excellent. Never resentful. |
| | RELIABILITY | The likelihood of continuing to perform as intended. | Fair. Subject to misunderstanding. | Good. Subject to wear and drift. |
| | FLEXIBILITY | Ability to vary mode, qualities, and sequences of action. | Excellent. Can control unexpected emergencies. | Very poor. Restricted to highly specialized actions. |
| | GROUP WORK | Ability to act in concert with other systems. | Poor. Man is the "weak link" in a system. | Good when suitably interconnected and safeguarded. |
| | JUDGMENT | The ability to evaluate information and to make decisions therefrom. | Fair, but has broad capabilities. | Good over very narrow range, depending on programming. |
| OBJECTIVE CHARACTERISTICS | SIZE | Cubic feet required for a system. | High results per cubic foot, and per pound, for a wide range of actions. | Large size and weight: justified only for large scale, fast, operations. |
| | WEIGHT | Weight required for an operating system. | | |
| | LIFE | Useful operating life, before replacement is necessary. | 30-45 year working life | 5-10 year work life |
| | DEPRECIATION | Loss in effectiveness or value, as time elapses. | Appreciates with experience | Depreciates rapidly, subject to obsolescence |
| | COSTS | per hour; per operation. | Low per hour; high per operation. | High per hour; low per operation. |
| | AVAILABILITY | Ease of procurement | Higher skills difficult to obtain. | Available by purchase, design, or leasing. |
| | EFFICIENCY | Results obtained per cost and per efforts. | Low efficiency at all times. | High efficiency if used continually for high duty cycle. |

Chart 12-2. Man versus Machine (Continued)

| | TERM | EXPLANATION | MAN | MACHINE |
|---|---|---|---|---|
| **SENSING FUNCTIONS** | SIGHT | The ability to detect and discriminate light, images, and colors. | Superior but limited as to visual band covered. | Good over narrowly restricted range only. Consistent results |
| | HEARING | The ability to detect and discriminate sounds, audio signals, and pitch. | Superior, especially in noisy locations. | |
| | TASTE | The ability to detect and discriminate tastes. | Superior, wide range and sensitivity. | Poor. Many tastes and odors cannot be sensed by automatic systems. |
| | SMELL | The ability to detect and discriminate odors. | Superior, wide range and sensitivity. | |
| | TOUCH | The ability to detect and discriminate physical pressures, motions, and relief. | Excellent for sensing qualities but not quantities | High sensitivity over very wide range. Readily accomplished. |
| | TEMPERATURE | The ability to detect and discriminate hot and cold. | Fair ability to sense comparative levels, but poor absolute sense. | |
| | BALANCE | The ability to sense level, plumb, and equilibrium. | Deficient ability | |
| | SUPER-HUMAN | The ability to detect properties by means beyond the ken of man. | Man can extend his senses only by use of instruments. | Machines can utilize X-ray, infrared, and induction effects for sensing. |
| **MENTAL FACULTIES AND OPERATIONS** | MEMORY | The ability to store information and recall from storage when necessary. | Superior long term memory. Fair recall ability; error prone. | Limited capacity, excellent recall ability, error free. Can also erase memories. |
| | LEARNING | The ability to associate new experiences with information in memory storage. | Wide range. Fair effectiveness. | Very limited selfprogramming ability. |
| | ARITHMETICAL | The ability to perform arithmetic operations: addition, subtraction, multiplication and division. | Slow, error prone. | Fast, error free. By calculators and digital computers. |
| | MATHEMATICAL | The ability to perform algebraic operations, relating functions and proportions. | Slow. Complex relationships cannot be solved. | Fast; practically unlimited capabilities. By mentors and general-purpose computers. |
| | LOGICAL | The ability to make decisions or commit action, according to specific criteria; deductive reasoning. | Slow. Subject to fallacies of reasoning and intuitive "short-cuts." | Reliable. Decision by controller and computers. Machine depends on correctly programmed premises. |
| | ORIGINALITY | The ability to create new patterns or meaningful combinations. | Good, but not all men have talent. | Remotely possible, to limited extent. |
| | CLEVERNESS | The possession of a broad scope of knowledge rather than mere intensive narrow knowledge. | Excellent. Man has versatile knowledge. | Very low due to machines' narrow field of knowledge. |
| | RESOURCEFUL-NESS | The ability to vary mode of action as required by circumstances. | Man can overcome unexpected obstacles. | Machine must depend on the cleverness of the man who prepared the program. |
| | CLASSIFYING | The ability to separate members of a group according to certain characteristics. | Yes, but inefficient for repetitive work. | Excellent. Machines sort by measurements very well. |
| | IDENTIFYING | The ability to detect basic similarities in diverse forms. | Yes. Man can recognize faces and photographs. | No. Can a machine recognize speech or handwriting? |

*"—and this machine does the work of nine men."*

Figure 12-3.   Labor saving machine.

## OBSOLESCENCE AND AUTOMATION

Men who are forced to leave their jobs due to mechanization are rendered *obsolete*. The men who are most versatile and who have the greatest adaptability to new conditions suffer obsolescence less than those who are not as resourceful. The characteristic of adaptability is desirable for machines as well as for men.

*Automaticity*, the level of mechanization utilized, develops in two ways:

1. The *intensive* development of automation. This consists of making a machine highly effective in performing a specialized task or series of operations. This is readily accomplished by skilled engineers and is often practical and justified. However, intensive development of automation has the principal drawback that such machines are not adaptable and can't deviate even slightly from the assigned task, even if such accommodation to instantaneous conditions should be desirable.

2. The *extensive* development of automation. This gives a machine or process latitude to vary the work process as necessary for the desired end result.

All machines must be of a more or less specialized nature. However, by use of automatic cognition, including feedback, machines can monitor the results of their operation and correct their actions.

All practical automation machines are neither entirely *intensive* nor *extensive* in their mode of operation but have some of each characteristic. Those that are more extensive have greater flexibility at the cost of greater expense and complexity. Those industrial machines that are mainly intensive attain automation more readily, at the risk of obsolescence, because they are so highly specialized and cannot have the advantages of feedback, which is the hallmark of the extensive machine.

Whereas feedback allows automatic compensation along extensive lines, the free use of external programming whereby a machine or process can be readily accommodated to changing conditions is also a trend toward extensive automation. In contrast, anything *special* that limits the breadth of operation of a machine or process tends toward intensive automation.

Specific purpose automation systems are basically inflexible, for a change in product leads to some obsolescence of equipment. Although this type of automation does its specific work very well, any product changes demand redesign and rebuilding, though some machine sections are salvageable.

The first users of *Detroit brand* automation paid heavily for its lack of convertibility. Much attention is now given to the use of standardized unit machines, which can be assembled into a variety of automation lines. This has considerably reduced the vulnerability of the largest automation fabrication systems (such as automatic engine factories) to obsolescence. However, even with highly standardized sections and units, a major change is expensive and takes a long time.

An obvious question now is: "How can you

attain the flexibility and adaptability so necessary to reduce the risk of obsolescence?" The answer is external control and feedback.

External control means that the control system is external to the machine's basic mechanisms, and that it is designed to be readily readjusted. Such external control is usually manual. All changes in operation, such as a change in program must be set in by an operator. External control, automatic or manual, is the best safeguard against supersedence of an industrial machine or process.

The difference between machines that function without feedback and those that do make use of closed-loop control resembles the difference between a semi-skilled industrial workman and the skilled craftsman. The skilled worker has a broad base of knowledge, resourcefulness, and judgment within his field. He can therefore adjust his performance as necessary to meet problems and varied requirements. A semi-skilled laborer, however, can only do the limited number of operations that he was taught to do.

For a man to obtain a craft skill (such as tool-and-die maker) is much more difficult and expensive than is obtaining proficiency at a limited task (such as drill-press operator). In like manner, the design and development of $A_4$ machines that make use of feedback and that have self-corrective properties is considerably more expensive and presents more technical control problems than do ordinary machines with no self-judgment characteristics.

One way to help combat the hazards of mechanical obsolescence is to rely more heavily on job-shop automation, whereby the manufacturing process makes use of a number of basic machine tools, each machine tool having considerable latitude in its mode of operation and making much use of programmed external control. This is particularly adaptable to small lot, batch, or special model production. Accomplishment of job-shop automation demands use of modern control techniques such as numerical control, computer control, and tape programs, and multitool do-everything, externally programmed machines.

## UNSOLVED PROBLEMS

It should not be inferred that the philosophical approach to automation has almost solved today's automation problems. For one thing, classifications and definitions of automation concepts must be kept up to date, for they are dynamic, changing with the times.

Thus far, the philosophy has done little towards showing actually when and how to design for automaticity. Not that technology is the philosopher's job, but the principles on which decisions are based are still *soft*.

The economic and sociological problems of automation are profound, yet little has been said about them here. Automation is a reality for high production fabrication at the price of extreme rigidity of the manufacturing process. How can automatic short-run production be attained with flexible machines? Furthermore, is the present day dependence upon cutting metal the last word in fabrication? It would appear that the chipless methods such as powdered metals and cold forming may offer greater promise for automation.

Another problem is cross-field communication. The production men do not know the full capabilities of automatic control. Men versed in control theory do not know the problems of the fabricating industries. Hence, control engineers should be encouraged to look into industrial operations. Manufacturing engineers, especially those who set up product fabrication lines, should look to the nonmanufacturing accomplishments of control engineers for hints and suggestions.

However, suggestions alone won't do much good. Each specialist is very busy with his own work. Furthermore, the information that is available, for example magazine articles, relates how automatic control serves in a specific case. Very seldom is it apparent how the same control techniques can be applied to other problems.

The philosophy of automation can seek out existing automation practice in one field and show how it can be used in another. It can show how military automation applies to the process industries, and how processing automation can be used for fabrication of pieceparts. The philosophical role having the greatest potential is to actively distribute automation techniques from field to field.

The automation specialist must have a scientific basis for his work. He must have definite ways to measure and evaluate results. Words alone cannot illustrate subtle relationships between seemingly remote types of systems. Designers must resort to quantitative methods as well as to experience and judgment.

Complex automation demands a mathematical basis for evaluation of control systems. Mathematics is needed for determining many of the key variables of automatic processes. Cybernetics unites information theory with control theory and thus provides a mathematical basis for automation.

The automation sciences are so interrelated, that for our purpose we can consider them together as one philosophy.

Figure 12-1 shows how the automation sciences embrace the automation engineering activities along with industrial, office, military, domestic, and collateral activities.

## EVOLUTION OF TOOLS

The first tools, as shown on the frontpaper (inside the front cover) were of stone. Some of these fist-held tools were chipped so that a single tool could do several functions; the point for drilling, a straight or serrated edge for cutting, scraping, or gouging, the side for pounding, and so on. No doubt the early fist tool was a good weapon, too.

Special purpose stone tools, which evolved from the primitive fist-tool, provided cutting edges better suited for slicing, for drilling, sawing, gouging, and so on. Later abraded (ground) stone tools provided more uniform and sharper cutting edges.

We are not entirely beyond the stone age, for many valuable modern tools are of stone. In fact, nonmetallic tools are having a revival.

Grinding wheels and honing stones are made of natural or artificial stone and even diamond is a stone of sorts. Now black granite, the basalt which constitutes the basic rock formation of the earth, is used for precision surface plates having first been used by the Egyptian pharaohs for official cubits, the standards of measure by which the monuments of antiquity, including the pyramids, were erected.

In addition to the natural stones, concrete (an artificial stone) is now being used for heavy press frames. There are signs that new epoxy concretes will be used more and more for production machinery.

Returning from the modern stone tools to the late stone age, the early stone tools were superseded in time by copper, then by bronze, then by iron, finally by steel. We can now see that steel is being partially superseded by aluminum and by the exotic metals such as titanium, and by plastics, too, to some extent. The changeover to copper, bronze, iron, and so on, was mainly to get a better cutting edge which could be readily resharpened.

To use the cutting edges most effectively, special purpose tool holders developed. These are the ancient but still used carpenter's, blacksmith's, and other mechanics' tools. These mechanics' hand tools helped man's hands control the cutting action. Examples are the drill brace, the plane frame, and the sawblade frame. Nevertheless, all hand tools continue to be $A_0$, hand-manipulated and muscle-actuated.

When such hand tools were driven by water power or by a horsepower treadmill, $A_1$ power tools came into being, such as the woodlathe, saw, and grindstone. However, these were not yet machine tools.

### EARLY MACHINE TOOLS

The first $A_2$ machine tools could provide automatic feed as well as the basic machining function. This automatic feed capability brought into use mechanical means for holding and controlling both the work piece and the tool. The work-holding devices, prototypes of today's jigs and fixtures, were supported and guided in their actions by the rigid metal framework of the machine. Thus, they replaced man's hands and arms as well as his muscle.

To a minor extent, limited by their design and

by the use of special shaped cutters and some use of patterns and templets, such machine tools replaced a small amount of man's brain action. With the new, improved, second generation machine tools and accessories for clamping and holding work pieces, mass production, based on interchangeable parts, became commonplace.

Once the new machine tools were developed (just preceding 1900), other highly efficient production tools followed. These included forges, presses, dies, shears, welders, and specialized casting and forming machines. The new machine tools also made it possible to develop special purpose machines for lumber mills, printing presses, power plants, steel mills, and farm machinery. They also set the stage for the large continuous-flow processing plants we have today for the production of paper, synthetic fibers, petroleum, and chemical products.

This, then, is how our tools developed; from stone, to copper, to bronze, to iron, to steel. Then they were driven by power. The power tool led to the self-feed, single-cycle, semi-automatic machine which set the stage for the repeat cycle, fully automatic machine. This leads to feed-back control, self-correcting action. Then, inevitably, we have mathematical control based on interrelated factors. Each new development is structured on its predecessors and borrows freely from contemporary developments in widely divergent fields often having nothing to do with manufacturing.

$A_1$ and $A_2$ machines practically superseded the need for man's hands, arms, body, and muscle for repetitive mass production, but they did not relieve him of much mental effort. Consequently, "brainwork" remains as a challenge. This is the frontier of automation, the mechanization of decision-making, measurements, and information.

As just discussed, the frontpaper depicts the evolution of automation starting with prehistorical hand tools through the seven basic machine tools and concluding with the automatic machines capable of working for an appreciable period unattended. This illustrates the natural development of tools that has paced the advances of civilization. Every new tool makes it possible for civilization to advance significantly by making possible new inventions. Significant discoveries of our civilization made possible by scientific developments based on tools are shown in the endpaper just inside the back cover.

The piece-part mass production industries, the fabricators, however, have used $A_4$ and $A_5$ machines but seldom thus far, for it is more difficult to do so with piece parts than with continuous flow products. In any event, the practical level of the machines we have today proved both in practice and in the laboratory are the $A_5$ machines controlled by limited purpose computers, the mentors.

Not yet a reality are the $A_6$ machine that can learn by conditioned reflex, the $A_7$ machine that can exercise some reasoning, the $A_8$ machine that is capable of original unprogrammed work, and the $A_9$ machine which is the master of man rather than his servant. These are all rather wild conjectures at present, but who knows?

The problem of the higher ordered machines is as much semantic as technical. What does learning mean? What is meant by reasoning? What constitutes original work? When is a machine the master rather than the servant?

## PRODUCTIVITY

Here *productivity* is taken to be the rate at which commodities (goods) and services are produced. In this sense productivity depends both on the effort applied to accomplish useful work and to the effectiveness of the tools used, tools meaning anything from hand tools to complete industrial or commercial plants.

In a sense, our productivity is an index of the efficiency of our national effort. Human effort can produce an appreciable amount of commodities and services only when aided by modern tools, namely, by the various powered and automatic machines for mechanizing both energy and information tasks.

Neither men nor machines are well utilized at present. Man can work with less physical effort than he is now doing, and do far more. Most machine work is also performed at less than the peak capability, at levels of automaticity far lower than what is desirable for highest productivity. Consequently, both men and machines must work more effectively if America's lead in productivity is to be maintained. Present indications are, however, that America's lead in productivity is dropping and may be overtaken by more aggressive, more recently industrialized nations.

Just as the U.S.A. superseded Great Britain, the pioneer industrial nation, the United States may be surpassed by newer countries that adopt the latest techniques immediately without being held back by excessive investment in outmoded plant and traditional production practices.

This does not mean mere intensification of effort is justified. Men must be reserved for the tasks best performed by them; all other work, be it physically arduous, mentally stultifying, or otherwise beyond practical human limitations, should be assigned to machines.

As explained in earlier chapters, man is best for nonroutine, low energy tasks. His principal qualifications are versatility and intellectual abilities. Machines perform routine energy converting and information processing jobs superbly, but they are relatively stupid and inflexible in their mode of operation. So man must concentrate on routinizing work for its mechanized accomplishment, and he must pace himself to accomplish more brainwork if he is to increase his productivity.

## INCREASING PRODUCTIVITY

The material welfare of any country is directly proportional to its productivity which, in turn, depends on the capabilities of its tools, the production machines, and how well they are used.

Human wants are expanding. However, taking the over-all view, only increased productivity can produce a net improvement for everyone. Redistributing the same "pie" (consumer goods and services) only helps a narrow group at the expense of the less politically powerful segment of the population. Obviously, the pie must be made bigger if there are to be more and larger slices to achieve the greatest good for the greatest number of people.

Economic growth of any nation depends largely on increasing the output per man hour. To accomplish this increase of output per man hour we must invest in better tools and use them most effectively. The *better* tools are those that increase productivity, which ordinarily increases when the thermodynamic and cybernetic efficiency is raised, as when a machine uses less power to do a job or uses control information more efficiently or accomplishes more "human" functions, by increasing its order of automaticity. Here is an example.

Man's primeval stone hand tools worked crudely. Today's hand tools are vastly more efficient, usually due to the better cutting action in more convenient form, but they are still classed $A_0$ as they do not work unaided. Power tools, $A_1$, became more productive as the power sources became more efficient, when water, wind, and steam replaced human and animal muscle and also as the cutters improved, such as by the adaption of tool steels and carbide cutting tools. However, even more important to productivity was not their inherent efficiency and capabilities, but how they were used.

Let us say, in a present day machine shop, 90 cubic inches of steel must be removed in producing a large die. If this material is removed a chip at a time, as by conventional milling, much time and energy is consumed and the metal removed is practically worthless. If, however, the metal is removed by cutting off a large piece at a time, as by a band machine or by an oxyacetylene torch, the only metal irrevocably wasted is in the kerf. The piece cut off has potential reclaim or salvage value and far less time and energy was consumed to do the job.

The point here is that both thermodynamic and cybernetic efficiency must be conserved. Obviously, the fewer kilowatt hours of energy expended in removing the 90 cubic inches of steel, the greater the thermodynamic efficiency of the job performed.

As will be further explained in the following chapter, which treats cybernetics and information theory, every organized "system" tends to lose its state of organization. The state of organization that exists must therefore be safeguarded if it is of value, which is usually the case. The steel die plate from which the 90 cubic inches was to be removed is an "organized system" in the sense that it was intentionally "organized" (formed) into its specific form. The large piece cut off by a torch or bandsaw also represents a greater state of organization than does the same mass of metal in the form of chips.

The less an organized system (such as materials or information) is allowed to disorganize during a production process, the greater is the cybernetic efficiency. The term "cybernetic efficiency" is used, for the science of cybernetics studies various organized systems and draws analogies to similar thermodynamic (heat) systems such as engines. Cybernetics uses analytical procedures similar to that customarily applied to thermodynamics to measure the state of organization or information in any system.

## CAPITAL INVESTMENT

The results per unit effort is usually greatest at the onset of any endeavor. This is the familiar *law of diminishing returns* of the economists. The law applies toward productivity, too. The early dollars invested into production facilities result in the largest incremental increase in productivity so the most backward producers have the most to gain by upgrading their equipment and methods.

In 1940 about $6,000 of capital equipment, such as production machine tools, was invested per industrial production worker in the U.S.A. He produced $1.78 worth of goods per hour with this equipment. By 1950, with tools worth $15,000, the typical U.S.A. production worker produced $3.15 worth of goods per hour. By 1960 an investment of $19,500 in capital equipment was needed to get $3.90 of productivity per man per hour.

Long range estimates are that by 1970 capital equipment worth $28,000 per man will produce $5.44 per hour.

The exact figures quoted here can be challenged, but the trend cannot. As investments at the lower orders of automaticity ($A_1$, $A_2$, and $A_3$ machines) result in greatest productivity per dollar invested, efforts are needed to upgrade the hand production tools, the power hand tools, the semiautomatic machine tools, and the automatic repeat cycle production machines. For greater productivity more and better tools and machines are needed.

Automation comes into the picture not so much because it can reduce the labor content but because it makes possible faster and better work and is more consistent.

The human and sociological aspects of productivity are beyond our scope here. Confining our attention to the historical technical aspects, we see that increases in productivity paced man's rise and the advance of our civilization. Forgetting all about automation for the moment, we are still far from using the most efficient $A_1$ and $A_2$ machines. Furthermore, we are still most prodigal with our use of materials and information. Here is where big pay-offs are possible, in the use of modern, high performance $A_1$, $A_2$, and $A_3$ machines, supported by semi-automatic aids to the operator, as explained in Chapter 5 where pre-automation activities are discussed.

Woollard's Basic Principles of Mass and Flow Production, Chart 3-8, clearly points out what must be done to increase productivity by intensifying production, whether by manual, semi-automatic, or automatic means.

The appendix lists a number of works expounding the views of leading automation thinkers. Many of these books are necessarily philosophical. As *The Anatomy of Automation* treats mainly industrial automation, any serious student of automation and its impact on our present day way of life who is interested in the portends of the future should complement this book with selections taken from the bibliography listed in the appendix.

# Cybernetics and Information Theory

13

## CYBERNETIC CONCEPTS

A new science that has great effect on the theory and practice of automation is *cybernetics*. It concerns itself with communications and control pertaining to living things and societies as well as to machines. Cybernetics, in fact, extends into mathematics, electronics, neurophysiology, anatomy, engineering, and one or two other disciplines. It is a crossroads meeting place where these specialities can exchange viewpoints and ideas.

Many physiological processes depend upon the existence of feedback (self-regulating actions). The heartbeat, oxygen intake, sense of balance, and body temperatures are known to be feedback controlled. Memory, learning, decision making, sight, hearing—all these human faculties have mechanical counterparts.

Chapter 7, "Anatomy of Automation," expands

the functional similarity between corpus automation and corpus man. It shows that the control system functions—sensing, decision, actuation—can be performed by man, by machine, or by both working together.

The subjects treated by cybernetics which are of particular interest to automation are the *theory of messages* and the *theory of control* which is a special interpretation of the theory of messages. Further concepts enveloped by cybernetics are computers and all self-acting devices and systems, including automation.

Figure 13-1. Computor composed music.

The thesis of cybernetics is that society can be understood by studying its messages and the facilities and methods available for communicating them. Prior to the industrial era, almost all messages were man to man. Now, however, messages between man and machine, machine to man, and machine to machine play an ever increasing role.

The tightest definition of cybernetics is: *cybernetics* is the *theory of messages; message* here meaning any organized pattern of information. Cybernetics takes the view that transmitting a mere informational message, "in the declarative mood" as grammarians would say, is not significantly different from transmitting control orders, a command message to a machine, "in the imperative mood." Such a man-machine message constitutes control. Cybernetics attempts to show the best form for such control messages.

Music is also a form of language, subject to cybernetic interpretation and synthesis.

Cybernetics compares various systems, including those of living things, societies and organizations, and machines. Their similarity is not limited to obvious *face* likeness but is based on the similar mathematical representations of the various systems.

Many have noticed the analogies and similarities of diverse systems. However, cybernetics systematically searches them out and shows how living systems resemble mechanical and electric systems. What is more important to the automation worker, cybernetics suggests machines for performing heretofore human functions.

Cybernetics explains that a natural tendency exists for all organized systems to continually lose more and more of their state of organization, to break down, to increase their entropy. *Organized system* refers to any thing that has a form, system, function, or control. Ultimately, all forms of organization, such as men, machines, and society, tend to become more random in behavior and less consistent in their actions until they meet death, breakdown, failure, collapse, or extinction.

## MEN AND MACHINES

*Automation* refers to the state of *organization* which permits work to be done without human intervention. Like all organized states, automation tends toward a less organized condition too, for tools and machines cannot ordinarily improve themselves but can only degenerate through wear and deterioration. The inherent tendency toward degradation of function in automation machines prevents uninterrupted long-range precision operation, unless antideterioration features are included.

A typical nonfeedback machine, one that represents a high state of organization, is an alarm clock. The level of organization of an alarm clock can never exceed the original condition. It can never be better than new. The natural tendency is to develop defects as it wears. The same statements apply to most simple automatic machines, those that do not use feedback.

The lesson to learn from cybernetics that particularly applies to automation is that a natural tendency for the work done by any machine to degrade, to deviate from the desired performance, must be combatted. Both active and passive anti-entropy efforts are possible.

## ENTROPY

The concept of *entropy* constitutes the core of cybernetics. *Entropy* originally refers to a mathematical factor which is a measure of the unavailable heat in a *thermodynamics* system. Cybernetics uses entropy in the sense of being an index of the state of disorder in *any* system. Although cybernetics embraces all organized systems, information systems are singled out for special study.

As an aid to understanding, information systems (such as messages and control signals) are commonly compared to energy systems (such as steam engines). Such comparisons of energy and information systems disclose that information and energy are similar in many ways and that the extent of their similarities has only been approached.

There seems to be much more than a mere superficial analogy here, for the likeness between thermodynamics systems and information systems exists in depth. Information seems to obey the same basic cybernetic laws as does thermodynamics. Information tends to flow and to degrade from a higher state of organization (potential) to a lower state of organization. Just as in the case of heat, an engine is needed to raise low potential information to higher (more organized) potential information.

In the case of mechanics, the engine that raises potential may be a compressor. In an information system, a man, or a computer can raise the potential or information by increasing the state of organization of information.

### Anti-Entropy

Animals, plant life, machines, buildings, and messages are typical organized systems that have a natural tendency to degenerate or decay, to increase their entropy. To create an organized system requires active anti-entropic agents. These anti-entropic agents are inherent in living matter, for as long as they live organisms organize matter for growth and repair of damage.

Biological growth is anti-entropic, for it works against the trend toward disorganization. Other anti-entropic agents are of greater interest to us. Man can be anti-entropic because he can create organization from *pi*. Reducing disorder or correcting an error reduces the entropy, the level of disorder of a system. Some machines can also (to a much lesser extent than can man) reduce disorder and correct errors; they too have anti-entropic agents. These can only be feedback machines, for nonfeedback machines can not be *actively* anti-entropic.

### Stability

In its simplest form, mere stability is anti-entropic, for a system with stability can self-correct a disturbance. The act of disturbing such systems, such as tilting a rocking chair, provides the energy necessary for the corrective action. The concept of *feedback* is a big step forward. It is a form of stability also. Feedback can accept energy from an external source to perform a corrective action.

In a general sense, feedback assumes that a specific condition or performance of a system is normal. As long as the system meets the desired condition, it is equivalent to being in a condition of stability. Any deviation from the normal is analogous to the displacement of a stable mechanical system. The feedback control system, usually a servomechanism, senses the amount and direction of the deviation and corrects the system to reduce the deviation from normal.

Feedback is therefore a *forced* form of stability. The cybernetic concept of *ultrastability* means that a control system can work toward a definite goal. That is, if an attempted corrective action aggravates the disturbance, the mode of corrective action is automatically changed. This is equivalent to learning. An $A_6$ automation device must necessarily have ultrastability.

The points to be made here are that nonliving anti-entropic means do exist, and that mechanical anti-entropic agents, such as feedback, are necessary to the higher orders of automation.

This does not mean that we must rely entirely on active anti-entropic agents. We have been relying mainly on *passive* anti-entropic methods.

All systems, machines for example, exhibit increased variability of performance, for they tend to degrade as time goes on. This cannot be prevented or avoided, but the tendency toward degradation of organization and performance can be greatly reduced so that a machine will continue to perform as desired over a long period of time. By proper design, the rate of deterioration of any system, such as a manufacturing process, can be rendered tolerable or negligible.

Passive anti-entropic measures, such as improved bearings or antibacklash gearing, are good enough for the greater number of systems and processes. But *active* methods of anti-entropy are necessary when requirements are exacting or when long term consistency of performance is needed.

Feedback does much more than reduce the rate of deterioration, by actually improving the performance of a process or system.

## INFORMATION THEORY

Information is the basis of all human activity. Speech, printing, telephone, TV, writing, photography, and machine control all are based on information. However, all forms of transmission result in some loss of meaning or reproduction of the original information.

For example, speech may be misunderstood if not distinct and if word meanings are not in agreement. Copying a photo loses definition. A TV picture is inferior in detail to a studio view, and a radio telephone message is obscured by noise, interference, and transmission losses.

Information theory teaches that the data content of messages can be measured, and that both energy and information must be expended to keep useful information from degrading during use or transmission. Just as an energy engine can raise the potential of energy at the expense of energy, so can an information engine (man, computer, or sorting device) raise the potential (usefulness) of information.

How many simultaneous messages can be sent on a transatlantic cable? What frequency band is necessary to transmit color TV? What forms of machine language can be used to direct an automatic profiling machine? These are representative questions in the field of information theory. Information theory is vital to automation because automatic measurements, punched cards, magnetic tapes, patterns, followers, machine programs, and computer control are all information handling functions.

Information has been found to be equivalent to negative entropy, and it can be evaluated (measured) numerically. Whereas *entropy* is an index of unavailability or obscurity, *information* indicates identifiable data. A short message may contain much information if the signals are a part of a large body of codes.

Numerically, the information content of a message is represented by the number of *bits* in its coded form. A signal transmitting a message is always subjected to unwanted changes termed *noise*. Noise also contains bits, though of an unwanted sort. The information on a phonograph record for example is less true than the original recorded sounds. Entropy is increased (fidelity lost) by both recording and by reproduction.

Any channel for transmitting information, as in a machine control system, can only handle a limited number of bits (basic information units) per second, including both the message (the wanted information) and the noise (the unwanted information). Absolutely noise-free and errorless transmission of messages is not possible. Therefore, some redundancy is necessary in a message to compensate for noise.

This has meant little to the automatic control designer thus far, who has found simple two-state signals (yes-no, go-no go) adequate for most controls in common use. However, fully automated processes increasingly make use of multiple sources of information and have a number of possible responses to these signals. Information theory shows how to best handle data from instructions, sensors, and computers to indicators or machine actuators.

## INFORMATION POTENTIAL

The refrigerator is an example of a thermodynamic process. Expending an adequate amount of energy (electric power) raises a smaller amount of heat energy up to a higher level. That is, we can transfer heat from within the box to the outside, opposite to natural flow. In a similar way, the state of organization of information can be raised to a higher level. A mass of data (census figures) can be worked on to result in an *answer* (population trends) which represents higher potential information.

In both cases, entropy (state of disorganization) decreased. In the thermal case, the heat from within the refrigerator was caused to flow uphill into the surrounding atmosphere. In the cybernetic case, dealing with information, the information represented by a mass of data was further concentrated.

As an example of increasing information potential, consider the levels of information for the manufacture of a special eccentric cam.

1. The part begins as a designer's concept. In this form, the information is almost useless unless the designer himself is a machinist who could form the part.
2. The designer makes a drawing of the part with all dimensions. This is a useful form of information but is not coded in machine language.
3. Next, this drawing is translated into a tabulated number code which represents the key points and changes of the cutting tool path.
4. As the machine control system cannot read typewritten numbers, the information is punched into paper tapes which automatically control the cutters through the actuators.

Each time the necessary information is translated to a higher level of usefulness, errors tend to be introduced. Considerable effort and know-how (energy and information) are required, to raise the information potential making the information usable.

## CYBERNETIC EFFICIENCY

Efficiency is a basic goal of all of our activities. The engineer considers efficiency to be the ratio of the *output* of a machine or process or system compared to the *input*. He knows the impossibility of achieving 100 per cent in a practical system, but he works incessantly to keep efficiency at a high level. The designer is concerned with thermodynamic (mechanical) efficiency pertaining to the transfer and conversion of energy.

Business management seeks higher efficiencies of accomplishment, such as more orders filled per day, or more truck miles per dollar. Business does not care about energy efficiency alone; the dollar is the basic unit by which efficiencies are determined.

However, few concern themselves with cybernetic efficiency. That is, few consider the ratio of information used to accomplish some useful work, compared to the theoretical minimum information necessary to do the job. Whereas thermodynamic efficiency requires the reduction of energy losses (usually heat or electricity), cybernetic efficiency requires the reduction of information losses.

Before automation, the cost of information handling to do a job was ignored. Everyone knew from common sense that all jobs required information, but there was nothing that could be done to evaluate it. So empirical and instinctive methods had to be relied on until the advent of the feedback machines.

Nowadays, the machine and control system designers know that refined information is expensive and they try not to waste it. However, because they do not yet have straightforward numerical methods for evaluating the information content at each stage of a process, they may needlessly transform information or permit it to degrade.

The time approaches when process designers must be able to evaluate the dollar costs of the information bound into products as well as the cost of the energy. For some time now, molten aluminum has been shipped directly from the refiners to the engine casting foundry. Hot steel billets are transported many miles from the blast furnace and converter to the rolling mill by placing them in railroad gondola cars and covering them with granular insulation. In both cases, great pains are taken to conserve heat, as heat losses are recognized as dollar losses.

When we know how to determine information content as readily as we can compute heat content and measure temperature, we will know how much information is wasted by scrambling parts in bulk containers between manufacturing stations. This will bring about greater appreciation for transporting parts in an oriented manner by use of kinetic package parts magazines which

Cybernetics machine tool?

contain items in the exact array required to facilitate their introduction into the manufacturing process, such as for the automatic assembly of electronic equipment.

Being able to compute information content does not mean that lengthy analytical methods will be obligatory. Most design decision will continue to be made according to experience, but the critical few decisions effecting the design of process information handling can then be done rigorously. Being aware of cybernetic information efficiency and choosing to ignore it if unimportant is quite different from not being aware of it at all.

## UNSOLVED CYBERNETIC PROBLEMS

Ultimately, *cybernetics* should teach us how to handle information efficiency in design considerations just as *thermodynamics* has done in energy matters. Cybernetics will probably further seek out similarities among the body of information theory and the thermodynamic theory to create the practical formulas that engineers need for a facile calculation of information efficiency. Because cybernetics sets the pace for automation by pointing out similarities between man and machine, many automation problems can be interpreted as being cybernetics problems. Many automation improvements however await cybernetics guidance.

What is learning? What is judgment? What is reasoning? What is intuition? What is imagination? In what ways are the brain and a computer similar? What are the parallels between biological control systems and machine control systems? These are some of the questions cybernetics tries to answer.

It has been pointed out that some organic and machine systems have the unique property of reversing the entropic process. Instead of succumbing to the natural tendency toward disorganization (breakdown), they can for an appreciable time actually improve their local state or organization. Living things can repair damage. Men can organize. Machines and animals make use of feedback.

Some characteristics indicate that evolution is also strongly anti-entropic in nature. Evolution can take simple forms and in the course of time adapt them to forms uniquely adapted for specific environments. We know that concepts and machines evolve as well as living things. Evolution implies obsolescence. Just as machines rendered obsolete the use of men for some types of work, even more so machines obsolete other machines. Jet aircraft have obsoleted propeller aircraft (for long distance trips) just as automation systems have to some extent obsoleted individually operated machines.

The law of the jungle seems to exist in the factory, too. If we had a theory on the evolutionary process as it applies to machines, we could evaluate the obsolescence hazards of our new automation schemes and lessen some of the risks and losses that have been encountered by automation pioneers. This is also a job for cybernetics.

## MACHINES THAT LEARN

What is a machine that learns? Mere submission to memory is not enough. To a large extent, learning consists of putting information into a memory and developing the ability to recognize connections. Two approaches to the mechanization of learning can be derived from the theory of association and the theory of the conditioned reflex. Some work has already been done with the mechanization of learning, but much still remains for the cyberneticists to do before we can have a practical automation machine that learns or has true inductive reasoning.

Indispensable to modern automatic control and to machines that learn are effective memory storage systems. Memory storage systems of large capacity do exist. Also existing are memory storage systems that can insert and recover information rapidly. However, as a rule, high speed recovery of information and high storage capacity are not compatible. Automation needs improved methods for storage and rapid recall of information. This is a job for the information theory corner of cybernetics.

A further area of cybernetic work is the application of feedback and control theory to the analysis and control of organizations, societies, and economic systems. This could smooth out booms and busts in business and prosperity. Here, too, some work has been done with economic analogs. Servomechanism theory has been applied to complex management decisions with some encouraging results.

This may not at first seem directly to concern the practice of automation, but automation does not exist in a vacuum. An industrial system embraces all pertinent aspects, management, men, money, machines, materials, and markets. Likewise, the automation system is a component of an over-all economic system. The control engineers, working to the directions of cybernetic revelations, have shown that their skills contain powerful methods for handling systems of extreme complexity, those that contain multiple feedback loops. It is only reasonable that similar techniques be used to analyze economic systems which show remarkable similarity to complex control systems. The mathematics of the control engineer and use of models and computers and analogs are of value here.

# Automation Trends

## 14

What are the frontiers of automation today? Which way is automation headed? What automation work is needed right now? What automation promises to pay off the best? The answers to these questions are of vital interest to all automation workers and potential automation workers. We have seen how automation evolved from hand tools to power tools to semi-automatic machines to fully automatic systems and automatic decision making.

Automation now appears to be developing along three lines. Efforts concentrated here should be most timely and most likely to meet acceptance:

1. The trend toward greater use of automatic instrumentation
2. The trend toward the use of computing elements for control
3. The trend toward greater compactness and versatility

Industrial automation is a blend of energy converting devices (mechanisms) and information devices (control elements). For production, energy has already been completely mechanized. Future developments in the use of energy can only consist of improvements in existing mechanical systems. They will be made more compact and will make even more use of standard elements. Electric power also seems destined to be used even more widely, almost replacing mechanical, hydraulic, and pneumatic systems except for special applications. Even automobiles may ultimately be powered by electricity, either from turbine generators or fuel cells.

The level of information that can be mechanized is not limited. Thus, radical developments can be expected here. A result will be that automatic control will enable machines to attain greater versatility and to be more adaptable to rapid changeover.

The fact that an entire process can be performed automatically has been well proved. In most cases, however, an automatic process can only accept a very narrow range of materials and can only produce products having a limited range of configurations. As more use is made of flexible *external* control instead of permanent *internal* control, processes can be made to use a variety of input materials and to produce a wider range of products. The point here is that automatic control broadens the functional capabilities of machines so that compact machines that are equivalent to versatile factories can be designed.

Special machines often develop into standard models; in such cases, design and development costs can be spread out on a broader base, greatly reducing the cost per machine. This has already been proved in the form of standardized machine loading devices, TV assembly machines, and unit heads for in-line transfer machines.

Examples of standardized specific product machines follow, in addition to examples of high versatility machines and transportable and mobile factories.

Full automaticity has its place, but partial automatic methods involving the automatic instrumentation of pertinent process factors are also valuable in their own right. Man-machine systems which depend heavily on automatic instrumentation (semi-automation) are often the most logical choice. Automatic instrumentation is also necessary for advanced orders of automaticity such as for feedback control $A_4$ and mentor control $A_5$.

Automatic measurements can be processed by mentors to accomplish automatic statistical quality control, an application where considerable work can be expected. Automatic dull tool detection is another growing application for partial automaticity.

Today's automation worker would therefore do well to watch carefully the use of automatic instrumentation and measurement techniques, the use of mentors to aid instrumentation and control, and the development of compact, high versatility machines.

## MOBILE FACTORIES

A large number of products are unique in the sense that only one manufacturer produces that exact product, but this is not always the case. Many products are staples, the "rice and potatoes" of manufacturing, rather than unique products.

Manufactured staples are items that are widely used, produced in a number of locations, and which change very little from year to year. General examples are containers, hardware, building materials, pipe products, electrical connectors, and so on. Because there is a consistently large demand for such items, their production has been highly mechanized for years. As a result of transportation costs, each country or locality generally manufactures most of the staple products it requires.

Chart 14-1 lists typical products which can be made anywhere in the world by special machines or processes. Such machines bring the factory to the raw material or to the user, thus reducing transportation.

The idea of such machines is not new and versions of them have existed for years. The wire nail machine, the ice cream machine, and the

Chart 14-1. Mobile Factories

| PRODUCTS | MATERIALS | CAPABILITIES |
|---|---|---|
| WOVEN WIRE PRODUCTS | Metal wire, plastics "wire" | Wire cloth, screening, fence wire, wire rope, metal lath. |
| WIRE HARDWARE PRODUCTS | Steel wire and rod | Nails, staples, rivets, pins, dowels, hooks, springs. |
| SHINGLES AND TILES | Asphalt, concrete, asbestos fiber, pigments. | Cement asbestos shingles for walls and roofs, asphalt floor tiles. |
| REINFORCED CONCRETE PRODUCTS | Wire, cement, aggregates | Pressure pipe, planks, panels, utility and fence posts, RR ties. Including prestressed beams, domes, poles. |
| CAST BUILDING PRODUCTS | Cement, aggregate, gypsum, solid industrial wastes (cinders, ashes), pigments, waste fibers. | Blocks, bricks, building tiles, drainage tilepipe, fireproof gypsum partition blocks. |
| CONSTRUCTION BOARDS | Gypsum, concrete, wood waste, fiber waste, paper | Lath board, interior wall board, sub-flooring, exterior sheathing, concrete form boards, fireproof cement-asbestos board. |
| CLAY PRODUCTS | Clay, glazes, pigments | Structural and face brick, roof tiles, drainage, tile pipe. |
| UNIVERSAL PACKAGING MACHINE | Strip and tubular plastics film | Slicing, weighing, marking, wrapping and sealing in transparent plastic. |
| DRY-CELL BATTERIES | Zinc sheet, carbon rods, steel sheet, plastic sheet chemicals | All sizes of flashlight and dry-cell and electronic power batteries. |
| SHEET METAL FABRICATION | Sheet metal coils or sheet | Cans, boxes, trays, buckets, kitchenware. |
| PLASTICS PRODUCTS | Plastics sheet or granules. | Jars, bottles, housewares. |
| PORTLAND CEMENT | Clay, limestone, chalk. | Any cement for concrete. |
| PLYWOOD MANUFACTURING | Logs, glue | All plywood grades and thicknesses. |
| PIPE AND TUBE FITTING MACHINE | Pipe or tubing | Threaded nipples, end assemblies, pipe and tubing fittings |
| OPTICAL MANUFACTURING MACHINE | Optical glass, plastics for frames | Eye glass lenses and frames. |

envelope making machine can be purchased from a catalog, ready-made.

The new trend of special machinery is to incorporate high versatility along with specific product capability, making such machines more usable to a wider market. Here are examples.

## WIRE HARDWARE PRODUCTS

Every locality requires wire products, such as screening and fence wire; but small countries and isolated regions can't use enough of any single item to justify building a specialized fac-tory. All the screening and types of wire fencing required added together amount to a significant total. A solution to supplying low demand is to develop a single machine that can produce any type of wire cloth or fence wire needed, utilizing easy changeover accessories. The automation innovation displayed by such a machine is the emphasis on high versatility, not on mere mecha-nization of a narrowly restricted process.

Whether a single machine or an integrated process of several stages, a standardized ready-made factory to do the job can be built. Trans-portability can be simplified by building the equipment in the form of railroad cars or truck trailers. A number of products, especially those that are large, heavy, and rather simple, are produced in regional manufacturing establishments. Most major population centers have local plants that produce cement block and panels, sewer pipe, clay drain tiles, wood products, and steel tanks. The trend to locate manufacturing plants near the point where the goods are needed to reduce transportation is sure to continue. This tendency has been limited only by the small range of products that lend themselves to being produced locally in this manner. The availability of a pre-engineered, packaged automatic factory to produce a product currently purchased from a distant source is certain to increase the number of small specialty manufacturers near large cities. This offers a big market to alert machinery manufacturers.

Specific purpose machines that can be used for only one or two items are being made obsolete by machines that produce a wide range of products and which can be rapidly converted from one item to another.

Items 1 and 2 on Chart 14-1 make products from wire. Many nonindustrial countries could supply most of their needs by merely buying each of the two machines. This would set up a requirement for wire drawing machines, ultimately leading to the need for a small steel mill.

The advantage is that there would be an immediate local outlet for the output of each stage of advancement. Therefore, the transition to industrialization would be smooth, whereas starting industrialization from the raw material end demands that all stages of manufacturing be developed concurrently. This is impossible to accomplish without great economic shock.

### SHINGLE AND TILE MACHINE

The machine that can produce exterior building siding, shingles, and floor tiles of various sizes, colors, and patterns, will be in demand. This machine will be capable of converting basic materials as asphalt, asbestos fibers, and portland cement into useful building materials. The shingle and tile machine could provide an unlimited number of colors and size variations

without warehouse expense. Undoubtedly, the products would be automatically wrapped and stacked on pallets for lift truck handling. Such a machine could also be built on a railroad car if desired.

### CONCRETE PRODUCTS

The machine for producing reinforced concrete products is actually a fair-sized factory, a combination of several machines. Now that the advantages of prestressed concrete are more widely appreciated, the demand for both prestressed and conventionally reinforced concrete items is increasing. In many cases, concrete lasts longer than steel and is cheaper than wood. Furthermore, many parts of the world have neither steel nor timber.

Close kin to the reinforced concrete product plant are the well-known concrete block, brick, and tile machines. If concrete product and block machines are available, along with a cement plant, almost any country in the world can erect buildings with semi-skilled labor.

These are not new machines but are being further improved for more automatic operation and increased versatility. The latest concrete block machines available are far superior to those of the 1950's, which were a big improvement over earlier machines.

### CONSTRUCTION BOARD

Construction uses many types of board for interior partitions, subfloors, roofs, exterior sheathing, and for plaster lath. These are commonly made from gypsum covered with paper concrete reinforced with asbestos or glass fibers, or cellulose materials such as cane, wood chips, straw, peanut shells, rice hulls, and so on. Most countries in the world have materials that can be used to make up building board. Ideally, a building board machine would be able to use a wide variety of materials to manufacture lath, wall panels, roofing, and exterior sheathing.

### CLAY PRODUCTS

Factories for manufacturing clay brick and ceramic tiles are usually fairly large. The products require lengthy baking and are made up in batches. Automation can be introduced here to make up a great variety of styles and patterns of items (such as tile or brick faces). Such items could be vitrified quickly by high power radio frequency induction and dielectric heating so that the production could be made on a continuous flow basis. An automatized products factory mounted on several railroad cars could do the entire job, from clay to finished products.

### METAL TUBE AND PIPE FITTING

The metal tube and pipe machine would obviate the need for most pipe fittings. By a process of metal gathering, extrusion, cold forming, drawing, upsetting, and forging, fittings can be made up from the parent metal of the pipe or tube. If separate fittings are needed, they can also be made up from pipe stock.

A machine of this type eliminates the need for huge stocks of pipe fittings. A typical application for such a machine would be a shipyard or large building construction site where fittings and connectors could be made to order on the spot. The Elmes machine produces copper tube solder fittings, even tees and elbows, on a mass production basis. The high pressure cold extrusion technique is also suitable for ferrous metals. The finished part is produced from seamless tubing without chips or waste.

### OPTICAL MANUFACTURING

A large part of the world's population must wear eyeglasses, which are expensive by present production methods. A machine can be designed to accept dial settings of the optometrist's prescription and turn out the proper lenses already mounted in a frame if desired. Perhaps a person could have his finished glasses fitted within one hour after his eye examination.

The high versatility machines discussed here are not far removed from reality. Every one of them either exists in prototype or represents the synthesis of several existing functional machines. In no case does it require designs that would seriously tax today's control engineering and machine design skills.

Such machines are attractive for the United States, for every locality can then supply itself with the staple manufactured goods, as already is the practice to a limited extent. However, such high versatility specific product machines are especially valuable for underdeveloped areas abroad that are far from factories but have raw materials. Among such locations are the Middle East, South America, Alaska, and Africa.

## LIMITED PURPOSE CONTROL COMPUTERS

Industrial machines and processes are becoming more comprehensive, their control systems automatically performing a number of functions formerly depending on man. To accomplish this increased scope of self-action, industrial process control systems must become cognizant of a greater number of the variables that affect the result of their operation. A machine becomes "aware" of prevailing conditions by means of sensors (such as a transducer) which report temperature, pressure, velocity, mass, dimension, liquid level, and so forth.

Automatic control often depends upon the cognition of the output of the process, *feedback*. The simplest case is one in which a feedback signal is used to adjust *one* process variable, such as controlling temperature by regulating steam input, by means of a standardized process controller.

Sometimes more than one variable condition must be regulated to achieve the desired output result. Some variable conditions cannot be regulated directly but must be compensated for by varying other factors. It is also possible to have a control system which does *not* rely on feedback signals at all but which measures several conditions of the process or raw material which are then balanced to achieve the desired output.

In every case of automatic control with more than one sensed or controlled variable (even without a feedback signal), some sort of device is needed to keep the variables in the proper relationship to achieve the desired output. This is a job for a computer, for a mathematical equation is the most direct way by which the relationship of several process variables can be established. Although huge general purpose computers are

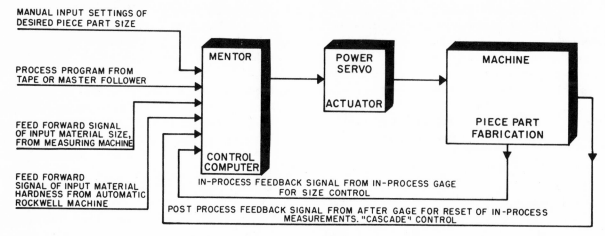

Figure 14-2.  Mentor control of fabricating machine.

sometimes used, *mentors,* small limited purpose computers, are suitable for automatic control problems of limited scope. With multiple inputs to the control system, automatic processes (and machines) must use computing process controllers (mentors) to resolve and reconcile the many interrelated input variables and constants.

### AUTOMATIC COGNITION, PRESET, AND CONTROL

The concept of feedback, the control of a process on the basis of its performance, has been useful in the development of systems for controlling both electronic and physical processes. The term is not appropriate when referring to the automatic sensing of process variables that are *not* the result of process performance alone.

A control system that performs the activity of *cognition* is capable of accepting feedback information concerning the performance (output) of the process. A control system that features cognition can *also* accept programmed input data, instructions, and can sense variations in the materials or environment which may affect the process. Process control systems must stress automatic cognition, for only by cognizance of the *multiple* information inputs (preprocess, inprocess, and postprocess) that a machine can automatically perform the manifold operations that must otherwise be done manually.

The control function of a "sophisticated" industrial manufacturing machine is shown in

Fig. 14-2, *Mentor Control of a Fabricating Machine.* Control is based on the automatic cognition of process factors obtained from sensors and input settings. The mentor receives open-loop signals (not self-correcting) from manual settings and from the process program; feedback signals from a postprocess gage; and preset signals from sensors that measure preprocess conditions such as hardness and piece-part size. The mentor reconciles these input signals algebraically, then controls the machine process according to a logical (sequence) procedure. In this way, the machine process anticipates the effect of preprocess conditions by automatic preset and by manual controls. It responds to postprocess conditions by zone control aftergaging. It may respond to inprocess conditions by short loop immediate feedback, similar to the cascade control of continuous processes.

### MENTORS

One reason for using computing devices for control purposes is that a machine can only work a routine. Seemingly nonroutine production processes can be handled as routines once they are defined by one or more equations. A mathematical equation expressing the interrelationship of the variables that affect a process renders the process a routine, capable of automatic control. This is a powerful technique, similar to Operations Research.

Most computers used for control purposes are not of the general purpose analog differential analyzer or of the digital computer type. Computer elements used mainly for control or instrumentation are usually of the specially designed fixed purpose type, making use of readily available standardized servomechanisms, discriminators, summing amplifiers, modulators, and so on. Such computers used for industrial machine control purposes are usually limited purpose, electromechanical, analog, equation solvers, similar to the computing elements of radar controls, fire control systems, flight simulators, and other electromechanical military electronics devices. These special purpose analog techniques are useful for industrial control too, although digital computers may also be used, as is the case with numerical control.

Because computers used for control purposes are not general purpose machines, the question arises what to call them. The term *mentor* is suggested.

One use for a mentor is to decode input data from numerical form into analog control signals. Another mentor application is to control several machines in unison so their output parts will assemble with the desired fit.

The interpolation of input data is still another application for a mentor. Any taped program can handle but a limited number of discrete points. Tool position (a milling cutter for example) between these points must be interpolated. Straight line proportional interpolation is adequate for straight work but falls down badly when curved surfaces are programmed. A machine tool control system that gives straight line motion between specific data points can be readily developed. However, such a simple machine control system burdens the information programmer because the number of specific data points that must be called out to define a curve increases sharply as the required tolerance on the accuracy of the contour is tightened.

To reduce the required machine information input data to a minimum, parabolic (curved) interpolation is used. This technique works out well for curved surfaces such as cams and is satisfactory for straight line proportionalizing also.

Parabolic interpolation between programmed points is successfully accomplished by a mentor which computes a smooth curve between three successive reference points so that a program controlled machine tool can proceed along the desired contour of the part.

Chart 14-3 lists possible ways by which mentors can be used to aid in the control of manufacturing machines and processes.

## MENTORS FOR THE PROCESS INDUSTRIES

We are all familiar with closed-loop negative feedback control, whereby process factors (such as temperature or rate of flow) are automatically controlled on the basis of actual process performance. Familiar too, is ordinary open-loop control, whereby process factors (such as electroplating current) are set on a predetermined basis and do not take into account process performance. Less familiar is automatic preset, which is neither negative feedback nor open-loop.

In the case of preset, control automatically adjusts a process to accommodate changing preprocess input conditions, not postprocess (output) conditions. Examples of preset and feedback (sometimes called *cascade control*) are shown in Figures 14-4 and 14-5.

### Mentor Controlled Process

Raw chemical material (crude oil, for example) must usually be heated to a specific temperature before passing to a process station such as a fractioning column. By conventional thermostat action, a temperature recording *controller* positions the valve operator so that fuel flow increases when temperature drops and vice versa.

If the amount of material flowing through the heater was constant, this mode of control might suffice. If, however, the flow of raw material varies over a wide range, such simple control is not adequate. One reason is that wide range control is not compatible with precision. Even more important, feedback control is postprocess, *after-the-fact*. Hence, with normal process lags overshooting would result because of the time delay between fuel throttling and the corresponding output temperature change.

Chart 14-3.  Mentors for Fabrication

| APPLICATION | EXPLANATION | EXAMPLES |
|---|---|---|
| AVERAGING | Computes average of machine output as index of center-line-of-machine-performance, $\bar{X}$, by averaging or integrating.  Necessary because most machine and process outputs (fabrication or processing) exhibit "normal" statistical variability. | A time integration of a continuous product, such as wire, paper, chemicals, etc.; an arithmetical averaging of the individual variates in a sample, such as piece-part sizes; averaging a number of measurements; averaging test data, such as color, hardness, and surface finish. |
| AUTOMATIC QUALITY CONTROL | In addition to computing $\bar{X}$ as above, computes and records the standard deviation $\sigma$ the index of variability.  This tells if a process is "under control," as $\pm 3 \sigma$ is the natural capability of the machine. $\bar{X}$ is called bar X. $\sigma$ is called sigma. | Provides $\bar{X}$ indicator and recording for the machine setter and machine feedback; provides $\sigma$ indicator and recording for "out of control" alarm and machine capability indication; provides SQC certification record strips to accompany product, in accordance with government specifications. |
| DATA PROCESSING AND INTERPOLATION | Codes and decodes (by computation) control data to and from "machine language"; converts (by computation) data from analogue to digital, digital to analogue; changes scale factors; linearizes; proportionizes.  Interpolates machine position between data points by linear proportionalizing, or by quadratic parabolic method. | Converts digital programmed data to analogue signals for machine control; digitizes analogue transducer data for digital control system; converts weights and measures data from Metric to English; provides trigonometric or logarithmic values of control signals from "built-in" tables; compensates for changed volume due to changed pressure and temperatures; computes "interest" and "percents."<br>Numerical machine control systems.  Analog control system, which uses a multiturn transformer having parabolic turn ratios to develop parabolic curvature interpolation. |
| MEASUREMENT AND INSPECTION | Determines measurements from reference points; performs trigonometric measurement computations; computes functions of measurements; discriminates-compares-segregates-classifies; senses system malfunction from "normal" sporadic error. | Compares positions to a reference to determine measurements; performs gearing calculations; solves gage lab calculations for checking cams, screws, tapers, etc.; averages measurements and determines least-square value of a number of measurements.  Computes areas, volumes, CG, etc., from measurements for inspection; automatic taper, runout, eccentricity evaluation. |
| MACHINING AND MACHINABILITY | Solves machining equations for compensation of tool diameter and tangential velocity.  Solves machinability equations to maintain correct speeds and feeds for optimum tool life and workpiece condition, even when working conditions are continually changing. | Aircraft skin-mill profile machine control, turbine blade milling, automatic lathe, cutting speed control, machinability computer.  Band saw cutting speed selector; automatic metal spinning rpm control. |
| DULL TOOL DETECTION | Integrates relative amount of energy (or function of energy such as torque or thrust) consumed by a tool in performing its work, as an index of tool condition. | Senses tool (drill) thrust or torque; senses motor drive current; averages value of load signal for greater accuracy and freedom from spurious indications; integrates total energy passing through cutting tool; computes normal tool flank temperature, as functions of cutting speed and load. |
| "OR" (OPERATION RESEARCH) CONTROL | Controls a machine or process by continuous solution of equations describing the interrelationships of the various process factors, similar to "operations research," alias the "scientific method." | Equations are written on a variational basis (not a priori) that relate the factors of a process.  Introduction of analogues of the independent variables, factors, and constants permits continual solution for the dependent variables which are the machine (or process) control signals.  Uses single equations, or simultaneous equations. |

Chart 14-3.  Mentors for Fabrication (Continued)

| APPLICATION | EXPLANATION | EXAMPLES |
|---|---|---|
| NEGATIVE ERROR FEEDBACK | Compensates for load induced error by sensing load; solving for anticipated error from empirical load-error relationship; introduces negative of anticipated error into process feedback loop, to accomplish effectively zero load induced positional error. | Power synchro receiver is used to position tool, as per synchro transmitter at master part. Tool load causes synchro positional error. Load is sensed (from synchro current) and solved for equivalent error. Negative of error is introduced into synchro transmission line, via synchro differential. Same technique applicable to compensate rate and acceleration and voltage error. |
| DYNAMIC MACHINE CONTROL | Continually solves differential equations of forces and motions, reconciling their instantaneous values and basic control on such dynamic transient conditions rather than on steady state conditions. | High order servomechanism controls provide such dynamic control. Instantaneous braking and acceleration control; compensation for stretch and deflection, error integration control; anticipation control; dynamic balancing. |
| POSITIONING AND INDEXING | Position determined by "navigational" computations, as well as by scaling; solving dynamic equations for obtaining absolute instantaneous position from rates and accelerations. | Positioning machine members and workpiece by "dead reckoning," by inertial navigation techniques; indexing to any position by controlling dynamics of moving parts and transfer mechanisms, without need of stops and detents; positioning by controlled catapulting, (a fire control practice). |
| SELECTIVE ASSEMBLY | Computes assembly dimensions from measurements of individual piece-part sizes, as basis for automatic selective assembly which rejects less piece parts, and results in a "tighter" assembly. | Determines size of assembly by evaluation of $\bar{X}$ and $\sigma$ of the piece parts; grouped machine operation, whereby several machines in a fabricating process compensate for each other's deficiencies; evaluates "best" assembly from parts in memory storage. |

The fuel required is a function of the raw material flow. Consequently, automatic preset can perform the *gross* fuel flow settings in accordance with raw material flow, via a feed forward control path. Concurrently, conventional feedback accomplishes the *precise* trimming up control function.

Another way of looking at preset is that the preprocess feed flow measurement *biases* the flow controller setting, *anticipating* the action of the feedback control. Though this mode of control is widely employed, it has not usually been recognized that a mentor is involved. A number of process controllers used by the flow industries include mentor computing characteristics for accomplishing algebraic and arithmetic operation on control signals.

PROCESS VARIABLES AND AUTOMATIC PROGRAMS

Process operation, whether controlled by electronics or servomechanisms, depends on a number of variables and constants. Factors that can be predicted such as sequence and mode of operation can be set up beforehand in the form of a program.

Setting up a program (instructions) to follow is the most common technique for rendering processes and machines automatic. However, the exact values of many of the factors known to affect a process are not always predictable, for many process factors (such as temperature, pressure, and environment) are interdependent. In the case of nonautomatic control, an operator performs the function of cognition. He makes extemporaneous settings of the machine in accordance with his sensing (observations and awareness) of the immediate prevailing conditions, as noted from instrument dial readings. In the case of automatic control, the sensing, cognition, and control must of course be done without the intervention of a man. An automatic control function similar to feedback may be necessary

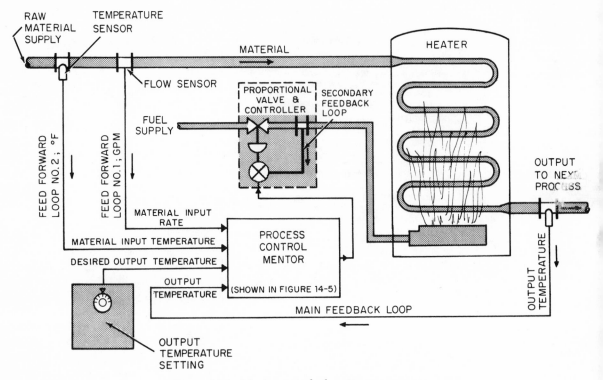

Figure 14-4. Mentor control of continuous process.

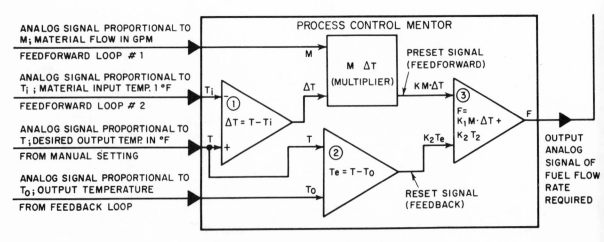

Figure 14-5. Process control mentor.

Chart 14-6. Mentors for Processing

| APPLICATION | EXPLANATION | EXAMPLES |
|---|---|---|
| DATA INTERPRETATION | Signals from process sensors are not always direct indications of the physical quality being measured. Thus, scale factors and calibration curves must be applied to linearize data, or data must be converted to a more usable form. | Introducing scale factors; calibration curves; corrections due to pressure-temperature changes. "Identity" operations; converting analogue to digital to pulse, to time modulation and vice versa; makes analogue signals from sensing transducers compatible to digital machine control; and makes digital taped signals compatible to analogue machine control. |
| DERIVED MEASUREMENTS AND TESTS | Some measurements, such as "length, time, mass" are fundamental. They can be measured directly. Other measurements, such as "density, elasticity, efficiency," must be derived from fundamental measurements, in accordance with a mathematical relationship (formula or equation). | Direct readings of "derived" concepts, such as entropy, air density, efficiency, humidity, dew point, specific gravity, index of refraction, viscosity. Slide rule, nomograph or alignment chart, calculations can be readily accomplished by a mentor, such as Mach numbers and module of compressibility, resilience, elasticity, rigidity, etc. |
| MIXING BLENDING PROPORTIONING | In many processes, the materials involved, whether reagents, fuels, catalysts, or principal agents, must be combined or used according to a specific recipe or ratio. The proportions of the mix or blend may be a linear or nonlinear function of the fluctuating materials used, and product cost. Proportioning is a role for a mentor computer. | Ratios of fuels, reagents, chemicals, and catalysts in a process. Mixes of grains and minerals; manures and minerals; fillers, granules and accelerator; water, aggregate and cement; base and trace metals. To develop feeds, fertilizers, plastics, concrete, or alloys, that have specific properties according to formulae. |
| AVERAGING INTEGRATING WEIGHING | Average value of a process measurement is commonly more valuable than is the instantaneous value. Averaging of continuous process "dimensions" is usually performed by a time integration. Time integrations of rate measurements give quantity. Integration of force at a given point in a conveyor system is a function of the weight (of the materials) that passed over the conveyor. | Determining the centerline of process performance, the "machine-mean" (process-mean) $\bar{X}$, as shown in Chart 14-8, is done by averaging and integrating; monitoring process energy consumed; weighing solids, liquids or gases, as they pass a point in a process. Also, planimeters and totalizers of process functions (such as yield or by-product). |
| MAXIMIZING MINIMIZING | It is commonly necessary that a process factor (dependent variable) be held to a maximum value, or to a minimum value, by manipulation (control) of the process factors that are more or less independent variables. In simple cases, this consists merely of adjusting the controlled variables, so that the "slope" of output to input is zero. | Maximizing product output from a catalyst reaction; maximizing temperature in a boiler by controlling air-fuel ratio; maximizing range of vehicle (truck, aircraft, ship, tractor, locomotive) by throttle control and fuel injection control; maximizing oil pumped from an old oil field by pumping cycle control; controlling binary columns by maximizing temperature difference from two sensors several "plates" apart. |
| OPTIMIZING | Optimizing frequently consists of working to a zero slope maxima-minima relationship, as above. Some optimization however, consists of working to a specific slope of the input-output curve, as would occur on a logarithmic curve, or on the "knee" of a saturable process. | Process control to specific pH value; optimum steam flow to tank temperature; optimum lbs steam to lbs product; magnetizing current to specific B-H curve slope; induction heating for optimum energy consummation. |
| CONTROL OF ELECTRIC PROCESSES | Most processes make use of electricity to some extent mainly for heat, energy, or for instrumentation. Many of these electric currents can be best controlled on the basis of computer action. Of special interest here are the "continuous" processes that make direct use of electric current as the active agent of the process. The amount of electric current desirable can be interpreted to be a mathematical function of a number of process factors. | Current used for electrolytic plating, anodizing, etching, (milling), as a function of area, materials, electrolyte, resistance, pH, and temperature; electric erosion arc machining as function of metal, thickness, temperature, diameter, etc; electric welding current control as function of metal, thickness, strength desired, electrodes, pressure, etc., including automatic setting of parameters on basis of automatic strip-tear-test. |

Chart 14-6.  Mentors for Processing (Continued)

| APPLICATION | EXPLANATION | EXAMPLES |
|---|---|---|
| SIMULATION | For reasons of safety and economy it is at times desirable to train process-operating personnel both routine operation and emergency procedures, prior to completion of the equipment installation, or else it is not permissible to tie-up operational equipment for training purposes, or it is desired to practice "impossible" conditions, such as fire, explosion, or atomic "scram" condition. | Nuclear reactor simulator; process trainer; "economic analog" simulator of business, operational flight trainers, dynamic analog of chemical plant process, in fast time or slow time; "synthetic training situation" mock-ups. Equipment for the practice of emergency conditions, such as fire and explosion. |

to avoid the need for continuous manual presetting of the process in compliance with changing input conditions.

Adjustments, manual or automatic, depend on the cognition of input conditions which are subject to variation. Following is a simplified mathematical development of an equation that describes the type of control desirable for an automatic process. Figures 14-4 and 14-5 illustrate a case where preprocess, inprocess, and postprocess variables must be considered, and where control by a mentor is necessary for the automatic cognition of several control variables. The algebra that describes the necessary control action is typical of many control systems, both for the fabrication processes and for the continuous processing industries. The object here is to demonstrate mentor control *function* to exemplify the mentor control method. Consequently, no explanation is offered of the equipment by which this can be accomplished.

### MENTOR ALGEBRA

The rate of fuel flow required for a typical continuous process is proportional to the product of the rate of flow of the material being heated times the temperature rise required. This can be represented by the equation

$$F = k_1 M \cdot \Delta T \qquad (1)$$

where $F$ is the fuel flow in pounds/minute and $M$ is the material flow in gallons per minute.

$\Delta T$ is the temperature rise required, equivalent to $T - T_i$, where $T$ is the desired output temperature and $T_i$ is the input temperature.

The proportionality factor, compensating for

the specific heat of the material, the thermal efficiency of the process, and the calorific value of the fuel, is $k_1$. Knowing the process factors $k_1$, $M$, and $\Delta T$, the correct rate of fuel flow for proper temperature rise can be readily determined.

However, control on this basis is open-loop. Any process variations (such as quality of the fuel, or combustion efficiency) would lead to an error. Control of process error requires conventional feedback regulation of output temperature by a process temperature controller.

A more realistic equation than Equation (1) above, is Equation (2)

$$F = k_1 M \cdot \Delta T + k_2 T_e \qquad (2)$$

where $T_e$ = Output temperature error, equivalent to $T - T_o$, $T$ being the desired output temperature and $T_o$ being the actual temperature.

The first term of Equation (2) contains the preprocess (feed forward) *preset* factor and proportionality constant $k_1$. The second term contains the postprocess (feedback) *reset* factor and its proportionality constant $k_2$. The control system is an example of automatic *cognition*, whereby error feedback is superimposed on computer function open-loop control. The mentor reconciles *forwardloop* and *feedback loop*, as well as manually set input information.

### SUPERVISORY CONTROL

There are two ways by which a mentor can serve a process control system. One can be termed the *supervisory* mode. This means that the direct regulation of the process factors is left to conventional industrial controllers acting with their associated sensor "transmitters" and "opera-

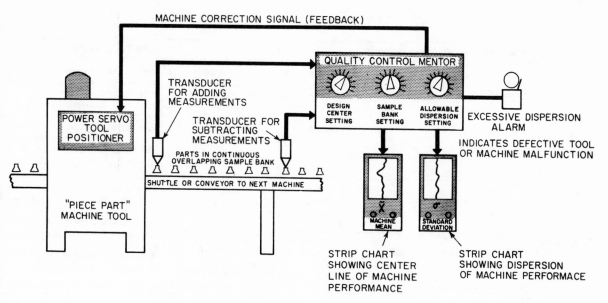

Figure 14-7. Feedback control by quality control mentor.

tor" valves. In this mode, the mentor merely readjusts the controllers. Mentor action here is similar to that of supervisory personnel. Should a failure occur in the computer, process control can readily revert to manual adjustment.

MASTER CONTROL

The second method can be termed the *master* mode of computer control. In this case, the mentor replaces the usual process controllers and acts directly on the valves or other actuators. The computer must not fail or automatic process control ceases entirely.

The master mentor control system uses somewhat less apparatus so it may have a lower first cost when equipping a new plant. However, this is not necessarily so when adapting an existing process to mentor control. Because of the extra safeguard of retaining industrial controllers for subordinate control, the trend for the future seems to be the supervisory mode rather than the master form of control by mentors and large scale computers.

Chart 14-6 discusses mentors functionally. The details of the equipment are not mentioned, for mentors (and signals) can be electromechanical,

pneumatic, electronic, or fully mechanical, depending on specific conditions.

Sensors, actuators, amplifiers, and analog units are usually commercially available, so design of a mentor for a specific control problem does not ordinarily require the design of components.

AUTOMATIC INSTRUMENTATION

MENTORS APPLIED TO MEASUREMENTS

One reason why mentors are needed on the industrial scene is to average discontinuous data as required for control purposes and to indicate the standard deviation of samples from the production being controlled.

Because most processes and machines exhibit a normal variation of output, the average of their performance is necessary for feedback control purposes. When the product is continuous, as in the process industries, a time integration of the output gives the average which is the centerline of machine (or process) performance, also called $\overline{X}$, the machine-mean. If the product consists of pieceparts, $\overline{X}$ is the arithmetical average.

Whether it is a continuous process or piece-

Chart 14-8.   Mentors Applied to Measurements

| MATHEMATICAL FUNCTION   EQUATIONS | | | DISCUSSION | CONTROL APPLICATIONS |
|---|---|---|---|---|
| 1.   **X**<br><br>called variable, or<br>dimension, or<br>measurement | | $X = kx$ | X is the measurement, the controlled dimension of the work being produced by the machine. Lower case x is the analogue of X, a voltage or shaft rotation proportional to X. The scale factor k, is the ratio $X/x$. | 1. Direct (uncompensated) in-process or post-process feedback control.<br>2. Automatic inspection and segregation.<br>3. Determining <u>range,</u> an indication of machine dispersion. The range of a sample lot, R, equals $X_{max} - X_{min}$ |
| 2a.   $\overline{X}$ | of discrete piece part dimensions | $\overline{X} = \dfrac{\Sigma X}{n}$ | Discrete dimensions: (piece-part fabrication), $\overline{X}$ is the average, the sum of n measurements X divided by n. | 1. Feedback control based on centerline of machine performance.<br>2. Statistical Quality Control.<br>3. Reference for computing standard deviation.<br>4. Actuating a "drift alarm." |
| 2b. called "bar-X" or <u>mean</u> | of continuous dimensions | $\overline{X} = \int_{t_0}^{t} X dt$ | Continuous dimensions: (processing, or continuous fabrication) $\overline{X}$ is the average, the time integral of the variable X divided by time t. | |
| 3.   $X^2$<br><br>square | | $X^2$ | Discrete dimensions: $X^2$ is the square of the measurement of an individual piece part.<br>Continuous dimensions: $X^2$ is the square of a point value of the continuous measurement. | 1. Comparing variable to a standard where the change of X is insufficient for reliable discrimination.<br>2. Computing the <u>mean-square,</u> $\overline{X^2}$ |
| 4a.   $\overline{X^2}$<br>mean square | of discrete piece-part dimensions | $\overline{X^2} = \dfrac{\Sigma X^2}{n}$ | Discrete dimensions: $\overline{X^2}$ is the average of the individual $X^2$ values. | 1. Computing root-mean-square of measurements, $X_{rms}$<br>2. Accentuating variations, to facilitate sensitive discriminations. |
| 4b. | of continuous dimensions | $\overline{X^2} = \int_{t_0}^{t} X^2 dt$ | Continuous dimensions: $X^2$ is the average of the square of the point values of X. | |
| 5.   $X_{rms}$<br><br>root-mean-square | | $X_{rms} = \sqrt{\overline{X^2}}$ | The root-mean-square is the "center-of-gravity" of the measurements, discrete or continuous. It is the square root of the average of the squares. | Used to compute $\sigma$ (sigma). The standard deviation $\overline{X}$ and $\sigma$ are the two prime criteria for Statistical Quality Control. |

part fabrication, an index of the centerline of process performance $\overline{X}$ is required for high precision feedback control. Not as indispensable but most valuable too, is the *standard deviation, $\sigma$,* an index of process variability. This is the root-mean-square deviation of the process with reference to the mean $\overline{X}$. Computation for $\sigma$ follows naturally from computation of the machine-mean.

Having $\overline{X}$ and $\sigma$ permits basic statistical quality control techniques to be applied. When the capability of the machine or process (ordinarily considered to equal $\pm 3\ \sigma$) is exceeded, the process is *out of control.*

The mathematics for automatic quality control are not difficult. $\overline{X}$ is the arithmetical average or time integration of the variable being measured. $X_{rms}$ is the root-mean-square value of the measurements. Then $\sigma^2 = X^2_{rms} - \overline{X}^2$, which is analogous to a simple right-triangle relationship readily solved by a mentor. Figure 14-7 shows piece-part fabrication with an auto-quality control mentor control computer.

Chart 14-8 discusses basic mathematical functions of measurements which can be readily solved by mentors.

Figure 14-9 shows how the statistical quality

Chart 14-8. Mentors Applied to Measurements (Continued)

| MATHEMATICAL FUNCTIONS    EQUATIONS | DISCUSSION | CONTROL APPLICATIONS |
|---|---|---|
| 6a. $\sigma$ (sigma) standard deviation $$\sigma = \sqrt{\frac{\Sigma (X - \bar{X})^2}{n}}$$ $$= \sqrt{\frac{\Sigma}{n}(X^2 - 2\bar{X}X + \bar{X}^2)}$$ | The standard deviation measures the dispersion of the measurements about the mean. Sigma is equal to the rms value of the dispersion of the measurements relative to the mean. This is a common form of the basic statistical equation as used for Statistical Quality Control. | 1. Automatic Statistical Quality Control. (Auto-QC)  2. Determining machine capability (a machine's natural tolerance)  3. Actuation of an "excessive-dispersion" alarm. |
| 6b. $$= \sqrt{\bar{X}^2 - 2\bar{X}\bar{X} + \bar{X}^2}$$ $$\sigma = \sqrt{\bar{X}^2 - \bar{X}^2}$$ | An equivalent form of the same equation (somewhat easier to use) for determining sigma. It shows that the standard deviation equals the square root of the average of the squares minus the square of the average. | In a right triangle $c^2 = a^2 + b^2$; or $b^2 = c^2 - a^2$  $X_{rms}$ is analagous to c  $\bar{X}$ is analagous to a  $\sigma$ is analagous to b  so $\sigma^2 = (X_{rms})^2 - \bar{X}^2$ |
| 6c. $$\sigma = \sqrt{(X_{rms})^2 - \bar{X}^2}$$ | An equivalent form of the same equation arranged to show the right-triangle relationships of the terms, analogous to Pythagoras' Theorem. (see box →) | |
| 6d. | The right-triangle relationships facilitate solution by simple computing devices, such as a synchro-resolver. (see box →) | |
| 7a. S capability $$S = \pm 3\sigma$$ | The "natural tolerance" (capability) of a machine equals $\pm 3\sigma$ The accumulated tolerance of several parts in an assembly is the root-sum-square of the natural tolerance of the assembled piece-parts. | 1. Determining tolerance of an assembly from piece parts, prior to assembly.  2. Group control of machine stations in an automation process.  3. For automatic selective assembly. |
| 7b. $S_{rss}$ (root-sum-square) Assembly tolerance $$S_{rss} = \sqrt{\Sigma S^2}$$ | | |

control terms $\bar{X}$ and $\sigma$ are developed from measurements of the workpiece signalled by sensors at the machine. Each mathematical operation is shown by a separate block. A sequencing controller is needed to add and subtract measurements from the sample bank.

ADVANTAGES OF AUTOMATIC-QUALITY CONTROL

Advantages of manual statistical quality control are retained when machines and manufacturing lines are instrumented for automatic quality control. Some additional features and advantages attained with auto-quality control are worth noting. One is the aid given to operators in properly setting manually controlled machines. A visual Machine-Mean Indicator is a great aid to a machine operator, telling him

when to make an adjustment and when to leave well enough alone. The indicator responds to changes in performance more quickly than does a hand-plotted control chart.

Firms that produce piece parts for sale to other manufactures or to the government must sometimes provide certification attesting that inspection and quality control procedures were followed in accordance with a particular specification. With 100 per cent automatic quality control, charts from automatic recording instruments could accompany each lot of parts that is shipped to facilitate receiving inspection or customers' acceptance.

Built-in automatic quality control could also prove to be a boon to machine tool builders, as proof of the stability and reliability of a ma-

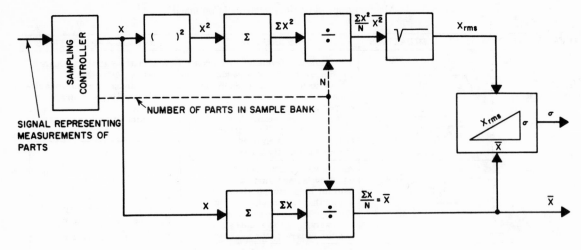

Figure 14-9. Mathematical block diagram of Q-C mentor.

chine. Each machine has a capability, depending on construction, design, and wear. A machine's freedom from drift, as shown by a $\overline{X}$ indicator and recorder, would prove the machine's inherent stability.

Another advantage in using auto-quality control is that it facilitates feedback control of piece-part manufacture. Although self-correcting machines are possible (by zone control) which do not rely on the automatic calculation of machine mean, auto-quality control makes possible consistently greater precision work from the *same* machine than is possible by any other mode of feedback control.

The following list describes quality control when routine activities are performed by automatic electromechanical devices.

1. A sample of parts is selected by an automatic programmer
2. The individual dimensions are measured by automatically sequenced sensors (automatic measurements)
3. Quality control formulas are solved automatically (by means of mentors) to determine the *machine-mean* (arithmetical average) and the *standard deviation* (index of dispersion) of the measurements
4. The machine-mean $(\overline{X})$ and the standard deviation $(\sigma)$ are both automatically plotted on charts

5. The machine-mean is continuously compared to the desired value machine output to determine machine drift
6. The machine compensates for drift automatically (feedback control) by means of power servo actuators
7. Excessive or erratic dispersion (observed from charts) indicates machine malfunction and sets off an alarm

## AUTOMATIC DEFECTIVE TOOL DETECTION

*Downtime* is a big factor in the success of an automated installation. Minimizing the shutdowns necessary to change worn and defective tools is a major concern of the production man. Spotting dull and defective tools before they fail has presented a continuing problem for industry.

Though the problem is cutting tools in general, only *drills* are discussed here, as the ubiquitous drill is the most frequently encountered tool in automation. The techniques suitable for automatic defective drill detection are transferable to other cutting tools, such as mills, routers, taps, and hobs.

### THE DEFECTIVE TOOL PROBLEM

The practice of group-changing all of the tools in a machine or line according to a strict schedule, or changing according to operation counts, helps reduce machine downtime caused by

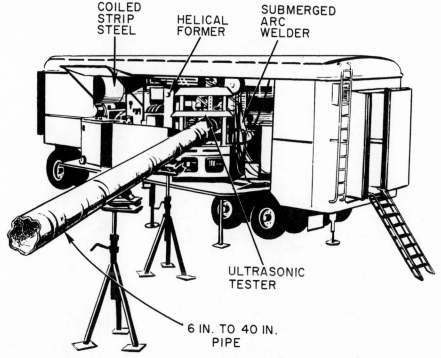

COILED STRIP STEEL

HELICAL FORMER

SUBMERGED ARC WELDER

ULTRASONIC TESTER

6 IN. TO 40 IN. PIPE

Figure 14-10.  Mobile pipe factory.

abrupt and unexpected tool failures. The most frequent tool replacement schedule however does not entirely eliminate *all* tool failures.

### WHEN IS A DRILL DULL?

Before discussing automatic methods of detecting dull drills, the standard methods for determining when a drill is dull should be explained. Considerable study, going back into the 1800's, has been made of twist drill life. These all point to the following indications of drill dullness:

1. The drill squeals
2. The thrust (force) required for constant feed drilling increases
3. A wear land (flatspot) develops at the cutting edge
4. Drive power requirements (watts input) increases up to 30 per cent over normal
5. A *sudden* increase in torque and thrust when drilling steel

6. A *continuous* increase in torque and thrust when drilling cast iron
7. Temperature at the cutting edge increases

As long as an operator handles a drilling machine, the squeal or wear land methods can be used. The operator of course has no way of knowing the torque, thrust, or horsepower demanded.

Replacement of the operator by automation brings about the dull tool problem. Lacking the operator's senses (including common sense), the machine continues to use drills regardless of condition. It is therefore desirable to instrument the machine to detect drill dullness. Neither the squeal nor wear-land are amenable to instrumentation by an electrical transducer. However, thrust, torque, and power input can be readily measured by electrical methods.

Experiments have shown that with the speed held constant, the thrust required to drill a hole

221

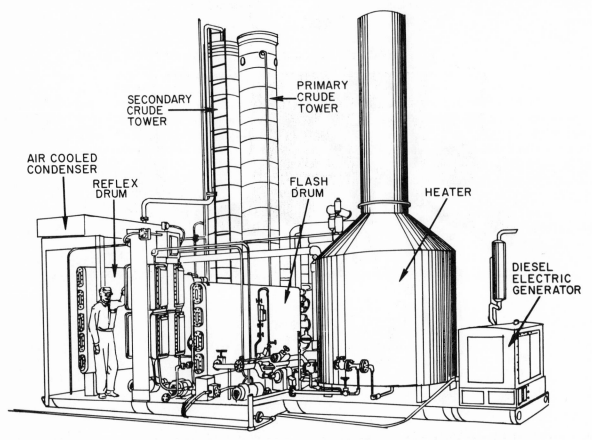

Figure 14-11. Transportable oil refinery.

at constant feed rate increases as the tool becomes dull. It is therefore apparent that monitoring the thrust exerted in forcing a drill into the material at a constant rate of feed can be used to indicate dullness. If the force required is too high, the drill is approaching failure due to dullness. Thrust value that is too low suggests that the drill is broken, missing, or that the work piece is not in position.

Measuring drill thrust does not require complex automatic control or instrumentation. Strain gage transducers in the form of large flat washers can be placed at the thrust bearing of each drill spindle.

There is no need to consider the specfic circuitry here but to note that the signal from the strain gage sensor at each drill spindle could be readily amplified and made to actuate an indicator or alarm. An electrical controller is needed to perform timing, switching, sequencing, and regulation functions, but these are all quite conventionally accomplished.

Dullness detection is not the only form of tool sensing desirable. A more simple method consists of a feeler-type switch that checks to see if the drill is broken or probes to see if the hole is clear. An induction coil arrangement is sometimes used to sense whether or not the drill is broken without coming in contact with the drill. The use of a strain gage thrust sensing dull tool detector accomplishes the drill surveillance task as well, obviating the need for separate feelers and proximity sensors.

By automatically weeding out the early tool

failures, the tool changing schedule can be prolonged, resulting in considerable savings of money and production time.

There is, however, a statistical point when it is economically sound to replace all or nearly all of the tools in a machine. Regardless of how long the tools last, eventually they must be replaced. In plain words, automatic dull tool detection does not replace the probability curve, but, in effect, negates the early failure probabilities that are the bane of machine designers and production engineers alike.

Automatic detection need not encompass every tool on a 500-operation transfer machine. Judgment and experience are needed to instrument the critical few, not the trivial many.

### Drill Replacement Policy

1. Determine the cost of replacing a single drill. Include tool setting labor, tool grinding labor, tool cost per grinding, and production loss.

2. Determine the cost of replacing all of the drills in the machine at once, include labor, tool cost, and production loss.

3. Calculate (or determine from production-records) how many individual drill replacements can be made more economically than replacing all of the drills in the machine.

4. Replace drills individually, on the basis of a dull tool detector, until the next scheduled general drill change.

5. When all drills are being replaced en masse, select the best ones (those showing least wear, by wear-land inspection), for use as spot replacement prior to the next scheduled drill replacement.

6. Schedule general drill change for off-shift maintenance, whenever possible, to reduce production time loss.

Chart 15-1. Systems Engineering Definitions

| TERM | DEFINITION | EXAMPLES | DISCUSSION |
|---|---|---|---|
| SYSTEMS ENGINEERING | Pertains to the design of complex systems comprised of many separate components and elements rather than to the design of individual pieces of equipment. Coordinates all development and design activities of a complex system and is responsible for satisfactory system performance. | Modern systems commonly include computer devices and automatic control techniques such as feedback. Typical systems are highway traffic control, airline ticket reservation, automatic manufacturing of complex assembled products, programmed education and training, medical instrumentation of entire hospital, automatic agriculture. | Systems engineering must be wholly objective. It can flourish only in an atmosphere of complete independence of approach, unfettered by encumbrances, such as sales quotas or predilection for particular pieces of proprietary equipment. "The whole is greater than a sum of the parts" in a system. |
| SYSTEMS ENGINEER | The person or persons engaged in the design and development of a system in its entirety. Commonly the system creator and innovator; the technical entrepreneur. | Also known as project engineer consulting engineer and principal engineer. Analogous to the architect in construction field, interne in medical field, producer in motion picture field, and publisher in publishing field. | He must always represent the system users or buyers interest alone, so he may not be connected to vendors or manufactures of the equipment. He is a generalist rather than a specialist, to embrace the entire problem on a broad front. |
| CONSULTING ENGINEER | A professional engineer who provides specific services, such as counsel, reports, investigations, designs, etc., on a fee or retainer basis, rather than for a salary. | Not necessarily an individual; may be a research and development organization, university laboratory, operations research group, or project task force, or, a small, independent firm, authoritative in their specialty. Does not include "job shop" establishments, doing routine drafting-board design work feasibility study. | Whereas a consultant is ordinarily an "outsider," in large organizations staff groups are sometimes set up to act as "captive" consultants to operating divisions of the organization. The unbiased consultant will recommend a minimum of equipment to do the job, possibly recommending against adoption of the system. |
| APPLICATIONS ENGINEER | A person engaged primarily in adapting existing products to suit the system in which they are to function, and who makes corrections and modifications in the field. | Service engineer, field engineer, electrical engineer, electromechanical engineer. The job is to modify more or less standard items, such as synchros, motors, computers, recorders, hydraulic pumps, conveyors, to meet the needs of a system. | The sales engineer may or may not also assume the role of applications engineer. The applications engineer's work is important, for systems can't exist without adequate equipment. However, his work precludes system-wide responsibility. |
| SALES ENGINEER | A person who uses his engineering competence and training primarily to promote sale of products and who also may interpret the characteristics of the product to the potential user. | Manufacturers' representatives or field men, selling anything from hardware and cabinets to complete computers and automatic manufacturing processes. | The sales engineer is needed to introduce technical equipment. As he is customarily paid according to sales, his recommendations tend to favor complex and costly devices. |
| VENDOR | The person or organization that manufacturers or sells components and equipment for use in systems. | Manufacturers of electronic devices, indicators, transducer pick-offs, machine tools, data processing units, simulators, transistors. | The vendor contributes applications engineering service covering the components and machines he supplies to the system. If his goods are to be fairly priced, he cannot provide "free" systems engineering. |

Chart 15-1. Systems Engineering Definitions (Continued)

| TERM | DEFINITION | EXAMPLES | DISCUSSION |
|---|---|---|---|
| CLIENT | The person or organization for whom a consultant performs his services. He is not a customer, for he receives only services, not goods from his consultant. | The user of the system, such as a city, insurance company, manufacturer, airline, railroad, or public utility. | The client ordinarily compensates a consultant on a fee basis not be a salary or percentage of costs or of profits basis, and engages him on a temporary assignment. |
| EMPLOYER | A form of client, who obtains a system engineer's exclusive services. | Large organizations are likely to employ staff systems engineers. | The employer compensates on a salary basis and usually offers a permanent assignment. |

# APPENDIX 2

Portions of the following previously published articles, written by Amber & Amber, are contained in the *Anatomy of Automation*. These articles were copyrighted by the magazine publishers in the year in which they appeared. Since publication of the articles, *Electrical Manufacturing* has been renamed *Electrotechnology* and is now published by Conover-Mast.

1. "Orders and Degrees of Automaticity," *Electrical Manufacturing* (New York: Gage Publishing Co., Jan. 1955). A method for classifying automation.

2. "Analog Computers for Machine Control, Part I," *Electrical Manufacturing* (New York: Gage Publishing Co., Aug. 1955). The basic principles and devices for computer controls.

3. "Analog Computers for Machine Control, Part II," *Electrical Manufacturing* (New York: Gage Publishing Co., Oct. 1955). How devices are made to compute.

4. "Automatic Dull Drill Detection," *Automation* (Penton, Cleveland: Publishing Co., Oct. 1955). How to detect dull drills automatically.

5. "Developments in Automatic Quality Control," *Tool and Manufacturing Engineer* (Detroit: American Institute of Tool and Manufacturing Engineers, Jan. 1956). How Automatic Quality Control can be obtained by means of small $\overline{X}$ and $\sigma$ computers.

6. "Automation vs. Automatization," *Automatic Control* (New York: Reinhold Publishing Co., Feb., 1956). Which term is preferred?

7. "QC Computers for Machine Control, Part I," *Electrical Manufacturing* (New York: Gage Publishing Co., July 1956). How automatic feedback control of industrial machines depends on Quality Control concepts $\overline{X}$ and $\sigma$.

8. "QC Computers for Machine Control, Part II," *Electrical Manufacturing* (New York: Gage Publishing Co., Aug. 1956). Design of QC Computers for the control of continuous processes and piece-part manufacturing machines.

9. "A Yardstick for Automation," *American Machinist* (New York: McGraw-Hill Publishing Co., Aug. 13, 1956). How to measure automation.

10. "Au-to-ma-tion," *Research and Engineering* (New York: Relya Publishing Co., Feb. 1957). Levels of automaticity.

11. "A Yardstick for Automation," *Instruments and Automation* (now called *Instruments and Control Systems*) (Pittsburgh: Instruments Publishing Co., April 1957). 10 Orders of Automaticity, from hand tools to science fiction.

12. "Measuring Automation," *Society of Automotive Engineers Journal*, SAE (New York: Society of Automotive Engineers, July 1957). Grading automation into ten orders.

13. "The Machine Designer, A Man and a Task," *Product Engineering* (New York: McGraw-Hill Book Company, Inc., Nov. 4, 1957). What, precisely, is machine design? Who does it and how?

14. "Anatomy of Automation," *Electrical Manufacturing* (New York: Gage Publishing Co., Jan. and Feb. 1958). Comprehensive article showing structure of automation, citing definitions and examples of automation terms.

15. "Computers for Production," *Production Handbook*, Section 16 (New York: Ronald Press Co., 1958). Electronic Computers as an aid to Production.

16. "Routine Means Machine," *Process Control & Automation* (London: Colliery Guardian Co. Ltd., Jan. 1958). A method of approach to the problem of when to apply automation.

17. "Applying Machine Control Computers," *Automatic Control,* (New York: Reinhold Publishing Co., March 1958). Use of a mentor (control computer) to reconcile preprocess, postprocess and inprocess conditions.

18. "Automatic Quality Control Computers and Other Machine Control Computers," *Computers and Automation* (Waltham, Mass.: Berkeley Enterprises, Inc., April 1958).

19. "Special Purpose Computers in the Control of Continuous Processes," *Automatic Control* (New York: Reinhold Publishing Co., May 1957). Examples.

20. "Proposed Standards for the Practice of Systems Engineering," *Instruments and Automation* (Pittsburgh: Instruments Publishing Co., May 1958).

21. "Controls—Internal and External," *Process Control & Automation* (London: Colliery Guardian Co. Ltd., May 1958). Automation external control has flexibility. Automaticity by internal control is fixed.

22. "How to Understand Automatic Control," Part I, *American Machinist* (New York: McGraw-Hill Publishing Co., Sept. 22, 1958). From ideas to signals.

23. "Special Purpose Computers Applied to Quality Control," *Automatic Control* (New York: Reinhold Publishing Co., Oct. 1958). Computer control of automatically measured dimensions.

24. "How to Understand Automatic Control," Part II, *American Machinist* (New York: McGraw-Hill Publishing Co., Oct. 6, 1958). From signals to servos to systems.

25. "Operations Research for Computer Control," *Institute of Radio Engineers Transactions on Automatic Control* (New York: IRE, Dec. 1958). Industrial applications of computer control, aided by OR.

26. "How Much Automation?" *Production* (Birmingham, Mich.: Bramson Publishing Co., Dec. 1959). Two manufacturers solve a comparable painting problem by automatic and manual methods.

27. "Super Mass Production." *Production* (Birmingham, Mich.: Bramson Publishing Co., Jan. 1960). How simple electrical counters and running meters in office of screw machine department monitor production.

28. "More Functions for a Single Part." *Product Engineering* (New York: McGraw-Hill Publishing Co., July 10, 1961). The proven technique of designing components to do several jobs simultaneously.

APPENDIX 3

Selected Bibliography of books on Automation, Production, and Cybernetics.

The following is not a survey of all of the books on automation in print, but a list of the books recommended for the reasons stated.

*A. Automation applied to Business and Industry*

1. *Automation,* HMSO (London: Department of Scientific and Industrial Research, 1956), 106 pp. Intended to be a guide for company executives. Fifteen automation workers discuss the basic concepts, approaches, experiences, on automation.

2. *Power to Produce, The Yearbook of Agriculture, 1960* (Washington: U.S. Government Printing Office, 1960). 480 pp. Discusses all aspects of the new highly mechanized agriculture, including automation, systems engineering, and special machines.

3. *Keeping Pace with Automation* (New York: American Management Association, Special Report No. 7, 1956). A practical guide for industrial executives, containing articles by 15 leading automation workers.

4. Amber, George H., and Paul S., *Production Handbook,* Sec. 16, 2nd Ed., "Electronic-Computers" (New York: Ronald Press Co., 1958). Covers the use of analog and digital computers as an aid to production.

5. Bailey, S. B., *Automation in North America* (London: HMSO, Overseas Technical Reports. No. 3, 1958), 66 pp. A report on visits to industrial, commercial, and research establishments in the U.S.A. and Canada.

6. Bright, James R., *Automation and Management* (Cambridge, Mass.: Harvard Business School, 1958), 270 pp. An authoritative explanation of the nature of automatic manufacturing, citing actual case histories and covering the nonengineering critical areas pertaining to sales, labor, and management.

7. Eary, Donald F., and Gerald E. Johnson, *Process Engineering* (Englewood Cliffs, N.J.: Prentice-Hall, 1962). Provides fundamental principles for developing a manufacturing plan. Establishes relationship between product design and process engineering, from part print to a commercially acceptable product.

8. Electronic Industries Association, *Automation Systems* (New York: Interscience Publishers).

9. Grabbe, Eugene M., editor, *Automation in Business and Industry* (New York: John Wiley & Sons, 1957), 611 pp. Lecture series in print of twenty-one contributors, each covering his specialty. Ranges from fundamentals to the future of automation, including computers, automatic control, manufacturing automation, and economics.

10. Hoos, Ida R., *Automation in the Office* (New York: Public Affairs Press, 1961).

11. Fairbanks, R. W., *Successful Office Automation* (Englewood Cliffs. N.J.: Prentice-Hall, Inc., 1956). Applications and technique of using automatic business machines and data processing equipment.

12. Hugh-Jones, E. M., editor, *The Push Button World* (Norman, Okla.: University of Oklahoma Press, 1956), 158 pp. Seven contributors discuss various aspects of automation for production and administration.

13. Hugh-Jones, E. M., editor, *Automation in Theory and Practice* (Oxford, 1956). The British version of *The Push Button World*. Either book will do.

14. Hurley, G. P., *Automating the Manufacturing Process* (New York: Reinhold, 1959). Concentrates on the mechanical aspects of automation.

15. June, Stephen A., and six co-authors, *The Automatic Factory—A Critical Examination* (Pittsburgh: Instruments Publishing Co., 1955), 81 pp. A quick look and explanation of the first wave of automatic production.

16. Levin, Howard S., *Office Work and Automation* (New York: Wiley, 1956), 203 pp.

17. Lossievskii, V. L., editor, *Automation of Production Processes* (New York: Pergamon Press, 1960). Translated from Russian.

18. Oates, J. A., *Automation in Production Engineering* (London: George Newnes, Ltd., 1958), 326 pp. A practical guide to automatic machines and automatic fabrication and measurements for both mass production and job-shop use. Excellent photographs illustrating pertinent details.

19. Rusinoff, S. E., *Automation in Practice* (Chicago: American Technical Society, 1957), 226 pp. A simplified explanation of industrial automation processes. Good illustrations.

20. Woollard, Frank G., *Principles of Mass and Flow Production* (London: Iliffe Books, Ltd., 1954), 195 pp. The classic on flow and mass production, establishing and detailing 18 basic principles. Includes transfer machines, the automatic factory, and human relations. Real how-to-do-it, by an expert.

*B. General, Social and Economic Aspects*

1. Booth, Andrew D., *Progress in Automation, V. 1* (New York: Academic Press, 1960; London: Butterworth & Co., 1960). Essays on automatic equipment.

2. *Impact of Automation* (Washington: U.S. Bureau of Labor Statistics, 1960), 114 pp. Twenty articles on technological change. Bulletin No. 1287.

3. *Mechanics Through the Ages* (Wheaton, Ill.: Hitchcock Publishing Co., 1953), 64 pp. A picture book of facts taken from the history of manufacturing.

4. Bramson, Roy T., *Highlights in the History of American Mass Production* (Birmingham, Mich.: Bramson Publishing Co., 1945), 144 pp. Covers period from 1730 Connecticut tinware production, to WW II.

5. Buckingham, W. S., *Automation, Its Impact on Business and People* (New York: Harper, 1961). Automation's fundamental principles, history, and social-economic implications. Written by a management man for laymen.

6. Burlingame, Roger, *Machines that Built America* (New York: Harcourt, Brace & Co., 1953), 166 pp. Pre-automation era production in the U.S.A. From automatic flour mill to automotive mass production. Easy reading.

7. Crossman, Edward Robert, *Automation and Skill* (London: HMSO, 1960), 59 pp.

8. Diebold, John, *Automation: Its Impact on Business and Labor* (Washington, D.C.: National Planning Association, Pamphlet No. 1061, 1959), 62 pp. Automation's pioneer voice of 1952, Diebold, discusses today's automation problems and suggests approaches to solving them.

9. Dreher, Carl, *Automation: What It Is, How It Works, Who Can Use It* (London: Victor Gollancz, Ltd., 1958), 128 pp. Amusing insight on a serious subject.

10. Einzig, P., *The Economic Consequences of Automation* (New York: W. W. Norton & Co., Inc.), 252 pp. Does far more than merely discuss the economic consequences, treating philosophical and sociological aspects as well. Discusses all non-technical aspects of automation.

11. Jacobson, H. B., and J. S. Roucek, editors, *Automation and Society* (New York: Philosophical Library, 1959), 553 pp. A nontechnical "current history" by 32 contributors covering the concept, application, and management of industrial automation, and its effect on society. Includes 37 short automation case histories.

12. Lilley, S., *Automation and Social Progress* (London: Lawrence & Wishart, 1957), 224 pp. Analyzes the trends in automation and shows why much more manpower should be put into services, and the advantages of intensified "services" to complement automatic production.

13. Macmillan, R. H., *Automation, Friend or Foe?* (London: Cambridge University Press, 1956), 100 pp. A nontechnical easy explanation by an expert in automatic control, automatic production, and computers.

14. Mann, Floyd C., and L. Richard Hoffmann, *Automation and the Worker* (New York: Holt, Rinehart & Winston, 1960), 272 pp. A study of social change in power plants when management decided to introduce automation.

15. May, J., *The Real Book About Robots and Thinking Machines* (New York: Garden City Publishers, 1961; Toronto: Doubleday). A book for juveniles on automatic machines and computers.

16. Pyke, Magnus, *Automation: Its Purpose and Future* (London: Hutchinson's Scientific and Technical Publications, 1956), 191 pp. A broad-scope nontechnical discussion of automatic methods from the British view.

17. Ross, Frank Xavier, *Automation, Servant to Man* (New York: Lothrop, Lee & Shepard, 1958), 212 pp. Another presentation of automation for juveniles.

18. Walker, Charles R., *Toward the Automatic Factory* (New Haven: Yale University Press, 1957). (London: Oxford University Press), 232 pp. A case study of men and machines at a modern steel hot mill.

## C. Productivity Charts

The following "study charts," essentially a new form of book, pertain to tools and productivity. They are available from the Wilkie Brothers Foundation, Des Plaines, Illinois.

1. "Productivity—Creates All Economic Growth," 44 x 22 inch, 1961. Depicts and explains nine areas of productivity including manufacturing, power generation, transportation, financing, and commerce. Includes instruction sheet on how to use this fact-filled guide to economics.

2. "This is the Industrial Revolution," 22 x 34 inch, 1959. Depicts and explains the principal inventions, discoveries, and concepts which collectively brought about our present day high level of productivity. Classified into ten logical groups.

3. "Civilization Through Tools," 36 x 17 inch, 1956. Illustrates by drawings and photographs the evolution of tools up to modern machine tools and presents the formula by which living standards may be improved for all for universal prosperity and permanent world peace through tools.

4. "Why Living Improves," 22 x 17 inch, 1951. Makes the point that natural resources, plus human mental effort, multiplied by power tools, produces man's material welfare.

## D. Philosophy of Automation and Cybernetics

1. Capek, Karel, *R. U. R.—Rossum's Universal Robots* (London: Oxford University Press, 1923), 102 pp. A play in three acts of the love life of $A_9$ machines and their revolt against their masters.

2. Chorafas, Dimitris N., *Factory Automation* (Washington: Catholic University of America, School of Engineering and Architecture, 1958), 144 pp. Dittographed lecture notes covering men, machines, automatic devices, and the function of the systems engineer. Includes dynamics of real time control, computation, and training for automation. Graduate level.

3. Diebold, John, *Automation, the Advent of the Automatic Factory* (New York: Van Nostrand, 1952), 181 pp. The pioneer automation book, first to use *automation* in the title. Still valid today.

4. George, Frank Honywill, *Automation, Cybernetics, and Society* (London: Leonard-Hill, 1958), 283 pp. Presents the point of view of the social scientist and logician. Philosophical and controversial.

5. Guilband, G. T. (V. MacKay, translator) *What Is Cybernetics?* (London: William Heinemann, Ltd., 1959), 126 pp. Attempts to portray cybernetics as a whole, as simply as the subject permits.

6. Hatfield, H. Stafford, *Automaton, Or The Future of the Mechanical Man* (London: Kegan Paul, Trench, Taubner & Co., Ltd., and New York: E. P. Dutton & Co., 1928), 100 pp. Dr. Hatfield explains most of the concepts we now collectively term *automation* in this little book, using less than 17,000 words of nontechnical language. The reader will recognize *industrial automation, cybernetics, feedback control, computer control, servomechanisms, punched cards, tape recording,* and *programmed machine tools.* He also explains the *autopilot, inertial navigation, radar, automatic letter sorting,* and *automatic traffic control.* Out of print, but a copy is available on loan from Amber & Amber.

7. Sluckin, W., *Minds and Machines* (Penguin Books, 1954), 223 pp. A nonmathematical treatment of cybernetics, including computers, control, and mental functions. Philosophical, not industrial.

8. Soule, George Henry, *Time for Living* (New York: Viking Press, 1955), 184 pp. Discusses automation's effect on U.S. social conditions and on our present day civilization.

9. Soule, George, *What Automation Does to Human Beings* (London: The Scientific Book Club), 184 pp. Appears to be London edition of above-mentioned book.

10. Weeks, Robert Percy (editor), *Machines & The Man* (New York: Appleton-Century-Crofts, 1961), 338 pp. A source book on automation.

11. Welford, Alan Traviss, *Ergonomics of Automation* (HMSO, 1960), 60 pp. Department of Scientific & Industrial Research. Problems in industry.

12. Wiener, Norbert, *The Human Use of Human Beings* (New York: Doubleday Anchor Books, 1954), 199 pp. MIT Professor Wiener, the founder of cybernetics, discusses man, machines, and society. This is the book which stimulated Amber & Amber to write *Anatomy of Automation.*

### E. The Future of Automation

1. Cleator, P. E., *The Robot Era* (London: George Allen & University, Ltd., 1955), 172 pp. The "gee-whiz" approach to mechanization, and automats, including industrial automation and computers.

2. Goodman, Leonard Landon, *Automation Today and Tomorrow* (London: Iota Services, Ltd., 1958), 158 pp. A technical survey of current progress with an extensive bibliography of the automatic factory.

3. Jungk, Rogert, *Tomorrow Is Already Here* (London: Rupert Hart-Davis, 1954), 239 pp. The author searched the United States for the most extreme examples of American technological developments and way of life. He sees many things clearer (and more sensationally) than we do ourselves. Translated from the German.

4. Soule, George, *The Shape of Tomorrow* (New American Library, Signet, 1958), 142

pp. A preview into the future, including the role of automatic technology.

5. Strehl, Rolf, *The Robots Are Among Us* (New York & London: Arco Publishers, 1955), 316 pp. A most sensational interpretation of automatic technology, translated from the German.

6. Steele, George, Paul Kircher, *The Crisis We Face* (New York: McGraw-Hill Book Co., 1960), 220 pp. Discusses U.S. military policy, electronics in military engineering, and economic policy.

7. Thomson, Sir George, *The Foreseeable Future* (London: Cambridge University Press, 1955), 166 pp. Easy to read discussions of tomorrow's energy, materials, transport, food, artificial thought, and the social consequences of advancing technology.

8. Vassilieve, M., and S. Gouschev (editors), *Life in the Twenty-First Century* (Harmondsworth, Middlesex: Penguin Books, Ltd., 1961), 222 pp. Translated from 1959 Russian book. Twenty-nine Russian scientists predict likely developments during the next 50 years. USA edition is called *Russian Science in 21st Century* (New York: McGraw-Hill, 1961).

F. *Computers, Automatic Control, and Dictionaries*

1. *Automatic Control in Soviet Industry* (London: Department of Scientific and Industrial Research, 1959), 64 pp. A report of a visit to the Soviet Union in May, 1959, to study automatic control applied to industrial production.

2. Berkeley, Edmund C., and Linda L. Lovett, *Glossary of Terms in Computers and Data Processing* (Newtonville, Mass.: Berkeley Enterprises, 1960), 90 pp. The 5th edition of the *Computers and Automation* magazine glossary, "de-Greeking" the many new terms of computation and control, emphasizing digital techniques.

3. Berkeley, Edmund C., and Lawrence Wainwright, *Computers, their Operation and Application* (New York: Reinhold, 1956), 366 pp. Also lists many sources of information.

4. Bibbero, Robert J., *Dictionary of Automatic Control* (New York: Reinhold, 1960), 296 pp.

5. Booth, Andrew Donald, *Automation and Computing* (London: Staples Press, 1958), 185 pp. Mainly about electronic calculating machines and electronic data processing.

6. Clason, W. E., *Elsevier's Dictionary of Automation, Computers, Control, and Measuring* (Amsterdam: Elsevier Publishing Co., 1961), 848 pp. Definitions in English/American, French, Spanish, Italian, Dutch, and German. Also distributed by Van Nostrand, Princeton, N.J.

7. Gorn, Saul, and Wallace Manheimer, *The Electronic Brain and What It Can Do* (Chicago: Science Research Associates, Inc., 1956), 64 pp. Basic facts about digital computers; who uses them, what they can do, and how information is coded for computers.

8. Holylock, W. G., *Automatic Control: Principles and Practice* (London: Chapman and Hall, 1958). A graphical nonmathematical explanation of process control.

9. Ivall, I. E., *Electronic Computers—Principles and Applications* (London: Iliffe Books, Ltd., 1960). Analog and digital computers for the layman.

10. Mandl, Matthew, *Fundamentals of Digital Computers* (Englewood Cliffs, N.J.: Prentice-Hall, Inc., 1958), 297 pp. From basics through programming, operation, and maintenance.

11. Warfield, John N., *Introduction to Electronic Analog Computers* (Englewood Cliffs, N.J.: Prentice-Hall, Inc., 1959), 192 pp. Suitable for nonelectrical engineers, as a detailed understanding of electronics is not necessary.

12. Woodbury, David Oakes, *Let Erma Do It; the Full Story of Automation* (New York: Harcourt, Brace & Co., 1956), 305 pp. A popular account of computer capabilities.

# APPENDIX 4

Periodical Publications Pertaining to Automation, Cybernetics, and Computer Application.

1. *American Machinist*, 330 West 42nd St., New York City 36, New York. Covers all metalworking production; job shop, tool room, and mass production.

2. *Automatic Control*, 430 Park Avenue, New York City 22, New York. Components and control systems of complex devices, mainly for electrical engineers.

3. *Automation*, 1213 West Third Street, Cleveland 13, Ohio. Case histories of actual practical automation systems in use, over the entire range of industry.

4. *Automation & Automatic Equipment News*, 9 Gough Square, Fleet Street, London E.C.4, England. New developments and equipment.

5. *Automation Progress*, Leonard Hill House, Eden Street, London, N.W.1, England. For nontechnical person who wants a broad survey of United States, United Kingdom, Russia, and Continental automation in all "areas" of automation. Covers philosophy of automation and cybernetics, too. Unsurpassed book reviews.

6. *Automotive Industries*, Chestnut & 56th Sts., Philadelphia 39, Pa. Illustrates Practices of the Automotive Industries, largest user of automation.

7. *Computers and Automation*, 815 Washington Street, Newtonville 60, Mass. Describes computers, data processing cybernetics, philosophy, and lists active participants in field.

8. *Control Engineering*, 330 W. 42nd Street, New York 36, N.Y. For professional control engineers. Mathematical approach used.

9. *Datamation*, 141 E. 44th St., New York 17. Covers the automatic handling of information including computers and office automation.

10. *Electro-Technology* (formerly named *Electrical Manufacturing*), 205 East 42nd St., New York 17, N.Y. The design magazine of Science and Engineering, describing the very latest in operational automatic devices. Covers basic principles too.

11. *Instruments and Control Systems*, 845 Ridge Road, Pittsburgh 12, Pa. Covers automation of the continuous process industries.

12. *Industrial Research*, Beverly Shores, Indiana. Attempts to reduce time lag between invention and application by discussing new scientific developments and their effect on industry. Covers the frontier of automation.

13. *Machinery*, 93 Worth Ave., New York 13, N.Y. Automatic production machines and machine tools.

14. *Management & Business Automation*, 600 W. Jackson Blvd., Chicago 6, Illinois. Office Automation and Data Processing Systems.

15. *Mass Production*, 4 Ludgate Circus, London, E.C.4, England. Covers practices of larger fabricating plants.

16. *Product Engineering*, 330 West 42nd St., New York 36, N.Y. Reports on new devices and developments, in addition to design details.

17. *Production*, Box 1, Birmingham, Mich. Covers mass production metalworking practice.

18. *Tool and Manufacturing Engineer*, 10700 Puritan Ave., Detroit 38, Mich. Coverage of tooling and manufacturing practices.

19. *Tooling and Production*, 1975 Lee Road, Cleveland 18, Ohio. Tooling and fabricating practices.

# Index

INDEX

# INDEX